# MATHEMATICAL ANALYSIS OF OBSERVATIONS

# MATHEMATICAL ANALYSIS OF OBSERVATIONS

B. M. SHCHIGOLEV

*Translated by Scripta Technica Inc*
*Editor* H. EAGLE

LONDON ILIFFE BOOKS LTD
NEW YORK AMERICAN ELSEVIER PUBLISHING COMPANY INC.

Originally published in the U.S.S.R. in 1960

English edition first published in 1965
by Iliffe Books Ltd, Dorset House
Stamford Street, London, S.E.1



Published in the U.S.A. by
American Elsevier Publishing Company Inc.
52 Vanderbilt Avenue, New York, N.Y. 10017

Library of Congress Catalog Card Number 65-16710

Printed and bound in England by
Butler & Tanner Ltd
Frome, Somerset

BKS 5052

# CONTENTS

Part III

Probability Theory

## Part V

## Analysis of Statistical Material

# PREFACE

This book was written as a text for courses in "Mathematical Analysis of Observations" for astronomy students in the applied mathematics and physics divisions of Universities. The book is based on lectures given at the Moscow State University and contains the material included in the semester program, as well as supplementary material not part of the course.

The subject matter is somewhat more extensive than the title would indicate since it includes not only problems connected with the processing of observations in a strict sense of the word but also problems on approximate calculations. These latter do not always involve analysis of observations, although it is convenient to solve them in connection with such a study. For example, the book discusses the problem of point interpolation from tables of a function whose values are computed from its definition (e.g., by means of a series).

The term "Mathematical Analysis of Observations" is thus intended in its broadest sense.

The problems considered in this book not only are applicable to astronomy but quite frequently need to be solved in various other branches of science and technology. Therefore, the author hopes that at least certain parts of the book will be useful to others besides astronomers.

The book is divided into parts and chapters. The chapters and sections are numbered from the beginning of the book. A double system of numbering was chosen for the formulas: Formula (16.10), for example, is the tenth formula in Chapter 16.

A small bibliography appears at the end of the book. It consists mostly of textbooks, and is divided into five parts, each part applying to one of the parts of the present book.

The author considers it his pleasant duty to thank his colleagues in the Department of Celestial Mechanics at Moscow State University, E. M. Slavtsev and A. I. Rybakov, for their help in preparing the manuscript for printing.

B. M. Shchigolev

# INTRODUCTION

Observations and experiments constitute the basis of all natural science. Observations and experiments that provide numbers—the results of measurements—are of special significance. A proper analysis of these numbers leads to a theoretical interpretation of the results of the observations and to the final goal of natural science, namely, the establishment of laws governing these phenomena, thus making possible the prediction of the future behavior of the phenomena.

All results of measurements contain errors of various origins. Therefore, the results of calculations with numbers, which in turn are the results of measurements, also contain errors. From a practical standpoint, it is very important to be able to estimate both the errors incurred in making the measurements and the errors resulting from operations on those measurements, because it is only then that we can safely use the conclusions drawn from observations.

It is no less important to organize the calculations and the observations in such a way as to ensure as small an error in the result as possible. All the information that we have on linear dimensions in the solar system, in the galaxy, etc. are based, in the last analysis, on direct measurements made on comparatively small quantities on the surface of the earth. These values contain errors. In order to obtain information on dimensions in the solar system, and (even to a greater extent) in the galaxy, we need to multiply these values by large numbers. The errors in measurements are then multiplied and this leads to large errors in the results. From these brief remarks, it is clear that the analysis of the results of observations cannot be carried out in an arbitrary manner. In order to have the results contain as small errors as possible, we need to develop both methods of estimating the errors and methods of computation that will ensure the most accurate results possible.

These remarks have to do with the analysis of observations in a narrow sense of the word, referring to operations on numbers that are obtained directly from observations. However, in forming a theory regarding phenomena and in computing quantities that are not directly observed but that are derived from the analysis of observations, it is necessary to use various mathematical devices; in particular, it is necessary to use various functional relations extensively.

As we know, a function can be defined in several different ways. In the simplest case, we are told what arithmetic operations must be performed on the values of the argument(s) in order to obtain the value of the function (a polynomial, a rational function, etc.). But a function may also be defined in such a way that we do not see from the definition how to calculate its value (e.g., the arcsine). In such cases, the definition is used to find those properties of the function that make possible its expansion in an infinite series; this infinite series may then be considered a new definition of the function. A function may be defined also by an integral, by a differential equation, etc. None of these methods of defining the function state directly how to calculate the value of the function from the value of the argument. In such cases, we need either to find an infinite series or to resort to numerical methods of solution that give the function in the form of a table. In those cases in which a function is determined by a convergent infinite series (usually a power series), that series is used for compiling a table of values for the function (especially if the function is encountered very often in practical problems). The compilation of a table is always an approximate operation since one must always cut off an infinite series at some term or other. Although tabular values of functions are not obtained from measurements, they contain unavoidable errors just as do the results of measurements. These errors must also be estimated. It is also necessary to estimate the errors incurred in performing operations on the tabular values of functions.

Thus, there are common features in the problems connected with measurements and in the problems of using tables of functions. Both types of problem are directly connected in that quite often the result of a measurement is the argument of a tabulated function. For these reasons, courses on the analysis of measurements usually include problems on operations on tabulated functions.

Among the errors of measurement a conspicuous place is occupied by random errors, that is, errors whose values cannot be estimated before the observations. We might also note that they cannot be evaluated even after observations, since the presence of random errors makes it impossible for us to determine the exact value of the quantity measured. In analyzing measurements containing random errors, one must use the theory of probability, which is also necessary in statistical work. This course in the mathematical analysis of observations includes the basic principles of probability theory so that the student may use a single textbook and have a single system of notation, terminology, etc.

Problems involving the analysis of observations and the somewhat allied problems of approximating the value of a function arose long ago, primarily in connection with astronomical problems. They were first stated in a completely explicit form in the works of the French mathematician Legendre (1752-1833) and the German mathematician Gauss (1777-1855).

The Russian mathematicians P. L. Chebyshev (1821-1894), A. A. Markov (1856-1922), and A. M. Lyapunov (1857-1918) played a special part in the development of the theory of errors and the theory of approximation of a function. The founders of the Soviet school of probability theory and of the constructive theory of functions, namely, S. N. Bernstein, B. V. Gnedenko, V. L. Goncharov, A. N. Kolmogorov, V. I. Romanovskii, A. Ya. Khinchin, and others, have conducted and are still conducting interesting research in these fields.

# Part I

# OPERATIONS WITH APPROXIMATE NUMBERS

Chapter 1

# ESTIMATION OF ERRORS OF APPROXIMATE NUMBERS

## 1. FUNDAMENTAL PROBLEMS IN THE THEORY OF APPROXIMATE CALCULATIONS

In the natural sciences, one has occasion to deal with exact numbers only very rarely. If an astronomer is investigating motions in a three-star system, the number 3 is, of course, exact. When a physicist is studying the structure of snowflakes, he can determine exactly the number of rays on each individual snowflake. However, the number of such examples is very limited.

The results of measurements are always approximate, primarily because of the limited accuracy of measuring instruments.

Every measuring instrument has a scale and the intervals between the dividing lines on this scale cannot be arbitrarily small. We sometimes speak of the "threshold of sensitivity" of the instrument. This is the smallest change in value that can be registered by the instrument. For example, if a circle designed for measuring angles has dividing lines every $10'$ and a vernier giving the individual minutes, the threshold of sensitivity of the instrument is $1'$, since a change in angle of $1'$ can be detected by the instrument, while a smaller change, though it can be perceived, cannot be accurately determined. If the needle of the instrument falls between two divisions, the tenth parts of the interval can still be evaluated either by the eye or with the help of the vernier. Thus, we may assert only that the errors in measurement are less than one tenth of the interval between the divisions of the scale. This assertion will be valid if there are no other sources of error besides the error caused by the limited accuracy of the measuring device.

There are a good many measurements, especially laboratory measurements, with regard to which we can find an upper bound on the absolute value of the error of measurement. We shall examine such cases below. Furthermore (quite apart from the question of the possibility of determining this upper bound accurately), it is always possible to assume the existence of this upper bound. Indeed, since an exact numerical value of the quantity measured exists as an objective reality independent of us, and since measurements give, generally speaking, some other value, the error is always bounded. In this part of the book, we shall assume that we are dealing with approximate numbers containing errors of arbitrary origin but for which we can find an upper bound on the absolute value of the error.

The first problem in the theory of approximate calculations will be to establish means of estimating errors.

We shall almost always need to perform arithmetic or other operations on approximate numbers. Of course, the results of these operations will also be of an approximate nature. We then encounter the second problem, that of estimating the error incurred in performing these operations if we already have estimates on the errors in the original numbers. We may call this problem the direct problem of the theory. If such a problem is solved in literal form, we can then set up two other very important problems:

(1) the inverse problem, that of determining the degree of accuracy in the original numbers that is necessary to ensure a specified degree of accuracy in the result of the operations performed;

(2) determining the conditions of measurements or calculations under which the error in the result of the operations will be as small as possible. We may vary either the choice of circumstances under which the measurements are made or the choice of formulas used in making calculations.

## 2. THE EXACT ERROR OF AN APPROXIMATE NUMBER

Let us suppose that a certain quantity (for example, an angle) has a definite numerical value $A$ that remains unchanged during the entire process of measurement. Let us suppose also that the measurement made of this quantity yields the value $a$.

The difference between the exact and approximate values

$$A - a = \Delta_a \tag{1.1}$$

is called the *exact error* of the approximate number $a$. This definition is convenient in that the concept of an exact error coincides with the concept of a correction since

$$A = a + \Delta_a, \tag{1.2}$$

that is, the exact error is the number that must be added to the approximate number in order to obtain the exact value.*

---

*Instead of an exact error, the concept of an *absolute error* is sometimes used. The absolute error $|\Delta|_a$ of an approximate number $a$ is the absolute value of the difference between the exact and approximate values of the quantity:

$$|\Delta|_a = |A - a|.$$

We shall not be using this concept.

The concept of an "exact error" is only of theoretical significance, since in the more common problems this error cannot in actuality be determined. We might only mention certain exceptional cases in which we wish to investigate the accuracy of measurements made by some technique or with the help of some instrument, and, to do so, we measure the same quantities in some other way (for example, with precision instruments) with an accuracy that is considerably greater than the accuracy of the technique or device for measuring that we are investigating. Although the more precise measurement also contains an error, we may assume that the second measurement yields a formally exact value and determine the "exact" error of the first measurement, confining ourselves to a certain number of significant figures.

Suppose, for example, that a measurement with a theodolite gives a value of $38° 43'$ with an accuracy of $1'$. Suppose that we measured the same angle with a universal compass with a maximum error of $5''$ and that the result of this measurement is $38° 43' 25''$. Formally considering the second value as exact, we may say that the exact error of the first measurement is $0.4'$ although in actuality this is only an approximate value of the exact error.

In what follows, we shall assume that the quantity $|\Delta_a|$ is so small in comparison with $|a|$ that we can neglect powers of $\Delta_a$ higher than the first. If we are considering several approximate numbers $a$, $b$, . . . at the same time, we shall also neglect products of the form $\Delta_a\Delta_b$.

## 3. LIMITING ABSOLUTE ERROR

As was shown in section 1, it is possible in exceptional cases to give an approximate value of the exact error, in the sense that the error of this determination is considerably less in absolute value than the error of the basic measurement. In many cases, it is easier to determine an upper bound on the absolute value of the exact error.

For an approximate number $a$, consider the smallest positive number $\varepsilon_a$ that contains one or two significant figures and that is at least equal to the absolute value of the exact error. In other words,

$$\varepsilon_a \geqslant |\Delta_a|. \tag{1.3}$$

We shall call this number $\varepsilon_a$ the limiting absolute error.

This definition requires some explanation. For the most part, it is not difficult to find a positive number that is known to be greater than the absolute value of the exact error, and we could take such a number as the limiting absolute error. If several such numbers can be found, the smallest of them must, by definition, be chosen. It is sometimes convenient to replace a value accepted as the limiting absolute error with another, simpler one, that is, one that contains fewer significant figures. In such cases, we can only increase the original value that was used.

If the limiting absolute error is known, we may write the obvious inequality*

$$a - \varepsilon_a \leqslant A \leqslant a + \varepsilon_a \tag{1.4}$$

for the exact value of $A$.

Let us consider the particular case in which the limiting absolute error of a number is determined by its decimal representation. Every approximate number, when written in this form, has a limited number of significant figures, depending on the accuracy of measurement or computation. For example, suppose that a length is measured by means of a ruler with dividing lines at each millimeter and a vernier that gives the tenth parts of a millimeter. Then, the length will contain whole centimeters, and the tenth and hundredth parts of a centimeter. From the nature of the process of such a measurement, we may assert that the absolute value of the error in this measurement is less than 0.01 cm if (as is usually the case) in using the vernier, we always observe a smaller (or larger) division of the vernier when the end of the interval does not coincide exactly with any division of the vernier. With such a measuring instrument, we can always give the sign of the exact error because the approximate value is known to be less (or, in the corresponding case, greater) than the exact value. This means of measurement can be called measurement without rounding off in analogy with the corresponding computational operation.

Measurement with rounding off in this example would consist in seeking the division of the vernier that is closest to the end of the segment that is being measured and in writing the corresponding number of hundredth parts. The exact error is equal to the distance from the division taken on the vernier to the end of the segment. In the case of a measurement with rounding off, the absolute value of this distance does not exceed one half the distance between the divisions of the vernier, the latter distance being equal to 0.01 cm.

Thus, if the result of the measurement indicates only hundredth parts of a centimeter and the measurement is taken without rounding off, the limiting absolute error of the measurement should be taken as 0.01 centimeters. On the other hand if there is rounding off of the measurements, the limiting absolute error should be taken as one half this amount. These conclusions are valid for arbitrary approximate numbers.

By generally accepted convention, the limiting absolute error of a number written in the decimal system of notation is taken equal to the unit corresponding to the last significant figure on the

---

*We call the reader's attention to the fact that the conditional notation that is sometimes suggested

$$A = a \pm \varepsilon_a$$

is not advised because a similar notation has long been used in the theory of random errors and there it has a different meaning.

right (in other words, equal to 10 taken to the power indicated by this last significant figure) if the number is taken without rounding off and equal to half this unit if the number is taken with rounding off. By "last," we mean the significant figure farthest to the right. If we have other information on the limiting absolute error, it must be stated, and when operations are performed on the numbers in question, we must be guided by this information rather than by convention.

This convention is used not only in cases in which the approximate number is obtained as the result of measurement but also in those cases in which it is obtained from calculation and is the result of discarding some number of significant figures on the right. The simplest example of this type is offered by the conversion of a simple fraction into a decimal fraction with the retention of only a certain number of digits to the right of the decimal point.

If digits are simply discarded (as in the case of a decimal fraction) or are replaced by zeros (as in the case of a whole number), then on the basis of the rule that was stated above, the limiting absolute error is taken to be the unit of the last digit that is kept. By "last," we mean the digit that has nothing to the right of it in the case of a decimal fraction and only zeros in the case of a whole number.* When we simply discard digits, we obtain an approximate value with an accuracy up to the unit of the last digit kept. This number will be *less* than the original number. We may possibly agree in such cases to increase the last significant figure by unity, in which case the limiting absolute error will still be equal to the unit of the last significant figure but the approximate value obtained will be *greater* than the original number.

Example 1. As we know, we may take $\pi = 3.1416$. Suppose that in organized calculations it is sufficient to take two digits to the right of the decimal. Then, we would take $\pi = 3.14$ (or $\pi = 3.15$), so that $\varepsilon_\pi = 0.01$. If we do not know how the approximating value of this number was obtained, we can only assert that

$$3.13 \leqslant \pi \leqslant 3.15.$$

On the other hand, if it is known that the number has a remainder (that is, that the exact value is greater than the approximate value), the lower bound will be 3.14.

---

*To avoid the possibility of confusion, we note the following about the method of defining the limiting error. Let us illustrate with a simple example. Suppose that in measuring a length with a precision instrument, we arrive at a result of 3.5003 cm. If we only need an accuracy of three decimal places, we should take the length as equal to 3.500 cm and not discard any of the zeros (in contrast with the rules of exact arithmetic). The reason is that, from what was agreed upon above with regard to our notation, the limiting error is equal to $(1/2) \cdot 10^{-3}$ cm, but if we discarded one of the zeros, this would indicate that it is equal to $(1/2) \cdot 10^{-2}$ cm. In this case, even the zeros to the right of the decimal point are significant figures.

Suppose that the same length is measured with a ruler graduated in millimeters. Then, we would obtain 3.5 cm with a limiting error of $(1/2) \cdot 10^{-1}$ cm. According to the formal rules of arithmetic, we might also write this as 3.500 cm, but this would change the estimate of the error.

Example 2. The equatorial radius of the earth $R$ is approximately equal to 6,384 km. Suppose that we wish to replace this number with a number containing only two significant figures. If we discard those digits that we consider superfluous, we may take $R = 6{,}300$ km with a remainder or $R = 6{,}400$ km with a surplus. In both cases, $\varepsilon_R \doteq 100$ km.

A simple discarding of digits is convenient in that the sign of the error is known, but when we do this we do not get an approximate value that is as close as it might be to the actual value. From this point of view it is more convenient to round off the approximate number in a manner equivalent to the rounding off in the case of a measurement. The rule for rounding a number off is generally known and we do not need to explain it: if the first discarded digit is less than 5, the last undiscarded digit is kept unchanged; if the first discarded digit is greater than 5, the last undiscarded digit is increased by 1. If only the digit 5 is discarded and the following digits are unknown, the most common convention is to keep the last undiscarded digit unchanged if it is even and to increase it by 1 if it is odd. This is rounding the number off to the nearest even digit. The error resulting from this rounding off is bounded by the following rule: the limiting absolute error of an approximation resulting from rounding off is equal to one half the unit of the last digit.

Example 1. For the number $\pi$, we obtain the approximate value $\pi = 3.14$ in rounding the number off to two decimal places. Therefore,

$$\varepsilon_\pi = \frac{1}{2}\, 0.01.$$

Example 2. For the equatorial radius of the earth, we have

$$R = 6400 \text{ km}, \quad \varepsilon_R = 50 \text{ km}.$$

A certain inconvenience with regard to rounding a figure off consists in the fact that the sign of the error of the approximate number is not known until we obtain the approximate number. In the case of the following operations, where only the approximate number is given and it is known that it is obtained by rounding off, we may only assert that

$$a - \varepsilon_a \leqslant A \leqslant a + \varepsilon_a, \quad \varepsilon_a = \frac{1}{2} \cdot 10^p,$$

where $10^p$ is the unit of the first significant figure on the right.

## 4. LIMITING RELATIVE ERROR

The bound that we gave above by means of the limiting absolute error makes it possible to exhibit bounds between which the exact value of a number lies but it does not sufficiently characterize the quality of the measurements made if the approximate number is the result of measurements or calculations drawn from the results of measurements. To be able to consider a measurement or a calculation satisfactory, we need to know not only the smallness of $\varepsilon_a$ alone but also the smallness of $\varepsilon_a$ in comparison with $a$. To clarify this, let us set

$$\varepsilon_a = \delta \cdot |a|,$$

where $\delta$ is a positive number. Then, we may write

$$a(1-\delta) \leqslant A \leqslant a(1+\delta), \text{ if } a > 0,$$

and

$$a(1+\delta) \leqslant A \leqslant a(1-\delta), \text{ if } a < 0.$$

It is clear from these inequalities that an approximate value $a$ does not determine even the sign of the number $A$ when $\delta > 1$ since the right and left sides of the inequalities in this case have different signs and the actual value can be either positive or negative. From this, it is clear that to characterize the quality of the approximation, it is important to know not just the magnitude of the limiting absolute error but also its relationship to the quantity $a$. A determination of the equatorial radius of the earth with $\varepsilon_R = 1$ m would be considered excellent, but a measurement of the dimensions of even a large auditorium with the same limiting absolute error would be poor. This example brings up another consideration concerning which we need to introduce an additional type of error estimate. In most problems, $a$ and $\varepsilon_a$ are denominate numbers and therefore, the numerical value of $\varepsilon_a$ depends on the choice of units of measurement; that is, it is not a sufficiently complete characteristic of the inaccuracy. Also, the values of the limiting absolute errors of different measurements cannot be compared in those cases in which quantities measured in different dimensions, such as weight and length, are measured.

In connection with these considerations, it is convenient to introduce the concept of a limiting relative error. The limiting relative error $\delta_a$ of an approximate number $a$ is defined as the ratio of its limiting absolute error $\varepsilon_a$ to the absolute value of the number $a$:*

$$\delta_a = \frac{\varepsilon_a}{|a|}. \tag{1.5}$$

If we know $\varepsilon_a$, we can find $\delta_a$ and vice versa.

Quite frequently, the quantity $\delta$ is expressed in percentages or in parts per thousand (indicated by [0/00]). In computing the limiting relative error, we try to obtain a number with only a few significant figures. As a rule, the calculation is made in one's head and $\delta$ is simplified in such a way that the number obtained is

*It would be more logical to call the ratio of $\varepsilon_a$ to $|A|$ the limiting relative error. But in practice, we cannot determine this value since we do not know the value of $A$. Let us consider the two quantities

$$\delta'_a = \frac{\varepsilon_a}{A}, \quad \delta_a = \frac{\varepsilon_a}{a}.$$

greater than what it must be according to the definition. For example, if $\pi = 3.14$ with rounding off, then

$$\varepsilon_\pi = \frac{1}{2} \cdot 10^{-2}, \quad \delta_\pi = \frac{0.5 \cdot 10^{-2}}{3.14} < \frac{1}{6} \cdot 10^{-2} < \frac{1}{5} \cdot 10^{-2}.$$

For the limiting relative error, we take

$$\delta_\pi = 2 \cdot 10^{-3} = 2‰.$$

## 5. ESTIMATE OF AN ERROR FROM THE NUMBER OF KNOWN DIGITS

In practice, the relation between the number of significant figures that are known with certainty in an approximate number and the limiting relative error is used extensively.

Suppose that a positive approximate number $a$ contains $s$ definitely known digits. Then, its decimal expansion is of the form

$$a = n_1 \cdot 10^r + n_2 \cdot 10^{r-1} + \ldots + n_s 10^p,$$

where $n_1, n_2, \ldots n_s$ are digits in the decimal representation with $n_1 \neq 0$. The integers $r$ and $p$ (with $r > p$) and the positive integer $s$ are related by the obvious equation $p - r = 1 - s$.

Suppose that the number $a$ is obtained with rounding off. Then,

$$\varepsilon_a = \frac{1}{2} \cdot 10^p.$$

---

Assuming for simplicity that $a$ and $A$ are both positive and using the definition of the exact error, we obtain

$$A = a + \Delta_a.$$

$$\delta'_a - \delta_a = \frac{\varepsilon_a}{a}\left(\frac{a}{A} - 1\right) = \frac{\varepsilon_a}{a}\left(\frac{a}{a + \Delta_a} - 1\right) =$$

$$= \frac{\varepsilon_a}{a}\left[\frac{1}{\left(1 + \frac{\Delta_a}{a}\right)} - 1\right] = \frac{\varepsilon_a}{a}\left[-\frac{\Delta_a}{a} + \left(\frac{\Delta_a}{a}\right)^2 - \ldots\right].$$

Remembering that $\frac{|\Delta_a|}{a} \leqslant \delta_a$, we obtain

$$|\delta'_a - \delta_a| \leqslant \delta_a[\delta_a + \delta_a^2 + \ldots].$$

Thus $\delta'_a - \delta_a$ is a quantity of the second order of magnitude if $\delta_a$ is of the first order. Consequently, which of the two quantities $\delta_a$ and $\delta'_a$ is used to characterize the relative error of the number $a$ is in practice of no significance.

From the definition of limiting relative error (1.5), we have

$$\delta_a = \frac{1}{2} \cdot \frac{10}{a}.$$

In the expression for $\delta_a$, let us now replace $a$ with its decimal expansion keeping only the *first* term. Obviously, this can only increase the value of $\delta_a$:

$$\delta_a < \frac{1}{2} \cdot \frac{10^p}{n_1 10^r} = \frac{1}{2} \cdot \frac{1}{n_1} \cdot 10^{1-s}.$$

This last expression can be taken for the limiting relative error

$$\delta_a = \frac{10}{2n_1} \cdot 10^{-s}. \tag{1.6}$$

Here $s$ is the number of definitely known significant figures in the approximate number and $n_1$ is the first digit of the number. We should note that in accordance with the formula that we have obtained, the limiting relative error depends only on the number of known digits and $n_1$, but not on the position of the decimal point.

We give a table of values of $\delta_a$ corresponding to different values of $n_1$ and $s$ (with $\delta_a$ expressed in percent):

| $n_1$ \ $s$ | 1 | 2 | 3 | 4 | 5 |
|---|---|---|---|---|---|
| 1 | 50 | 5.0 | 0.50 | 0.050 | 0.0050 |
| 2 | 25 | 2.5 | 0.25 | 0.025 | 0.0025 |
| 3 | 17 | 1.7 | 0.17 | 0.017 | 0.0017 |
| 4 | 13 | 1.3 | 0.13 | 0.013 | 0.0013 |
| 5 | 10 | 1.0 | 0.10 | 0.010 | 0.0010 |
| 6 | 8.4 | 0.84 | 0.084 | 0.0084 | 0.00084 |
| 7 | 7.2 | 0.72 | 0.072 | 0.0072 | 0.00072 |
| 8 | 6.7 | 0.67 | 0.067 | 0.0067 | 0.00067 |
| 9 | 5.6 | 0.56 | 0.056 | 0.0056 | 0.00056 |

To get an approximate evaluation of the relative error, we may take the average value of the first digit; that is, we may set $n_1 = 5$. Then, the limiting relative error of a number with one definitely known digit is a number of the order of ten percent; in the case of two definitely known digits, it is one percent; in the case of three, it is 0.1 percent, etc. We should note that in many applied problems, a limiting relative error of the order of a tenth of a percent is sufficient. It is enough to carry out such calculations with three significant figures.

We have just determined the limiting relative error from the number of known digits. It is easy to solve the inverse problem also, namely, the problem of determining the necessary number of known digits for a given limiting relative error. Suppose that we need to determine $s$ in such a way that $\delta_a = 10^{-q}$. Then, from formula (1.6),

$$\frac{10}{2n_1} \cdot 10^{-s} \leqslant 10^{-q}, \quad 10^q \leqslant 10^s \cdot \frac{2n_1}{10}, \quad 10^s \geqslant 10^q \cdot \frac{10}{2n_1}.$$

If we replace $n_1$ with the average number 5 (where $n_1$ can take any integral value between 1 and 9), we get $10^s \geqslant 10^q$ and $s \geqslant q$. Consequently, on the average, the number of known digits must be equal to the absolute value of the power of 10 in the given value of $\delta_a$. For example, if we need to find $\delta_a$ of an order of one percent, the number must have no fewer than two definitely known digits.

Let us obtain a more reliable estimate than the average. We begin with the decimal expansion of the number $a$:

$$a = n_1 \cdot 10^r + n_2 \cdot 10^{r-1} + \ldots + n_s \cdot 10^p.$$

Then,

$$(n_1 + 1) \cdot 10^r > a \geqslant n_1 \cdot 10^r.$$

Hence,

$$\delta'_a = \frac{1}{2} \cdot \frac{10^p}{a}, \quad \delta'_a \geqslant \frac{1}{2} \cdot \frac{10^p}{(n_1 + 1)\, 10^r} = \frac{10}{2\,(n_1 + 1)} \cdot 10^{-s}$$

if $a$ is an approximate number obtained upon rounding off. If it is given that $\delta_a = 10^{-q}$, we need to take $s$ such that $\delta'_a$ will be less than $\delta_a$; that is,

$$10^s \geqslant \frac{10^{q+1}}{2\,(n_1 + 1)}. \tag{1.7}$$

For the necessary number of known digits, we need to take the smallest integer $s$ that satisfies this inequality. We can get something like the average value if we take $n_1 = 4$. Then, $s \geqslant q$.

The table below, giving the number of known digits for a given relative error, was compiled from formula (1.7):

| $\delta\%$ / $q$ / $n_1$ | 100<br>0 | 10<br>1 | 1<br>2 | 0.1<br>3 | 0.01<br>4 | 0.001<br>5 |
|---|---|---|---|---|---|---|
| 1–3 | 1 | 2 | 3 | 4 | 5 | 6 |
| 4–9 | 0 | 1 | 2 | 3 | 4 | 5 |

This table can be replaced with the simple formula: if the first digit does not exceed 3, the number of known digits must exceed by 1 the absolute value of the power of 10 in the given relative error. In the remaining cases, these numbers are equal. The value of 0 for $q = 0$ and $n_1 = 4$–9 means that there will be a 100-percent error if we do not know a single digit in the number for certain but only that the first digit is less than 4. To see this, suppose that the exact value of a one-digit number is 5. If an error of 100 percent is allowed for the number, the absolute value of the error can attain the value of 5 and the approximate number can have any value from 0 to 10; that is, the first digit will not be known.

Chapter 2

# ERRORS INCURRED IN FUNDAMENTAL ARITHMETIC OPERATIONS

In this chapter, we shall consider the following problem: if the limiting absolute and relative errors of numbers upon which the operations of addition, subtraction, multiplication, and division are performed are known, what error will exist in the result?

## 6. ADDITION

Suppose that

$$u = a_1 + a_2 + \dots + a_n, \tag{2.1}$$

where $a_1, a_2, \dots, a_n$ are approximate numbers, either positive or negative or both. Let us denote their limiting absolute errors by $\varepsilon_1, \varepsilon_2, \dots, \varepsilon_n$. Also, let us denote by $\Delta_1, \Delta_2, \dots, \Delta_n$ the exact errors in the individual addends and by $\Delta_u$ the exact error in $u$. Obviously,

$$\Delta_u = \Delta_1 + \Delta_2 + \dots + \Delta_n, \tag{2.2}$$

and hence

$$|\Delta_u| \leqslant \sum_{k=1}^{n} |\Delta_k|. \tag{2.3}$$

Since by definition (see (1.3)),

$$|\Delta_k| \leqslant \varepsilon_k, \quad k = 1, 2, \dots, n,$$

we have

$$|\Delta_u| \leqslant \sum_{k=1}^{n} \varepsilon_k.$$

Therefore, $\varepsilon_u$ can be determined from the equation

$$\varepsilon_u = \sum_{k=1}^{n} \varepsilon_k. \tag{2.4}$$

Thus, *for the limiting absolute error of the sum, we may take the sum of the individual absolute errors in the addends.*

Example. Let us set $u = 3.14 + 0.843 + 0.0365$. Let us suppose that the approximating addends are given with accuracy up to the unit of the last digit. Then,

$$\varepsilon_u = 0.01 + 0.001 + 0.0001 = 0.0111$$

If we need to write this estimate more simply, we should take

$$\varepsilon_u = 0.02.$$

From this example, it is clear that there is no sense in trying to obtain approximate addends with different numbers of digits to the right of the decimal point. According to the value obtained for $\varepsilon_u$ in this example, the error can exceed one hundredth and, therefore, there is no sense in writing the thousandth and ten-thousandth parts in the result, and in fact we cannot vouch for the accuracy even of the hundredth part. In adding approximate numbers, we may proceed in two ways.

The first consists in "trimming" all the terms to be added to fit the least exact one. Since the limiting absolute errors of the terms will be equal, the limiting absolute error of the sum will be equal to the product of the limiting absolute error of a single term and the number of terms. However, it immediately follows from this that in the sum we lose exactly one digit after the decimal if the number of terms is a one-digit number, two digits if the number of terms is a two-digit number, etc.

However, it should be noted that this estimate of the error is suitable only when there are only a few terms to be added. If there are twenty or fifty terms, for example, the estimate of the error can be quite excessive since with this method it is actually assumed that all the approximate values for the terms have the largest errors in absolute value and that all are of the same sign. Such a case can, of course, be encountered in calculation, but it is very rare. As a rule, the numbers $\Delta_k$ have different signs and these errors partially cancel each other out in the sum of a large number of terms. Therefore, the actual error in the sum of a large number of terms can be considerably less than the number that would be obtained from assigning each term the maximum error (see next section).

The second method of adding numbers with different numbers of digits to the right of the decimal point consists in adding separately by groups those numbers with the same number of digits to the right of the decimal point place and then rounding off the sums to the smallest number of digits to the right of the decimal point.

Example.

$$u = 3.14 + (0.847 + 0.936) + (0.0746 + 0.0358) =$$
$$= 3.14 + 1.783 + 0.1104 \approx 3.14 + 1.783 + 0.110 =$$
$$= 3.14 + 1.893 \approx 3.14 + 1.89 = 5.03.$$

If two terms are given with accuracy up to half of the unit of the last digit, calculation of the error in the result in this example takes the following form: The limiting error of the sum of the fourth and fifth terms is equal to 2•0.00005 = 0.0001. After we round this sum off to three digits to the right of the decimal, we add the limiting error 0.0005. We then have in all 0.0006. Addition of the third and fourth terms in the preceding sum gives a limiting error of 2•0.0005 + 0.0006 = 0.0016. Discarding the third digit to the right of the decimal increases the error by 0.005, giving us in all a value of 0.0066, which we may replace with 0.007. Addition of the last sum to the first of the terms gives a limiting error 0.005 + 0.007 = 0.012.

If we had used the first method, we would have needed to round off all the terms to two digits to the right of the decimal point. We would then have obtained

$$u = 3.14 + 0.85 + 0.94 + 0.07 + 0.04 = 5.04$$

with a limiting absolute error of

$$(1/2) \cdot 0.01 \cdot 5 = 0.025.$$

The second method can be applied in those cases in which the number of terms is not very small.

## 7. STATISTICAL ESTIMATE OF THE ERROR OF A SUM*

Suppose that

$$u = \sum_{k=1}^{n} a_k,$$

where the $a_k$ are approximate numbers with exact errors $\Delta_k$. For each of these numbers, we know the limiting absolute error $\varepsilon_k$; that is, $\varepsilon_k \geqslant |\Delta_k|$. The exact error of the sum is

$$\Delta_u = \sum_{k=1}^{n} \Delta_k.$$

In order to construct the probable characteristics of the sum $u$, we need to make certain assumptions about the distribution function of the quantities $\Delta_k$. In ordinary calculations with a definite number of digits to the right of the decimal point, we assume that the error of a randomly chosen term is a random number subject to a uniform law of distribution in the interval from $-\varepsilon_k$ to $\varepsilon_k$. According to the preceeding section, the accuracy of calculations is only slightly increased if we take terms with equal limiting absolute errors. Therefore, we shall assume that all the $\varepsilon_k$ are equal to a single number $\varepsilon$.

Under these assumptions, the probability density of each of the terms $\Delta_k$ will be equal to $1/(2\varepsilon)$ and the center of distribution will be equal to 0. Therefore, the variance (or dispersion) of each of the exact errors is determined by the formula

$$\operatorname{Var}\Delta_k = \int_{-\varepsilon}^{+\varepsilon} \frac{1}{2\varepsilon} \alpha^2 \, d\alpha = \frac{1}{3} \varepsilon^2.$$

*This section should be read after completing the third part of the book.

Assuming that the exact errors are independent, we then obtain by using the theorem on the variance of a sum

$$\operatorname{Var}\Delta_u = \frac{1}{3} n\varepsilon^2.$$

For a statistical estimate of $\Delta_u$ we still need to construct the distribution function for $u$. The law of distribution for a sum of a finite number of terms is rather tedious to obtain, but we can manage without it. Let us assume that the sum obeys the normal law with center 0 and variance $n\varepsilon^2/3$. From the sigma rule, we may assume

$$P\left(|\Delta_u| < \varepsilon\sqrt{\frac{n}{3}}\right) = 0.68.$$

where $\Delta_u$ is the exact error of the sum, and from the three-sigma rule,

$$P(|\Delta_u| < \varepsilon\sqrt{3n}) = 0.9973.$$

The quantity $\varepsilon\sqrt{3n}$ can be taken as the limiting absolute error of the sum of $n$ terms. If we used the maximum limiting error method, we would obtain $n\varepsilon$.

It is easy to see that if $n > 3$, the statistical estimate of the error of the sum gives a lower limiting error than the usual estimate. If we add fifty terms together each with an accuracy up to 0.005, the exact limiting error will be 0.25; that is, even the hundredths are not reliable in the sum and the probable error will be $0.005\cdot\sqrt{150} \approx 0.06$. With a probability of 0.9973, we may expect the total error not to exceed 0.06 in absolute value.*

Of course, this leaves unanswered the question of the closeness of the distribution of the overall error to a normal distribution, which we shall use to determine the probability. Let us make the calculations for the simplest case.

Suppose that $n = 2$. From the formula for the distribution of the sum of two addends, we have Simpson's distribution with base from $-2\varepsilon$ to $+2\varepsilon$., for which the probability density $\varphi(\Delta_u)$ is given by the formulas

$$\varphi(\Delta_u) = \frac{1}{2\varepsilon}\left(1 + \frac{\Delta}{2\varepsilon}\right), \quad \text{if} \quad -2\varepsilon \leqslant 0 \leqslant 0$$

and

$$\varphi(\Delta_u) = \frac{1}{2\varepsilon}\left(1 - \frac{\Delta}{2\varepsilon}\right), \quad \text{when} \quad 0 \leqslant \Delta_u \leqslant 2\varepsilon.$$

(The factor $1/(2\varepsilon)$ in front of the parenthesized expressions is obtained from the condition of normalization of the probability density, according to which the area bounded by the distribution curve is equal to unity.)

The variance of the sum is determined by the formula

$$\operatorname{Var}_2 \Delta_u = \frac{2}{3}\varepsilon^2$$

---

*If we do not know the law of distribution of the sum of the errors, we may calculate the probabilities from a single variance by using Chebyshev's inequality:

$$P(|\Delta_u| < t\sigma_u) > 1 - \frac{1}{t^2}, \quad \sigma_u = \sqrt{\operatorname{Var}\Delta_u}.$$

If we wish to obtain limiting errors with a probability greater than 0.99, then $t^{-2} = 0.01$, and $t = 10$, so that

$$P(|\Delta_u| < 10\sigma_u) > 0.99.$$

In our problem, $\sigma_u = \varepsilon\sqrt{\frac{n}{3}}$. Therefore, in our example, the limiting error is equal to $10\cdot 0.005\sqrt{\frac{50}{3}} \approx 0.2$ with a probability exceeding 0.99. This result is still somewhat better than an estimate by using the maximum limiting errors.

C

(where the subscript 2 on the "var" indicates that the number of terms is equal to 2). Let us calculate the probability that the absolute value of the error of the sum would not exceed its mean square deviation:

$$P\left(|\Delta_u| < \varepsilon\sqrt{\frac{2}{3}}\right) = \int_{-\varepsilon\sqrt{\frac{2}{3}}}^{\varepsilon\sqrt{\frac{2}{3}}} \varphi(\Delta)\, d\Delta = \int_{-\varepsilon\sqrt{\frac{2}{3}}}^{0} \frac{1}{2\varepsilon}\left(1 + \frac{\Delta}{2\varepsilon}\right) d\Delta +$$

$$+ \int_{0}^{\varepsilon\sqrt{\frac{2}{3}}} \frac{1}{2\varepsilon}\left(1 - \frac{\Delta}{2\varepsilon}\right) d\Delta = \frac{1}{2\varepsilon}\left(\Delta - \frac{\Delta^2}{4\varepsilon}\right)\Big|_{-\varepsilon\sqrt{\frac{2}{3}}}^{0} +$$

$$+ \frac{1}{2\varepsilon}\left(\Delta - \frac{\Delta^2}{4\varepsilon}\right)\Big|_{0}^{\varepsilon\sqrt{\frac{2}{3}}} = 2\left(\frac{1}{2}\sqrt{\frac{2}{3}} - \frac{1}{12}\right) = \sqrt{\frac{2}{3}} - \frac{1}{6},$$

$$P\left(|\Delta_u| < \varepsilon\sqrt{\frac{2}{3}}\right) \approx 0.65.$$

Thus, even in the case of two terms, the probability of an error not exceeding the mean square error is equal to 0.65 instead of the 0.68 obtained by the normal law. To find the probability of a deviation not exceeding $3\sigma$ has no meaning here since the limiting error in the absolute value is equal to $2\varepsilon$ and the tripled mean square error will be

$$3\varepsilon\sqrt{\frac{2}{3}} = \varepsilon\sqrt{6} > 2.4\varepsilon.$$

## 8. SUBTRACTION OF CLOSE NUMBERS

Subtraction can be considered algebraic addition and in estimating the error of a difference we may use the result obtained in Section 6. If

$$u = a - b, \tag{2.5}$$

then

$$\left.\begin{aligned} \varepsilon_u &= \varepsilon_a + \varepsilon_b, \\ \delta_u &= \frac{\varepsilon_a + \varepsilon_b}{|u|}. \end{aligned}\right\} \tag{2.6}$$

In subtracting, we sometimes encounter cases presenting difficulties in the matter of computation. Suppose that $b$ differs only slightly from $a$. Since $a$ and $b$ have a finite number of significant figures, there will be few significant figures in the difference, and this means that the relative error of the difference will be great. A special difficulty arises in the case in which the result of such a subtraction will be used in subsequent calculations. For example, if there are only two digits known with certainty in the minuend and subtrahend, we may not have more than one digit in the result of an operation between this number and other numbers; at best, there will be only two certain digits. In such cases, we say that accuracy is lost since no increase in the accuracy of the other numbers (besides $a$ and $b$) can correct the result.

There are two ways out of this situation. First, we may try to increase in a significant manner the number of digits known with certainty in the numbers $a$ and $b$ in order to have the number of known digits needed in the result. However, it may not be possible to increase the accuracy of $a$ and $b$ very much (as, for example, when $a$ and $b$ are obtained from observations). Then, we try to rewrite the computational formulas in such a way as to remove the difference between close numbers.

If the minuend is only slightly different from the subtrahend, both these numbers can be represented in the form

$$a = m + \alpha, \qquad b = m + \beta,$$

where $\alpha$ and $\beta$ are numbers that differ from each other by a large amount. The simplest transformation of the formulas consists in trying to remove the common part $m$ by a transformation of the formulas such that the calculation is reduced to the following:

$$u = \alpha - \beta.$$

If this technique is not possible either, we shall need a more complicated transformation of the formulas.

Example. Suppose that we need to compute the left side of the formula

$$(r_1 + r_2 + s)^{\frac{3}{2}} - (r_1 + r_2 - s)^{\frac{3}{2}} = u$$

(a well-known formula of Euler expressing the relationship between two radius vectors of a parabola, the chord length, and the time). In ordinary problems, $s$ is a small number in comparison with $r_1 + r_2$. Therefore, a direct calculation by using this formula leads to a loss of accuracy. We may make the following transformation:

$$u = (r_1 + r_2)^{\frac{3}{2}} \left[ \left(1 + \frac{s}{r_1 + r_2}\right)^{\frac{3}{2}} - \left(1 - \frac{s}{r_1 + r_2}\right)^{\frac{3}{2}} \right].$$

By hypothesis, the fraction $s/(r_1 + r_2)$ is small in comparison with unity. Therefore, the expressions in the parentheses can be expanded in a binomial series.

When this is done, we obtain

$$u = (r_1 + r_2)^{\frac{3}{2}} \left(3\sigma - \frac{1}{8}\sigma^3 + \dots\right), \qquad \sigma = \frac{s}{r_1 + r_2}.$$

This transformation eliminated the common part in the minuend and subtrahend (unity), which made it possible to increase the accuracy of the remainder. Suppose, for example, that $r_1 + r_2 = 2.000$ and that $s = 0.01423$ (note that these numbers are given with four definitely known digits). A direct calculation will give $u = 0.060$ (when we make the calculation with 4-place tables of logarithms); that is, the result contains only two definitely known digits although the original numbers contained four. However, if we make the calculation by using the transformed formula, we obtain 0.06031 with a doubtful last digit.*

---

*We might note that in this example it would have been possible to get rid of the close difference in a simpler manner. If we multiply and divide the left side of the original formula by the sum

$$(r_1 + r_2 + s)^{\frac{3}{2}} + (r_1 + r_2 - s)^{\frac{3}{2}},$$

## 9. MULTIPLICATION

Suppose that

$$u = a \cdot b. \tag{2.7}$$

Let us determine $\varepsilon_u$ and $\delta_u$, assuming that we know $\varepsilon_a$ and $\varepsilon_b$. To simplify the calculations, let us assume that $a$ and $b$ are both positive. The exact product will be

$$U = A \cdot B = (a + \Delta_a)(b + \Delta_b) \tag{2.8}$$

or

$$U = u + a\Delta_b + b\Delta_a + \Delta_b\Delta_a.$$

Assuming that $\Delta_a$ and $\Delta_b$ are small in comparison with $a$ and $b$, we discard the product $\Delta_b\Delta_a$ as a second-order infinitesimal. Then,

$$U - u = a\Delta_b + b\Delta_a \tag{2.9}$$

and

$$|U - u| \leqslant a|\Delta_b| + b|\Delta_a|. \tag{2.10}$$

If we replace the absolute values of the exact errors with the limiting absolute errors, we shall obtain an upper bound on the absolute value of the exact error, which we may take as the limiting absolute error of the product of the two factors

$$\varepsilon_u = a\varepsilon_b + b\varepsilon_a. \tag{2.11}$$

This formula is easily extended to the product of an arbitrary number of factors. If

$$u = a_1 a_2 \ldots a_s, \tag{2.12}$$

then,

$$\varepsilon_u = a_1 a_2 \ldots a_{s-1}\varepsilon_s + a_1 a_2 \ldots a_{s-2} a_s \varepsilon_{s-1} + \ldots + a_2 a_3 \ldots a_s \varepsilon_1. \tag{2.13}$$

---

we obtain

$$u = \frac{2(r_1 + r_2)^{\frac{3}{2}}(3\sigma - \sigma^3)}{(1+\sigma)^{\frac{3}{2}} + (1-\sigma)^{\frac{3}{2}}}.$$

However, we note that the method of expansion in a series is more general than the particular method that we have just given.

Here, it is assumed that all the factors are positive. If any of them are negative, they should be replaced by their absolute values.

Example. Suppose that we are determining the circumference of a circle of radius $R = 3.484$ m. The number $\pi$ can be taken with whatever number of definitely known digits we may need. Let us take $2\pi = 6.283$. Each of the factors is given with an accuracy up to $(1/2) \cdot 10^{-3}$. Therefore, the limiting absolute error is given by the formula

$$\varepsilon_c = (R + 2\pi) \cdot \frac{1}{2} 10^{-3}.$$

We note that to calculate the error, there is no need to take those values of $R$ and $\pi$ that are directly given since the labor required in evaluating the error can become more complicated than the basic calculation.

Let us substitute 10 for $R + 2\pi$ in the expression for $\varepsilon_c$ (which is admissible since the estimate will become cruder). Then,

$$\varepsilon_c = \frac{1}{2} \cdot 10^{-2},$$

that is, we need to limit ourselves to hundredths in the product. It is easy to see that the product will contain four definitely known digits.

The multiplication of approximate numbers can be carried out by different methods depending on the desired accuracy of the result. In a direct multiplication, there is no need to count all the digits that are obtained when the calculation is made. In particular, various methods of shortened multiplication that make it possible to simplify the labor have been worked out.* Usually, in this shortened multiplication, the digit following the last abbreviation is determined and it is discarded when the figure is rounded off. In our example, we need to consider the thousandth parts, but these are discarded after the addition. Thus,

$$c = 21.89 \text{ m}.$$

If tables of logarithms are used for the calculations, the number of digits to be counted is automatically determined by the number of digits in the table.

But today multiplications are often carried out on calculating machines. These machines automatically have all the digits that may formally be obtained. In the result, the decimal point appears in accordance with the familiar rules of arithmetic. A calculation of the accuracy is made, and the number of digits after the decimal point that can be assumed as certain is determined. Then, a second marker is used to denote which digits must be kept.

Let us now determine the limiting relative error in the product. From the general formula for an arbitrary number of factors, we obtain

$$\delta_u = \frac{\varepsilon_u}{u} = \sum_{k=1}^{s} \frac{\varepsilon_k}{a_k}.$$

---

*See the book by Ya. S. Bezikovich in the bibliography to part I at the end of the present book.

By definition, $\delta_k = \varepsilon_k / a_k$; therefore,

$$\delta_u = \sum_{k=1}^{8} \delta_k. \tag{2.14}$$

Thus, the limiting relative error of a product is equal to the sum of the limiting relative errors of the factors.

This result is of great significance. Let us recall that the limiting relative error is closely related to the number of known (definitely known) digits. Therefore, when we multiply, there is no sense in taking factors with different numbers of known digits. For if, for example, there are three known digits in one factor and five in another, the product will have a relative error corresponding to a number of known digits not exceeding three. Consequently, in the product, the number of known digits will be equal to or less than the smallest number of known digits in any one of the various factors. If the number of factors is a one-digit number, we may formulate the following rule: the product of a one-digit number of factors has as many known digits as does the factor with the smallest number of known digits, or possibly one fewer.

Example. Let us calculate the area of a circle of radius 2.37 cm. The area $P$ is equal to the product of three factors of which two have three definitely known digits each. Therefore, we need only take the first three digits of $\pi$ as well, that is, 3.14. The relative error of the product is approximately equal to

$$\delta_P = \frac{1}{4}\cdot 10^{-2} + \frac{1}{4}\cdot 10^{-2} + \frac{1}{6}\cdot 10^{-2} = \frac{2}{3}\cdot 10^{-3}$$

Here, we used 2 instead of 2.37 and 3 instead of 3.14. (Since these simplifications increase the limiting error, they are admissible.) By a crude estimate that one can do in one's head, the area will be close to 20. Therefore, the limiting absolute error is equal to $1.4 \cdot 10^{-1}$. Consequently, we should take only the tenths in the product; the last digit in this product is not known with certainty. When we calculate the error, we obtain $P = 17.6$ cm. Each of the factors had three known digits with rounding off and the product has two known digits and one uncertain digit with a limiting absolute error of 0.14.

Let us apply the rule that we have obtained to an integral power of a number. If

$$u = x^n, \tag{2.15}$$

then,

$$\left.\begin{aligned} \varepsilon_u &= n x^{n-1} \varepsilon_x, \\ \delta_u &= n \delta_x \quad (x > 0). \end{aligned}\right\} \tag{2.16}$$

The number of known digits is found just as with ordinary multiplication. In determining $\varepsilon_u$, there is, of course, no need to take the given value of $x$ with many digits. Ordinarily, we take only the first increased by 1.

Example.

$$u = 3.458^3; \qquad \varepsilon_u = 3.4^2 \cdot \frac{1}{2} \cdot 10^{-3}$$

or (increasing this value) $\varepsilon_u = 3 \cdot 10^{-2}$. It follows from this that we need to take only tenths in the product. The result will be accurate up to $(1/2) \cdot 10^{-1}$ since $\varepsilon_u < 5 \cdot 10^{-2}$.

From this example, it is clear that we can vouch for only three digits when the number that is taken to a power has four known digits. The calculation will be crude, but in an exact calculation, we cannot vouch for the hundredths in the product. This can be shown in the following manner: If we wish to calculate with reserve digits, then $x^2 = 11.958$ and $x^3 = 41.351$. Let us now take the cube of the bounds between which the exact value of the number lies. The cube of the number lies between $3.4575^2 = 41.33$ and $3.4585^3 = 41.37$. This calculation shows clearly that the hundredths in the product are unreliable but that the error in the hundredths does not exceed four units. Therefore, in making calculations, we often introduce an extra digit (in comparison with the estimate). In the present example, we could have taken the product equal to 41.36, but in making subsequent use of this number, we would have needed to calculate that its limiting absolute error is not $(1/2) \cdot 10^{-1}$ but 0.03. In the example given above, a convenient order in which to perform the calculations on a calculating machine would be as follows: First square the number, take four digits (hundredths) from the machine, namely, 11.96, multiply by 3.458, and then round the figure off to get $u = 41.36$.

Thus, we can take the square or cube of a number and be certain that we do not lose more than one known digit. One may take as many digits as there are in the number that is being raised to the power, but the last digit will be doubtful. Of course, it is not permissible to take more digits in the result than in the original number.

## 10. DIVISION

Suppose that

$$u = \frac{a}{b} \tag{2.17}$$

and that $\varepsilon_a$ and $\varepsilon_b$ are known. We need to determine $\varepsilon_u$. We have

$$U = \frac{A}{B} = \frac{a + \Delta_a}{b + \Delta_b}, \tag{2.18}$$

$$\Delta_u = U - u = \frac{a + \Delta_a}{b + \Delta_b} - \frac{a}{b} \tag{2.19}$$

or

$$\Delta_u = \frac{b\Delta_a - a\Delta_b}{b^2 + b\Delta_b}. \tag{2.20}$$

We introduce the notation

$$\Delta'_u = \frac{b\Delta_a - a\Delta_b}{b^2}$$

and we find the difference $\Delta'_u - \Delta_u$:

$$\Delta'_u - \Delta_u = \frac{(b\Delta_a - a\Delta_b)\,\Delta_b}{b\,(b^2 + b\Delta_b)}.$$

This difference is a second-order infinitesimal if $\Delta_a$ and $\Delta_b$ are considered first-order infinitesimals. Therefore, we may take

$$\Delta_u = \frac{b\Delta_a - a\Delta_b}{b^2},$$

so that

$$|\Delta_u| \leqslant \frac{|b|\,|\Delta_a| + |a|\,|\Delta_b|}{b^2}. \tag{2.21}$$

Replacing the unknowns $|\Delta_a|$ and $|\Delta_b|$ with their maximum values $\varepsilon_a$ and $\varepsilon_b$, we get

$$\varepsilon_u = \frac{|a|\,\varepsilon_b + |b|\,\varepsilon_a}{b^2}. \tag{2.22}$$

Example. Let us set $a = 5.36$, $b = 0.748$, $\varepsilon_a = 0.5 \cdot 10^{-2}$, and $\varepsilon_b = 0.5 \cdot 10^{-3}$. To simplify the calculation of $\varepsilon_u$, let us take 6 instead of $a$ and 0.8 instead of $b$ in the numerator and 0.5 instead of $b^2$ in the denominator. Then we obtain

$$\varepsilon_u = \frac{3 \cdot 10^{-3} + 4 \cdot 10^{-3}}{0.5} = 1.4 \cdot 10^{-2};$$

and finally, $\varepsilon_u = 2 \cdot 10^{-2}$ (increasing the estimate for simplification).

Strictly speaking, it follows from this example that we cannot vouch for the hundredths in the quotient. In such a case as this, the hundredths are taken in the quotient because the error in that digit is shown to exceed unity only slightly and the calculation is made in accordance with the maximum possible error. However, if we should need to carry out further operations on the quotient, in calculating the error incurred in performing these other operations, we should bear in mind the estimate of the error obtained, namely, $2 \cdot 10^{-2}$, and we should set the fraction equal to $7.17(2 \cdot 10^{-2})$, where the limiting error is shown in parentheses.*

Let us now find the limiting relative error of a quotient. By definition, we have

$$\left.\begin{aligned} \delta_u &= \frac{|a|\,\varepsilon_b + |c|\,\varepsilon_a}{b^2} : \frac{|a|}{|b|} = \frac{\varepsilon_a}{|a|} + \frac{\varepsilon_b}{|b|};\\ \delta_u &= \delta_a + \delta_b. \end{aligned}\right\} \tag{2.23}$$

---

*Sometimes, it is desirable to write the result in the form

$$7.15 < u < 7.19.$$

This result shows that the question of the number of known digits in the case of division is solved just as in the case of multiplication. Therefore, the rule given in the preceding section can be extended to the set of multiplications and divisions. The same statement applies to the uselessness of keeping factors, numerators, or denominators with greatly differing numbers of known digits.

Example 1.

$$a = 2.43, \qquad b = 0.216, \qquad u = \frac{a}{b},$$

$$\varepsilon_a = 0.5 \cdot 10^{-2}, \qquad \varepsilon_b = 0.5 \cdot 10^{-3}.$$

To make it possible to estimate the error in one's head, it is customary to increase somewhat the number $a$ in the numerator of the formula for $\varepsilon_u$ and to decrease the value of $b$ in the denominator. In the present case,

$$\varepsilon_u = \frac{3 \cdot 0.5 \cdot 10^{-3} + 0.3 \cdot 0.5 \cdot 10^{-2}}{0.2^2} = 75 \cdot 10^{-3}.$$

We may take $\varepsilon_u = 10^{-1}$. Consequently, we can be sure only of the tenths in the quotient:

$$u = 11.2.$$

A second calculation can be made from the limiting relative error:

$$\delta_a = \frac{1}{4} \cdot 10^{-2}, \qquad \delta_b = \frac{1}{4} \cdot 10^{-2}, \qquad \delta_u = \frac{1}{2} \cdot 10^{-2}.$$

Since the first digit of the quotient is equal to unity, on the basis of the table at the end of Chapter 1, it has three definitely known digits.

Both conclusions agree with the general rule: since the dividend and the divisor have three definitely known digits each, the quotient cannot have more than three definitely known digits.

Example 2. Suppose that $a = 3.144$ and that $b = 0.0536$. Let us determine the value of $u = a/b$ and let us estimate the error. From the table at the end of Chapter 1, we find

$$\delta_a = 0.017\% \approx 0.02\%, \qquad \delta_b = 0.10\%, \qquad \delta_u = 0.12\%.$$

Since the first digit of the quotient is 5, we take $\delta_u = 0.1\%$ (not altogether legitimately). We find from the table that there will be three known digits in the quotient. Although we obtain in the quotient the same number of known digits as in the original number with the fewer number of known digits, it is still significant with such a small divisor that $a$ is given with four digits. If we were to take $a$ with only three definitely known digits, we would obtain

$$\delta_a = 0.10\%, \; \delta_b = 0.10\%, \; \delta_u = 0.2\%,$$

and from the table we could be sure only of two digits. We have $u = 58.7$. If we take the fraction correctly to the nearest half of a hundredth, $u$ will then be 58.66.

The control of the fraction in terms of its maximum and minimum yields $58.59 < u < 58.72$, which shows clearly the inexactness of the hundredths and even some unreliability in the tenths, since the digit in that position can be either 6 or 7 in accordance with these bounds. It should be noted that the average of the lower and upper bounds coincides with what is obtained in calculating the hundredths. To some extent, this justifies the use of the extra digit in cases like this. If the dividend has four digits and the divisor only three, we frequently take four digits in the quotient, remembering, of course, that the fourth digit is unreliable.

Chapter 3

# ESTIMATE OF THE ERROR IN A FUNCTION WITH APPROXIMATE ARGUMENTS

## 11. LIMITING ERRORS OF A FUNCTION OF A SINGLE INDEPENDENT VARIABLE

Suppose that

$$U = f(X), \tag{3.1}$$

where $f(X)$ is a continuously differentiable function. If, in place of the exact value of the argument $A$, we substitute its approximate value $a$, the value $f(a)$ of the function will also be an approximation. Let us find an expression for the limiting absolute error of the function $\varepsilon_u$ in terms of the limiting absolute error in the approximate value of the argument $\varepsilon_a$. The exact value of $f(A)$ can be represented in the form

$$U = f(A) = f(a + \Delta_a) = f(a) + f'(a)\Delta_a + \dots, \tag{3.2}$$

where $\Delta_a$ is the exact error $a$. Treating $\Delta_a$ as an infinitesimal and assuming that we may neglect terms containing second- and higher-order infinitesimals, we obtain

$$\Delta_u \approx f'(a)\Delta_a; \tag{3.3}$$

hence,

$$\varepsilon_u = |f'(a)|\,\varepsilon_a. \tag{3.4}$$

Thus, *the limiting absolute error of a function of a single argument is equal to the product of the absolute value of the derivative and the limiting absolute error of the argument.*

For the limiting absolute error, we obtain the formula

$$\delta_u = \left|\frac{f'(a)}{f(a)}\right| \cdot |a| \cdot \delta_a. \tag{3.5}$$

From this formula, it is clear that the limiting relative error is proportional to the logarithmic derivative of the function and the value of the argument. However, we note that the estimate obtained in this manner for the error of the function can be too crude in some cases.

Example. Let us evaluate tan 85°, assuming the angle given with an accuracy up to 0.5° = 0.0087 radians. Then,

$$\varepsilon_{\tan}=\frac{1}{\cos^2 85^\circ}\cdot 0.0087 = 0.0087\cdot 132 = 1.15.$$

From the tables, tan 85° = 11.4. Therefore, the unknown actual value lies somewhere between 11.4 - 1.15 = 10.25 and 11.4 + 1.15 = 12.55. Let us check this by a direct determination of the tangents of the bounds

$$\tan 84.5^\circ = 10.4; \qquad \tan 85.5^\circ = 12.7$$

These bounds can be considered as exact. The same bounds which we established by means of the limiting absolute error should coincide with the exact bounds up to three significant figures. The significant difference between the bounds, which exceeds the admissible error in the calculations, indicates that the limiting absolute error is not exact. It is easy to show that in the present case the discarding of terms of second- and higher-order infinitesimals in the series was inadmissible for 3-digit calculations. The first discarded term in the series exceeds 0.1, and, consequently, even the tenths in the error are not reliable.

A general rule can be given for checking the suitability of a method of determining the limiting absolute error of a function. If we assume the existence and continuity of the second derivative of the function in question, we may use Taylor's formula to write

$$f(A)-f(a)=f'(a)\,\Delta_a+\frac{1}{2}f''(\xi)\,\Delta_a^2, \tag{3.6}$$

where $\xi$ is a number somewhere between $a$ and $a+\Delta a$. In "linearizing" the right side, we incur the error

$$R=\frac{1}{2}f''(\xi)\,\Delta_a^2.$$

From this we obtain the estimate

$$|R|\leqslant\frac{1}{2}M_2\varepsilon_a^2, \tag{3.7}$$

where $M_2\geqslant|f''(x)|$ for $a-\varepsilon_a\leqslant x\leqslant a+\varepsilon_a$. If $|R|$ is a number exceeding the unit of the first discarded digit, the "linearization" will be crude. We must make the calculation with a smaller degree of accuracy or introduce the correction $M_2\varepsilon_a^2/2$ in the estimate of the error.

## 12. ERRORS IN THE SIMPLER ELEMENTARY FUNCTIONS

In this section, we shall examine the errors in the basic elementary functions.

### 1. The functions $\sin x$ and $\cos x$.

If $u = \sin a$, from the general formula (3.4), we have

$$\varepsilon_u = |\cos a| \cdot \varepsilon_a. \tag{3.8}$$

From this it is clear that

$$\varepsilon_u \leqslant \varepsilon_a. \tag{3.9}$$

Analogously, we obtain

$$\varepsilon_{\cos a} = |\sin a| \, \varepsilon_a. \tag{3.10}$$

From these expressions, we may derive the following procedure for carrying out the calculations. Because of the nature of the sine function, we lose little generality in assuming that the angle belongs to the first quadrant. Then, if the values of the angles in the formulas are approximate, to reduce the error, we need to take the sine of the angle if the angle exceeds 45° and the cosine if the angle is less than 45°. This rule should be taken in those cases in which it is possible to choose a computed trigonometric function.

Example. In a number of astronomical problems, we need to make calculations of the following type: Suppose that $\alpha = r \sin \delta$ and $\beta = r \cos \delta$ are known. Find $\delta$ and $r$. We evaluate $\tan \delta = \alpha / \beta$. From the tangent, we find an approximate value of the angle $\delta$. To determine the value of $r$, we may use either of the formulas $r = \alpha / \sin \delta$ or $r = \beta / \cos \delta$. Which of these two formulas to use should be determined by the rule stated above.

Suppose $\alpha = 2.364$, that $\beta = 1.575$, that $\tan \delta = 1.501$, and that $\delta = 56° 20$. Since $\delta > 45°$, to determine the value of $r$, it is advisable to use the sine since the error in the sine is less than that in the cosine. The values given or calculated for these quantities are as follows:

| | | |
|---|---|---|
| $\alpha^* = r \sin \delta$ | 2.364* | |
| $\sin \delta$ | 0.832 | (3) |
| $\beta^* = r \cos \delta$ | 1.575* | |
| $\tan \delta$ | 1.501 | (1) |
| $\delta$ | 56° 20′ | (2) |
| $r$ | 2.841 | (5) |
| $\cos \delta$ | 0.554 | (4) |
| $(r)$ | 2.843. | (6) |

The asterisks denote the given values for $\alpha$ and $\beta$ and the numbers in parentheses indicate the order in which the operations are made. The last two entries give a control for the calculations. The last entry is the control value of $r$.

### 2. The functions $\tan x$ and $\cot x$.

If $u = \tan a$ and $v = \cot a$, we have

$$\left.\begin{aligned} \varepsilon_u &= \frac{\varepsilon_a}{\cos^2 a}, \\ \varepsilon_v &= \frac{\varepsilon_a}{\sin^2 a}. \end{aligned}\right\} \tag{3.11}$$

It is clear from these formulas that

$$\varepsilon_{\tan a} \geqslant \varepsilon_a; \qquad \varepsilon_{\cot a} \geqslant \varepsilon_a. \tag{3.12}$$

If the angle $a$ is close to 0, the error in the tangent is close to its minimum and the error in the cotangent is great; consequently, the suitability of the formula for $\varepsilon$ should be examined. The opposite conclusions hold when the angle is close to 90°. Accordingly, we need to arrange our calculations in such a way as to be able to choose formulas containing either the tangent or the cotangent.

### 3. *Determination of angle from a trigonometric function.*

Suppose that $u = \arcsin a$. Then,

$$\varepsilon_u = \frac{\varepsilon_a}{\sqrt{1-a^2}}. \tag{3.13}$$

We can draw the following conclusions from this formula:

(a) $\varepsilon_u \geqslant \varepsilon_a$. Equality holds when $a = 0$, that is, when $u = 0$.

(b) If we need to determine the angle from the sine, the error will be small only if the angle (still assumed to belong to the first quadrant) is small.

(c) It is not advisable to determine the value of the angle from the sine for angles close to 90° because the error in the angle will be much greater than the error in the sine. For example, if $u =$ arcsin 0.984,

$$\varepsilon_u = \frac{5 \cdot 10^{-4}}{0.17} = 3 \cdot 10^{-3},$$

that is, the error in the angle can exceed 10′. This can be seen directly from the tables in which, correct to three decimal places, sin 79° 40′ = 0.984 and sin 79° 50′ = 0.984.

The same remarks hold with regard to making determinations of the angle from the cosine with the difference that it is convenient to determine the angle from the cosine when the angle is close to 90° but not when it is close to 0.

Suppose that $u = \arctan a$ and $v = \operatorname{arccot} a$. Then,

$$\varepsilon_u = \frac{\varepsilon_a}{1+a^2}, \qquad \varepsilon_v = \frac{\varepsilon_u}{1+a^2}. \tag{3.14}$$

It is clear from these formulas that it is most suitable of all to determine the angle from the tangent or cotangent because the error in the angle is less than the error in the tangent. The most undesirable case is the one in which a small angle is determined from the tangent or a large one, close to 90°, is determined from the cotangent, but in even these cases the error in the angle will be close to the error in the function. Therefore, our computational plans should be such as to make our calculations from the tangent or cotangent.

Example. Let us consider a problem that is frequently encountered in astronomical calculations, namely, that of determining the equatorial spherical coordinates from the rectangular coordinates $x$, $y$, and $z$. From the formulas relating these coordinates, we can make the following table of the calculations:

| | | |
|---|---|---|
| $x^* = r \cos \delta \cos \alpha$ | 3.1448* | |
| $\cos \alpha$ | 0.82509 | (3) |
| $y^* = r \cos \delta \sin \alpha$ | —2.1534* | |
| $y : x = \tan \alpha$ | —0.68475 | (1) |
| $x : \cos \alpha = r \cos \delta$ | 3.8115 | (4) |
| $\cos \delta$ | 0.98906 | (7) |
| $z^* = r \sin \delta$ | 0.56843* | |
| $z : r \cos \delta = \tan \delta$ | 0.14914 | (5) |
| $\alpha$ | 325° 35′ 54″ | (2) |
| $\delta$ | 8° 28′ 58″ | (6) |
| $r \cos \delta : \cos \delta = r$ | 3.8537 | (8) |

These calculations involve five significant figures. Therefore, the angles are given with an accuracy up to 1″. The values with the asterisks are given. The numbers in the parentheses indicate the order in which the operations are performed.

## 4. Powers and roots.

If $u = a^n$, then

$$\left.\begin{aligned} \varepsilon_u &= |n|\, a^{n-1}\varepsilon_a, \\ \delta_u &= |n|\, \delta_a. \end{aligned}\right\} \qquad (3.15)$$

It follows from these simple formulas that if $|n| > 1$, the relative error of the power is greater than the relative error of the original number. On the other hand, if $|n| < 1$ (that is, if we are taking an integral root of a number), the operation decreases the error. If the number $n$ is of the order of two or three on the one hand or 1/2 or 1/3 on the other, it follows from the formula for the relative error that we can take as many significant figures in the result as in the original number.

Example.

$\pi^2 = 9.86$, $\sqrt{\pi} = 1.77$, if we take $\pi = 3.14$,

$\pi^2 = 9.8696$, $\sqrt{\pi} = 1.7725$, if we take $\pi = 3.1416$.

We can agree to consider the values of $\pi^2$ and $\sqrt{\pi}$ shown with five significant figures as exact and the values shown with three significant figures as approximate. Comparison of the approximate with the "exact" figures shows in this case that the result contains either three known digits (as in the case of the root) or, to be formally rigorous, two digits (as in the case of the power) since in rounding off the five-digit value of $\pi^2$ to three digits, we need, by the rule of rounding off, to take 9.87, whereas the figure obtained is 9.86.

## 5. Logarithms and exponentials.

Suppose that $u = \log a$. Since $a = 10^u$, we have $u = (\log e) \ln a$, where $\ln a$ is the natural logarithm and $\log e = 0.4343 < 0.5$. Therefore, we need to take

$$\varepsilon_u = \frac{1}{2}\frac{\varepsilon_a}{a} = \frac{1}{2}\delta_a. \tag{3.16}$$

The limiting relative error $\delta_a$ in the approximate number $a$ does not depend on the position of the decimal, as was shown in Section 5 of Chapter 1, but depends primarily on the number of known digits in that number. If $a$ is rounded off, according to Section 5, we may take

$$\delta_a = \frac{1}{2C \cdot 10^{s-1}}, \tag{3.17}$$

where $C$ is the first significant figure and $s$ is the number of definitely known digits. It follows from this that

$$\varepsilon_u = \frac{1}{4C} \cdot \frac{1}{10^{s-1}}. \tag{3.18}$$

Here, if $C > 2.5$,

$$\varepsilon_u < \frac{1}{10^s}, \tag{3.19a}$$

and if $C < 2.5$,

$$\varepsilon_u > \frac{1}{10^s}. \tag{3.19b}$$

On the basis of this, we may formulate the following rule: if the first digit of the approximate number is greater than 2, its logarithm will have as many known digits after the decimal as there are known digits in the number; if the first digit is less than 3, the last digit of the logarithm, taken with five digits, may not be completely reliable: an error of one or two units in the last digit is possible (as, when $C = 1$, we have $\varepsilon_u = 2.5 \cdot 10^{-5}$). A somewhat simplified rule is usually followed: the number of digits to the right of the decimal in a logarithm should be equal to the number of definitely known digits in the approximate number. In many applied problems of a technological nature, it is sufficient to get a relative error corresponding to three or four known digits since the original data contains only that many digits. If observations yield three digits, the calculations can be performed on a slide rule. In the case of 4-digit results of observation, either a calculating machine or a 4-digit table of logarithms can be used. When the number of digits is greater than three or four, calculating machines are most often used at the present time.

It is easy to investigate the error of the inverse operation, that is, to determine a number from its logarithm. The result of this inverse operation is the exponential function or antilogarithm.

It follows from the formula for the limiting absolute error of a logarithm that

$$\delta_a = \frac{1}{0.4343}\varepsilon_u. \tag{3.20}$$

From the definition of a limiting error, the right side can be increased; therefore, we take

$$\delta_a = 2.4\varepsilon_u \qquad (\text{ if } \quad u = \log a). \tag{3.21}$$

If the logarithm ($u$) has $s$ digits to the right of the decimal, in the case that $u$ is rounded off,

$$\left.\begin{aligned} \varepsilon_u &= \frac{1}{2}\cdot 10^{-8} \\ \delta_a &= 1.2\cdot 10^{-8} \end{aligned}\right\} \tag{3.22}$$

which means that the number almost always has $s$ known digits. If the logarithm is obtained without rounding off, the relative error of the antilogarithm will be 2.5 times as great as the limiting error of the logarithm. Therefore, the number has either $s$ or $s-1$ known digits.

## 6. Logarithms of trigonometric functions.

(a) $u = \log \sin a$. Then,

$$\varepsilon_u = 0.4343 \cot a \cdot \varepsilon_a. \tag{3.23}$$

Let us assume that the angle is in the first quadrant. For the limiting error to be less than the limiting error of the angle, it will be necessary that $\cot a \leqslant 0.4343$ or $\tan a \geqslant 0.4343$, in other words, that $a > 23°\ 20'$.

From this it is clear that it is not suitable in calculations to take the logarithm of the sine of an angle less than 23.5°. It is suggested that the reader verify that it is not suitable to take the logarithm of the cosine of an angle if the angle is greater than 66.5°.* If the angle is less than 66.5° but greater than 23.5°, the limiting errors of the logarithms of both sine and cosine are less than the limiting error in the angle. (We note that the concept of "suitability" of calculation has to do with just this.)

---

*It should be recalled that the limiting error of the angle has to be expressed in radians in these error calculations.

(b) $u = \log \tan a$. Then,

$$\varepsilon_u = 0.4343 \cot a \sec^2 a \cdot \varepsilon_a = \frac{0.8686}{\sin 2a} \varepsilon_a. \quad (3.24)$$

In order for the error in the function to be less than the error in the angle, it will be necessary that $\sin 2a \geqslant 0.8686$, that is, that $59°\ 30' < 2a < 120°\ 30'$ or (more crudely) $30° < a < 60°$. Since $\log \cot a = - \log \tan a$, the estimate of the error for the logarithm of the cotangent is the same as for the logarithm of the tangent.

On the basis of what has been said, we can formulate the following rule for a rational organization of the calculations when using logarithms of trigonometric functions.

If the angle is less than 23.5°, we should take the logarithm of the cosine (recasting the formulas if possible). If the angle lies between 23.5° and 30°, it is best to take the logarithms of the sine and cosine. If the angle lies between 30° and 60°, we may use the logarithms of any of the four functions—sine, cosine, tangent, or cotangent. If the angle lies between 60° and 66.5°, we should take the logarithms of the sine and cosine. Finally, if the angle is greater than 66.5°, it is best to take only the logarithm of the sine.

## 7. *Determination of angles from the logarithms of the trigonometric functions.*

(a) If $\log \sin u = a$, then $\sin u = 10^a$ and $u = \arcsin 10^a$. Therefore,

$$\varepsilon_u = \frac{10^a}{\sqrt{1 - 10^{2a}}} \cdot \frac{1}{0.4343} \varepsilon_a \quad (3.25a)$$

or

$$\varepsilon_u = \frac{\tan u}{0.4343} \varepsilon_a. \quad (3.25b)$$

As in the preceeding sections, we shall take the condition $\varepsilon_u \leqslant \varepsilon_a$ as the criterion of suitability of an approximate calculation. In the present case, this condition leads to the inequality $u \leqslant 23.5°$. Thus, the calculation of an angle from the logarithm of its sine is most satisfactory in the case of angles less than 23.5°. Analogously, we may show that calculating an angle from the logarithm of its cosine is suitable if the angle is greater than 66.5°.

In a case where we *must* calculate an angle from the logarithm of its sine or cosine, the following rules are followed: if possible, angles less than 45° are calculated from the logarithm of the sine, and angles greater than 45° from the logarithm of the cosine. In the case of angles between 23.5° and 66.5°, this leads to a greater limiting error than the error of the logarithm that is used. In particular, if the angle is equal to 45°, the error in the angle will be 2.3 times as great as the error in the logarithm of the sine (or cosine).

D

Example. Suppose that $\log \sin u = 9.3847 - 10$. From 4-place tables of the logarithms of trigonometric functions, we find that $u = 14° \, 02'$. From tables of the trigonometric functions, we find that $\tan u = 0.2425$. Therefore,

$$\varepsilon_u = \frac{0.2425}{0.4343} \cdot \frac{1}{2} \cdot 10^{-4} = 3 \cdot 10^{-5}.$$

The estimate of the error in the angle is obtained in radians. Conversion to degree measure gives $\varepsilon_u = 6'' = 0.1'$. Since the angle is sufficiently small, it can be calculated with an accuracy up to 0.1. By interpolation, we obtain $u = 14° \, 02.0'$.

(b) If $\log \tan u = a$, then $\tan u = 10^a$ and $u = \arctan 10^a$. Then,

$$\varepsilon_u = \frac{10^a}{1 + 10^{2a}} \cdot \frac{\varepsilon_a}{0.4343} \tag{3.26a}$$

or

$$\varepsilon_u = \frac{\sin 2u}{0.8686} \varepsilon_a. \tag{3.26b}$$

The condition under which it is suitable to calculate the angle from the logarithm of its tangent is that

$$\sin 2u \leqslant 0.8686,$$

that is, that $2u < 60°$ or $2u > 120°$. From this it follows that it is suitable to determine angles between 0 and 30° and between 60° and 90° from the logarithm of the tangent. In the interval between 30° and 60°, the error in the angle is greater than that in the logarithm of the tangent being used, but this increase is not great: if the angle is close to 45°, its limiting error will be 1.15 times as great as the error in the logarithm of the tangent.

Since $\log \cot u = -\log \tan u$, the limiting error of the angle is obtained from the logarithm of the cotangent in the same way as in the preceding case.

Comparison of the errors in determining an angle from the logarithms of the trigonometric functions shows that it is most satisfactory to determine the angle from the logarithm of the tangent or the cotangent (since throughout the entire interval from 0 to 90° the limiting error of the angle does not exceed the product of the limiting error of the given logarithm and the number 1.15) and that in two thirds of this interval (from 0 to 30° and from 60° to 90°) the limiting error of the angle is less than the limiting error of the logarithm of the tangent. Therefore, with logarithmic calculations also we try to choose formulas and schemes that will allow us to calculate the angles from the logarithms of the tangents or cotangents.

## 13. THE ERROR INVOLVED IN FUNCTIONS OF SEVERAL VARIABLES

To shorten the writing, we shall confine ourselves to seeking the error involved in the case of functions of two variables. The formula that we shall derive is easily generalized to the case of an arbitrary number of variables.

Suppose that $U=f(x, y)$ is a continuously differentiable function defined on some set of values of the arguments $x$ and $y$. Suppose that we replace the exact values of the arguments with their approximate values $a$ and $b$. Then, we shall obtain an approximate value of the function $u=f(a, b)$. Let us calculate the limiting absolute error of the approximate value of the function, assuming that we know the limiting absolute errors of the arguments $\varepsilon_a$ and $\varepsilon_b$.

We shall denote the exact errors in the arguments by $\Delta_a$ and $\Delta_b$. From the definition of exact error (1.1), we have

$$A=a+\Delta_a, \quad B=b+\Delta_b,$$

where $A$ and $B$ are the exact values of the arguments. The exact value of the function is

$$U=f(a+\Delta_a, b+\Delta_b).$$

Let us assume that the exact errors are small, so that we can neglect their squares and higher powers. Let us expand the right side of the above equation in powers of the exact errors and let us cut off the expansion at the terms containing the first powers of the errors. Then, we obtain

$$\Delta_u=U-u=\left(\frac{\partial U}{\partial x}\right)_{\substack{x=a\\y=b}} \cdot \Delta_a+\left(\frac{\partial U}{\partial y}\right)_{\substack{x=a\\y=b}} \cdot \Delta_b. \tag{3.27}$$

In this equation, $\Delta_u$ represents an approximate value of the exact error since only the first two terms in the expansion are kept. It follows from this equation that

$$|\Delta_u| \leqslant \left|\frac{\partial U}{\partial x}\right|_{\substack{x=a\\y=b}} \cdot |\Delta_a|+\left|\frac{\partial U}{\partial y}\right|_{\substack{x=a\\y=b}} \cdot |\Delta_b|.$$

If we replace the absolute values of the exact errors with their limiting absolute errors, we shall obtain an upper bound on the absolute value of the error in the function—a value that we can take as the limiting absolute error in the function:

$$\varepsilon_u=\left|\frac{\partial U}{\partial x}\right|_{\substack{x=a\\y=b}} \cdot \varepsilon_a+\left|\frac{\partial U}{\partial y}\right|_{\substack{x=a\\y=b}} \cdot \varepsilon_b. \tag{3.28}$$

This formula is sometimes called the differential formula for the estimate of an error, since the right side is analogous to the expression for the total differential. For if we replace the differentials of the arguments in such an expression with the limiting absolute errors, and if we replace the partial derivatives of the function with their absolute values, we obtain the formula just derived. It is used both for computing an estimate in specific numerical values and for analyzing the accuracy and clarifying the conditions under which the accuracy of the result can be improved (that is, under which the limiting absolute error of the function will be decreased).

We note that the formula with which we began (that is, the formula containing the first two terms of the expansion) is sometimes given for the problem in question. This is meaningful only in those cases in which the exact errors in the arguments are considered as given. Then, the formula gives an approximate value of the error of the function. However, if the exact errors in the arguments are unknown, as is usually the case, and only the limiting errors are known, we need to apply the formula derived in this section.

Let us consider some examples of the application of this formula.

Example 1. The simplest formula for determining the time at which a star will rise and set is of the form

$$t = \arccos\,[(-\tan\varphi)\tan\delta]$$

where $\varphi$ is the latitude of the point at which an observation is made, $\delta$ is the declination of the star, and $t$ is the hour angle (defined by some convention). In using this formula, we assume that $|(\tan\varphi)\tan\delta| < 1$, that is, that the star does actually rise and set.

From the formula derived above, we obtain the following expression for the limiting absolute error of the hour angle:

$$\varepsilon_t = \frac{|\sin\delta\sec\varphi|\,\varepsilon_\varphi + |\sin\varphi\sec\delta|\,\varepsilon_\delta}{\sqrt{\cos(\varphi+\delta)\cos(\varphi-\delta)}}.$$

The symmetry of the formula with regard to $\varphi$ and $\delta$ is a result of the symmetry in the formula from which the calculations are made.

Let us calculate the limiting error for the calculation of the hour angle for the rise of Mars at Simferopol on February 3, 1948.

From the table of latitudes of the more important cities in the Soviet Union contained in the book *Kurs obshchei astronomii* (Course in General Astronomy) by S. N. Blazhko, we find that $\varphi = 44°\,57'$. From the astronomical calendar for the year 1948, we find that $\delta = 14°\,20'$. Since these numbers are taken from more exact tables with rounding off, we may take $\varepsilon_\varphi = \varepsilon_\delta = 0.5'$ or $\varepsilon_\varphi = \varepsilon_\delta = 0.00015$ radians. (We recall that in these calculations, the limiting error of an angle must be given in radians. Therefore, the quantity $0.5' = 30''$ must be divided by the number of seconds in a radian, which is 206,265. As a simplification, we take 200,000, which is permissible since such a substitution does not decrease but increases the limiting error.) For simplicity, all the factors should be replaced with as simple ones as possible, but in such a way that the error is not decreased. It is easy to see that in the present problem all the angles should be increased. Therefore, we take $\varphi = 45°$, $\delta = 15°$, $\varphi + \delta = 60°$, and $\varphi - \delta = 31°$. By using these values for the angles and a 2- or 3-place table of trigonometric functions or a slide rule, we obtain

$$\varepsilon_t = 0{,}37\,\varepsilon_\varphi + 0{,}74\,\varepsilon_\delta = 0{,}00018 \text{ radians}$$

The hour angle is calculated from the formula with a limiting absolute error of about $36''$.

Let us now consider the question of the most satisfactory conditions of observation, that is, those under which the limiting error will be the smallest. Since neither the choice of point of observation nor the choice of the celestial body is arbitrary in this problem, the solution of the question can be, so to speak, only passive; that is, we can only ascertain which celestial bodies and which latitudes enable us to calculate the hour angle of the rising and setting of the body with the least and which with the greatest accuracy. Since the two arguments $\varphi$ and $\delta$ are symmetric, we need only investigate the effect of one of them on the result. It is easy to see that as $\varphi$ increases from 0 to 90° with $\delta$ held constant, the coefficients of $\varepsilon_\varphi$ and $\varepsilon_\delta$ increase monotonically. We would obtain an analogous conclusion with $\delta$ increasing monotonically and $\varphi$ held constant. It follows from this that the hour angles of rising and setting of the body are determined with least error close to the equator of the earth and for bodies that are close to the celestial equator.

Example 2. Determination of the astronomical latitude of the point of observation depends on the basic formula

$$\cos z = \sin\varphi \sin\delta + \cos\varphi \cos\delta \cos t,$$

where $z$ is the geocentric zenithal distance of the body in question, $\varphi$ is the unknown latitude, and $\delta$ is the declination of the star. Let us set

$$t = \tau - \alpha, \qquad \tau = T + u;$$

where $\alpha$ is the right ascension of the body, $T$ is the reading of a chronometer, and $u$ is the correction of the chronometer. The declination and the right ascension can be obtained from an almanac at the instant of observation. Here, the geocentric values must be taken. Let us suppose that $\alpha$ and $\delta$ do not contain errors or, more precisely, that the errors in the coordinates are considerably less than the errors in those quantities that are obtained from observations.

Therefore, we shall assume that errors are contained only in the measured value of the zenithal distance and in the value of $\tau$., since it is impossible to separate the error in the reading of the chronometer from the error in the correction of the chronometer. Instead of expressing the latitude when it is determined explicitly in terms of the other quantities, we shall proceed in the following fashion. First we differentiate both sides of the formula. After replacing the differentials with the exact errors, we obtain

$$-\sin z\,\Delta_z = \cos\varphi \sin\delta\,\Delta_\varphi - \sin\varphi \cos\delta \cos t\,\Delta_\varphi - \cos\varphi \cos\delta \sin t\,\Delta_\tau.$$

For the spherical triangle with vertices at the zenith, the pole, and the star, we obtain the formulas

$$\cos\varphi \sin\delta - \sin\varphi \cos\delta \cos t = -\sin z \cos A,$$
$$\cos\delta \sin t = \sin z \sin A,$$

where $A$ is the azimuth.

By using these formulas, we can write the expression for the exact error in the latitude in a sufficiently simple form:

$$\Delta_\varphi = \sec A\,\Delta_z - \cos\varphi\ \tan A\,\Delta_\tau.$$

Replacing the errors with the limiting values of the errors and taking the absolute values of all the factors gives a formula for calculating the limiting absolute error in the latitude:

$$\varepsilon_\varphi = |\sec A|\,\varepsilon_z + \cos\varphi\,|\ \tan A|\,\varepsilon_\tau.$$

The method of application of this formula in particular cases is obvious. Therefore, we shall not consider a numerical example. From the formula, it is easy to derive conditions under which the limiting error in the latitude will be at a minimum, namely when the star rises at meridian ($A = 0$ or 180°). In this case, the coefficient of $\varepsilon_z$ will have its minimum value, namely, unity and the coefficient of $\varepsilon_\tau$ will vanish.

Two practical deductions can be made from this: (1) Observations for determining the latitude should be made when the star is close to a meridian (since it is not easy to ensure observations exactly at a meridian), and (2) it is extremely important for the zenithal distance to be measured as exactly as possible since under all circumstances we have the obvious inequality $\varepsilon_\varphi \geqslant \varepsilon_z$, with equality holding only when the observations are on the meridian.

Example 3. To determine the correction in the hours, we use the same formula as in determining the latitude, but here we assume the latitude known.

For calculating the correction in the hours, we must write the formula in the form

$$\cos z = \sin\varphi \sin\delta + \cos\varphi \cos\delta \cos(T - \alpha + u)$$

(with the same notations as in the preceding example).

As in the preceding example, we shall disregard errors in the spherical equatorial coordinates. We make the substitution

$$\Delta_\tau = \Delta_T + \Delta_u$$

in the formula of the preceding section to calculate the error. Let us solve for $\Delta_u$. Then,

$$\Delta_u = -\Delta_T - \sec\varphi \cot A\,\Delta_\varphi.$$

Passage to the limiting absolute errors gives the formula

$$\varepsilon_u = \varepsilon_T + \sec\varphi\,|\cot A|\,\varepsilon_\varphi + \sec\varphi\,|\csc A|\,\varepsilon_z.$$

There are no difficulties involved in calculating the limiting error from this formula. As is usual in such calculations, we may make crude approximations to the values of the angles $A$ and $\varphi$ in such a way that the limiting error will not decrease but increase.

It is clear from the formula that we have obtained that the determination of the correction in the hours will be made with the minimum error if the heavenly body is on the first vertical (azimuth equal to 90° or 270°). The minimum value of $\varepsilon_u$ is equal to $\varepsilon_T + \varepsilon_z \sec\varphi$.

Example 4. The acceleration due to gravity is determined by means of a swinging pendulum from the formula

$$g = \pi^2 \frac{l}{P^2};$$

here $l$ is the reduced length of the pendulum and $P$ is the period of oscillation. Observations yield the following values and their limiting errors:

$$l = 50.02 \text{ cm}, \quad \varepsilon_l = 0.01 \text{ cm},$$

$$P = 0.7098 \text{ sec}, \quad \varepsilon_P = 0.0001 \text{ sec}.$$

Let us calculate the acceleration due to gravity $g$ and its limiting error. We shall take 3.1416 as the value of $\pi$; that is, we shall set $\varepsilon_\pi = 0.00005$.

If we apply the basic formula to the present case, we obtain

$$\varepsilon_g = \frac{2\pi l}{P^2}\varepsilon_\pi + \frac{\pi^2}{P^2}\varepsilon_l + \frac{2\pi^2 l}{P^3}\varepsilon_P,$$

which can be conveniently written in the form

$$\varepsilon_g = \pi P^{-3}(2Pl\varepsilon_\pi + \pi P\varepsilon_l + 2\pi l\varepsilon_P).$$

For simplicity's sake, let us take $P = 1$, $l = 50$, $\pi = 4$, and $2\pi = 7$ in parentheses and let us take the factor in front of the parentheses equal to 10 (on the basis of the rough estimate made by taking $\pi = 3.14$ and $0.7^3 = 0.343$). Therefore, the product has a value of about 9, but we decreased the value somewhat so that it will be more accurate to take the value 10. Then, we obtain $\varepsilon_g = 10\cdot(100\cdot 5\cdot 10^{-5} + 4\cdot 10^{-2} + 7\cdot 10^{-4})$ or $\varepsilon_g = 0.8$ cm/sec. The error is noticeably increased, but the result is obtained quite simply anyway and, in fact, the entire calculation can be done in one's head. A more accurate calculation, explained in the book *Matematicheskaya obrabotka rezul'tatov izmerenii* (Mathematical Analysis of the Results of Measurements) by K. P. Yakovlev, from which this example is borrowed, gives an estimate of the error of 0.5 cm/sec². When the calculations are performed, we obtain $g = 978.0$. Considering the estimate of the error that we have obtained, we must take

$$g = 978 \text{ cm/sec}^2; \quad \varepsilon_g = 1 \text{ cm/sec}^2.$$

Example 5. To calculate the orbit of a small planet from three observations, we need to calculate the average anomaly $M$ when we know the eccentricity $e$ and the eccentric anomaly $E$. This calculation is made on the basis of Kepler's equation

$$M = E - e\sin E.$$

Let us take $E = 43°\,35'\,16''$ and $e = 0.14136$. We need to calculate the average anomaly $M$ and to estimate its limiting absolute error. Suppose that all the significant figures written in the expressions for $E$ and $e$ are definitely known and that we know that these numbers are obtained by rounding off. The limiting absolute error in the eccentricity is equal to 0.000005. The error in the eccentric anomaly is equal to 0.5″. If we convert this value to radian measure (dividing by 200,000 instead of 206,265—see example 1), we obtain $\varepsilon_E = 0.0000025$. We then compute the limiting error of the average anomaly from the formula

$$\varepsilon_M = (1 - e \cos E)\,\varepsilon_E + |\sin E|\,\varepsilon_l.$$

In this formula, we do not need to write the absolute value of the derivative with respect to the eccentric anomaly, since the value appearing in parentheses has to be positive since $e < 1$ and the absolute value of the cosine never exceeds unity.

To calculate the limiting error, we take $\cos E = 0.72$ (estimating too low), $e = 0.14$ (estimating too low) and $\sin E = 0.70$ (estimating too high). Then, $e \cos E = 0.10$ and $1 - e \cos E = 0.9$. Thus,

$$\varepsilon_M = 0.9 \cdot 2.5 \cdot 10^{-6} + 0.7 \cdot 5 \cdot 10^{-6}.$$

Increasing the limiting error only slightly, we obtain $\varepsilon_M = 0.000006$ radians. Conversion to an estimate in seconds of arc by multiplying by 206,265 (we actually multiply by a slightly greater number) gives $\varepsilon_M = 1.3''$.

*Remark:* To calculate $M$, we must either express the angle $E$ in radians or express the eccentricity in seconds or degrees of arc. This is explained by the fact that Kepler's equation $M = E - e \sin E$ is a formula derived using the tools of analysis and therefore the angles in it are naturally expressed in radians. To make possible the use of ordinary tables of trigonometric functions (in which the argument is expressed in degree measure), we need to multiply all the terms in the equation by the number of seconds (or degrees) in a radian. Then, the angles $E$ and $M$ are expressed in seconds and in the term $e \sin E$ the conversion factor can be applied either to $e$ or to $\sin E$. It is customary to treat the eccentricity formally as an angle in radians. Therefore, it is converted into seconds of arc. When we express the eccentricity in seconds, multiplying by 206,265, we obtain the value $e = 29{,}158''$ in our problem. If we now multiply this number by the 5-place value of the sine, 0.68947, we obtain $(E - M)'' = 20{,}104''$. Therefore, $E - M = 5°35'04''$. Finally, we have $M = 38°\,00'\,12''$ and $\varepsilon_M = 1.3''$. Consequently, in the value of the average anomaly, we cannot vouch for whole seconds. An error in either direction of one second is possible (that is, it can be 11″, 12″, or 13″).

Example 6. Let us calculate the total surface area $P$ of a right circular cone whose base has radius $r = 3.4$ cm and whose generator has length $l = 7.6$ cm. Let us find the limiting relative error of the result $P$.

The total area is given by the formula

$$P = \pi r^2 + 2\pi r l.$$

The formula for calculating the limiting absolute error is of the form

$$\varepsilon_P = (r^2 + 2rl)\,\varepsilon_\pi + \pi\,(2r + 2l)\,\varepsilon_r + 2\pi r \varepsilon_l.$$

Taking $\pi = 3.14$, we obtain for the limiting absolute errors of the arguments

$$\varepsilon_\pi = 0.5 \cdot 10^{-2}, \qquad \varepsilon_r = \varepsilon_l = 0.5 \cdot 10^{-1}.$$

If the coefficients of the limiting errors in the arguments are calculated with the values given for them,

$$\varepsilon_P = 64\varepsilon_\pi + 70\varepsilon_r + 22\varepsilon_l \quad \text{or} \quad \varepsilon_P = 5 \text{ cm}^2.$$

Thus, in the value for the total area, we have certainty only up to one tenth of a square centimeter. Calculation gives $P = 200$ cm² and $\varepsilon_P = 5$ cm². In the expression for $P$, the digits 2 and 0 are certain; $\delta_P = 2.5\%$.

## 14. THE CONCEPT OF THE INVERSE PROBLEM IN THE THEORY OF APPROXIMATE CALCULATIONS

Suppose that $U$ is a function of $n$ independent variables $x, z, \ldots, w$, whose approximate values can vary somewhat in accuracy.

Let us suppose that a certain required accuracy for a function is given in advance, that is, that the limiting absolute error of the quantity $u$ is given. The problem is to determine the limiting absolute errors in the arguments in such a way as to ensure this given accuracy in the function. We shall call this problem the inverse problem of approximate calculations.

If the function has more than one argument, the solution obviously will not be determined since only one number (the error $\varepsilon_u$) is given and, to solve the problem, we need as many unknown limiting errors as there are arguments. In practical problems, a convention, called the *method of equal influences*, is often used. The principle of this convention consists in the following: in accordance with (3.28), let us write the expression for the limiting error of the function in terms of the limiting errors of the argument:

$$\varepsilon_u = \left|\frac{\partial U}{\partial x}\right|_{\substack{x=a\\ y=b\\ \cdots\\ w=m}} \cdot \varepsilon_a + \left|\frac{\partial U}{\partial y}\right|_{\substack{x=a\\ y=b\\ \cdots\\ w=m}} \cdot \varepsilon_b + \cdots + \left|\frac{\partial U}{\partial w}\right|_{\substack{x=a\\ y=b\\ \cdots\\ w=m}} \cdot \varepsilon_m.$$

The method of equal influences consists in choosing errors of the arguments in such a way that all the terms on the right side of this equation will have the same value:

$$\left|\frac{\partial U}{\partial x}\right| \varepsilon_a = \left|\frac{\partial U}{\partial y}\right| \varepsilon_b = \cdots = \frac{\varepsilon_u}{n}, \tag{3.29}$$

where $n$ is the number of arguments. These equations give the expressions for the limiting errors in the arguments:

$$\varepsilon_a = \frac{\varepsilon_u}{n\left|\frac{\partial U}{\partial x}\right|}, \qquad \varepsilon_b = \frac{\varepsilon_u}{n\left|\frac{\partial U}{\partial y}\right|}, \ \ldots \tag{3.30}$$

It may be that the limiting errors obtained in this manner are not all admissible from the conditions of the observations. In such cases, we obviously must make some sort of modification in the convention, but we should still take an accuracy as close as possible to the one obtained from the method of equal influences. A justification for this method cannot be easily demonstrated; it is only a convenient convention.

A second variation on the method of equal influences is the convention of setting all the terms in the expression for the limiting relative error of the function equal to each other. This leads to the equations

$$\delta_u = \left|\frac{a}{u}\right| \left|\frac{\partial U}{\partial x}\right|_{\substack{x=a\\ y=b\\ \cdots\\ w=m}} \cdot \delta_a + \left|\frac{b}{u}\right| \left|\frac{\partial U}{\partial y}\right|_{\substack{x=a\\ y=b\\ \cdots\\ w=m}} \cdot \delta_y + \cdots; \tag{3.31}$$

$$\left.\begin{aligned}\delta_a &= \frac{\delta_u}{n\left|\frac{a}{u}\right|\left|\frac{\partial U}{\partial x}\right|},\\ \delta_b &= \frac{\delta_u}{n\left|\frac{b}{u}\right|\left|\frac{\partial U}{\partial y}\right|}.\end{aligned}\right\} \tag{3.32}$$

It is easy to see that the expressions for the limiting relative errors of the arguments are formally equivalent to the expressions for the limiting absolute errors, since by means of elementary transformations, one can obtain an expression for $\delta_a$ from the expression for $\varepsilon_a$, etc. However, it often happens in approximate calculations that from a practical standpoint there can be a significant difference, since two formally equivalent formulas can (as a result of the fact that we necessarily use a finite number of digits) give two numbers that are different both in magnitude and in accuracy. Therefore, in more important problems, we should try to write both expressions and compare the suitability and accuracy of calculating with each.

Example. The volume of a cone is computed from the familiar formula

$$V = \frac{1}{3}\pi r^2 h,$$

where $r$ is the radius of the base and $h$ is the altitude of the cone. Suppose that the approximate values of these quantities are 3.2 cm and 4.7 cm, respectively. The differential formula will be of the form

$$3\varepsilon_V = r^2 h\varepsilon_\pi + 2\pi r h\varepsilon_r + \pi r^2 \varepsilon_h.$$

We are given $\varepsilon_V$. From the method of equal influences, we have

$$r^2 h\varepsilon_\pi = \varepsilon_V, \qquad 2\pi r h\varepsilon_r = \varepsilon_V, \qquad \pi r^2 \varepsilon_h = \varepsilon_V.$$

When we determine the limiting absolute errors of the arguments from these equations, we may decrease them; that is, we may increase the values of the partial derivatives. Therefore, for calculation, we have

$$r = 3.5, \qquad r^2 = 11, \qquad h = 5, \qquad \pi h = 16, \qquad \pi r^3 = 32.$$

We then obtain

$$\varepsilon_\pi = \frac{\varepsilon_V}{55}, \qquad \varepsilon_r = \frac{\varepsilon_V}{112}, \qquad \varepsilon_h = \frac{\varepsilon_V}{32}.$$

If, for example, $\varepsilon_V = 1$ cm$^3$, we obtain $\varepsilon_\pi \approx 0.02$, $\varepsilon_r \approx 0.01$ cm, and $\varepsilon_h \approx 0.03$ cm. Here, we departed slightly from the general rule by taking values somewhat higher than they could be (0.02 instead of 1/55, etc.). The necessary accuracy in measurements can be obtained.

# Part II

# POINT INTERPOLATION

Chapter 4

# GENERAL REMARKS

## 15. THE APPROXIMATION OF TABULATED FUNCTIONS. THE CONCEPT OF POINT INTERPOLATION

Various functions are used in investigating natural phenomena mathematically. The functions may be defined in various ways. The simplest of these is a definition by means of an *analytic expression*, which makes it possible to determine the value of the function from any (admissible) value of the argument or arguments. In practice, such cases occur only rarely. However, even when they do occur, the operations indicated in the definition of the function can be extremely tedious. Therefore, the use of a given analytic expression to compute directly the values of the function at arbitrary values of the argument can present difficulties.

Frequently, functions are defined by means of *infinite series*. Calculation of the values of a function by means of an infinite series is a rather tedious operation, requiring investigation as to the convergence of the series and a determination of the number of terms that must be kept to ensure a specified degree of accuracy. Therefore, it is a tedious matter to use a series for calculating the values of a function at an arbitrary value of the argument.

A function may also be determined by means of an *indefinite integral* or by a *differential equation.* Some physical problems give rise to indefinite integrals or solutions of differential equations that can be expressed in closed form, but even then they can be cumbersome. As an example, let us consider the function $f(x)$ defined by the equation

$$f(x)=\int \frac{dx}{(x^2+1)^3(x^2+x+1)^2}.$$

As we know, such an integral can be expressed in closed form in terms of elementary functions, but such an expression will be so cumbersome that it is hardly advisable to calculate $f(x)$ from the exact formula every time that we use it. And, in most cases, functions defined by integrals or by differential equations cannot be expressed in closed form in terms of the elementary functions. The numerical values of such a function need to be determined by some approximate method for the various values of the argument.

In all those cases in which it is either impossible to calculate the values of a function exactly or the calculation is too tedious, we resort to a table that has been compiled for the function (which will be the case if the function occurs fairly frequently in various contexts).

We should mention one other method of defining a function, one that leads directly to a table of its values. This is the case in which we may assert, on the basis of general physical considerations, that a certain value represents a function of one or several arguments,* but the phenomenon is not sufficiently well studied to show the connection in a mathematical expression. In such cases, observations are made leading to a table of values of the function for various values of the argument. For the most part, such a table can be obtained only for a rather limited number of values of the argument. Here, expansion of the table is either impossible or it presents great difficulties.

In all the cases that we have listed and in others similar to them, we come, in the last analysis, to a tabular value of the function. The function $x = f(t)$ is determined by a table of its values $x_k$ for given values of the argument $t_k$ (for $k = 1, 2, \ldots, n$). The tabular values of a function and its argument are called the basic points of the table. If we construct a graph of a tabular function of a single argument, the points on the graph are also called basic points.

The values $t_k$ and $x_k$ are given with a definite number of sure digits, usually with a certain number of digits to the right of the decimal. If the table is computed by means of an exact analytic expression or a device allowing an estimate of the error (for example, by means of an infinite series), these digits in the tabular values of the function can, except for the last one, be considered as correct. The last digit cannot deviate by more than a unit from what it would be if the computations had been carried out with a greater number of digits.

For example, consider the set of digits to the right of the decimal in the expression $\sin 22° 19' = 0.4104697$. In rounding this figure off to five decimal places, the fifth digit that we obtain

---

*Natural phenomena are in general quite complicated, the relationships between the different quantities are quite varied, and it rarely happens that we can consider some quantity *exactly* as a function of 1 or 2 or 3 arguments. When the quantity observed is considered to be precisely a function of only one observed argument, this almost always means that this one argument is the *principal* factor determining the value of the function and that the influence of other arguments on the value of the function can be neglected under the conditions of accuracy with which the observations are made. For example, the heliocentric coordinates of a small planet or comet can, in the course of a brief interval of time, be considered as functions of the osculating elements and time, and these coordinates may be calculated from the 2-body formulas since the disturbances are small and may be neglected.

differs by one from the corresponding digit in the more exact value of the function, namely, sin 22° 19′ = 0.41047.

If a table is obtained for a function by means of a numerical solution to a system of differential equations (or to a single equation), the situation becomes more complicated because there is as yet no sufficiently reliable and simple method of estimating the error of a numerical solution of a differential equation. An even greater complication arises when a tabular function is obtained from observations. In this case, the values of the function contain a number of errors of different origins and, therefore, the functional relationship must be sought. If observations give several significant figures, at least one and sometimes the last two or three are unreliable. Generally speaking, in this last case, we may not apply the convention of determining the limiting error from an expression for an approximate number (see Part I).*

Thus, the values of a function are quite frequently given by tables; that is, a value of the function is given for each of a certain set of values of the argument. Usually, the table is arranged in such a way that values of the argument are listed in increasing order. The values of the argument are given at certain intervals, known as steps. When feasible, tables are compiled with a constant step, but this is not always suitable, since it requires an extra amount of work without increasing the usefulness, if there are regions in which the function changes slowly or almost linearly. In such cases, the entire tabulated domain of values of the argument is broken into several parts and a constant step is chosen for each. Generally speaking, these steps cannot be small; otherwise, the size of the table would be too great.

In solving problems that occur in nature, we usually deal with cases in which we need to know the values of the function at other values of the argument than those listed in the table. For example, we often need to find the coordinates of the sun relative to the center of the earth, but it is usually not at $0^h$ universal time (which is given in the almanacs) but at quite different instants of time situated between those that are tabulated. Therefore, the following problem is of great practical significance: suppose that values of a function have been tabulated. We must find a method of determining approximately the values of the function for arbitrary values of the argument other than those listed in the table.

If the value of the argument for which we wish to find the value of the function lies between values of the argument that appear in the table, the problem is one of *interpolation*. If the value of the argument in question is greater than or less than every value appearing in the table, it is a problem of *extrapolation*.

*The convention that the limiting error is less than one half the unit of the last digit has to do only with errors in rounding off that are incurred in measurements and calculations under the condition that the units of the last digit are determined from a scale and not by the eye. It is usual to speak in this fashion if the position of the needle between the divisions of the scale is determined by a visual estimate in terms of tenths of the interval between these divisions.

The simplest procedure for interpolating, which is still sometimes used, consists in tracing by hand a smooth curve through the points on a graph representing the basic points of the table. This curve is used as an approximate graph of the function and an interpolation is made from this graph in an obvious fashion. The accuracy of this method is quite limited, as is the accuracy of every graph. Also, the tracing of the curve is somewhat arbitrary and indefinite. Therefore, such a method is not applicable to tabulated functions all of whose digits are reliable, since a loss in accuracy would ensue; that is, the interpolated values would be less exact than the tabulated values. A graphical interpolation can be applied only in those cases in which the table is obtained from insufficiently reliable observations and the functional relationship itself is not sufficiently reliable.

Even in Newton's time (and earlier) the development of a method of interpolation from a tabulated function had been reduced to an approximation of the tabulated function by means of another function that allows easier calculations. The approximate expression of the given function that is constructed is used for interpolation. The given value of the argument is substituted into it and the calculations are made. Usually, an approximate representation of a small part of the table in the neighborhood of a given value of the argument is constructed.

The construction of an approximation of a tabulated function is an indefinite problem and is impossible without the preliminary introduction of two conventions or assumptions.

In the first place, some agreement must be made with regard to the class of functions used for approximation. In practical problems, a natural requirement is that it be easy to calculate the value of the function from a given value of the argument. This condition is satisfied by algebraic polynomials, which are almost exclusively used for approximation. If a function possesses properties that algebraic polynomials do not satisfy, other functions are used. Trigonometric polynomials are used most often if a function is periodic and an approximation is necessary in a region containing the entire period. If a function increases more rapidly than a polynomial, it would be natural to use exponential functions, but in practice, this is rarely done. When we need to approximate a periodic function over only a small part of its period, algebraic polynomials are usually used. The chosen approximating function must contain some number of literal parameters, which must be determined from the given table. If an algebraic polynomial of degree $n$ is used for approximation, the $n+1$ coefficients in the polynomial are examples of such parameters.

It is natural to demand that the approximation be as good as possible, but the meaning of the word "good" needs to be defined. This is the second requirement imposed on the problem.

In practice, various criteria for the best approximation are used.

In this part of the book (in the solution of the problem of approximating a function), we shall use the following criterion: *the approximating polynomial must, exactly, fit the basic points of the table.** It follows from this criterion that the degree of the

*Another criterion will be considered in Chapter 17.

polynomial used for interpolation must be one unit less than the number of basic points that are taken. This is because an $n$th-degree polynomial has $n+1$ coefficients and to determine them, $n+1$ statements are necessary.

The problem of interpolation of a function of a single variable $x=x(t)$ can be represented graphically as follows: suppose that points $(t_k, x_k)$ for $k=0, 1, 2, \ldots, n$ are given in the $tx$-plane. These are the basic points of the table. We must construct an $n$th-degree parabola that will pass exactly through these basic points. For this reason, interpolation under this requirement is called *point interpolation.*

## 16. A THEOREM ON THE EXISTENCE OF AN INTERPOLATIONAL POLYNOMIAL

Before deriving specific formulas for interpolational polynomials, we need to see what the conditions are under which a polynomial satisfying the requirement of point interpolation exists, and whether such a polynomial is unique or not. The answer to this problem is given by the following.

THEOREM. *If all the tabulated values of the argument are different, an interpolational polynomial satisfying the condition of point interpolation exists and is unique.*

Proof: Suppose that the $n+1$ basic points $(t_0, x_0), (t_1, x_1), \ldots (t_n, x_n)$ of a function $x=F(t)$ are given, and that $t_k \neq t_s$ for $s \neq k$. An $n$th-degree interpolational polynomial

$$P(t)=a_0+a_1t+a_2t^2+\ldots+a_nt^n \tag{4.1}$$

must, by the definition of point interpolation, satisfy the conditions

$$P(t_0)=x_0, \quad P(t_1)=x_1, \quad P(t_2)=x_2, \quad \ldots, \quad P(t_n)=x_n. \tag{4.2}$$

From this, we obtain the following system of $n+1$ linear algebraic equations with unknown coefficients $a_s$ (for $s=0, 1, 2, \ldots, n$):

$$\left.\begin{array}{l} a_0+a_1t_0+a_2t_0^2+\ldots+a_nt_0^n=x_0, \\ a_0+a_1t_1+a_2t_1^2+\ldots+a_nt_1^n=x_1, \\ a_0+a_1t_2+a_2t_2^2+\ldots+a_nt_2^n=x_2, \\ \cdots\cdots\cdots\cdots\cdots\cdots \\ \cdots\cdots\cdots\cdots\cdots\cdots \\ a_0+a_1t_n+a_2t_n^2+\ldots+a_nt_n^n=x_n. \end{array}\right\} \tag{4.3}$$

The question of the existence of an interpolational polynomial reduces to the question of the vanishing of the determinant of this system:

$$W=\begin{vmatrix} 1 & t_0 & t_0^2 & \dots & t_0^n \\ 1 & t_1 & t_1^2 & \dots & t_1^n \\ \cdot & \cdot & \cdot & \cdot & \cdot \\ \cdot & \cdot & \cdot & \cdot & \cdot \\ 1 & t_n & t_n^2 & \dots & t_n^n \end{vmatrix} \tag{4.4}$$

It is known from algebra that the value of this determinant, known as *van der Monde's determinant,* is given by the formula

$$W=[(t_n-t_0)(t_n-t_1)\dots(t_n-t_{n-1})]\times$$
$$\times[(t_{n-1}-t_0)(t_{n-1}-t_1)\dots(t_{n-1}-t_{n-2})]\times\dots$$
$$\dots\times[(t_2-t_0)(t_2-t_1)](t_1-t_0).$$

By hypothesis, $t_k \neq t_s$ if $k \neq s$; hence,

$$W \neq 0. \tag{4.5}$$

Since the determinant of the linear system is not 0, this system has a uniquely defined solution $a_0, a_1, \dots, a_n$. Consequently, one and only one interpolational polynomial exists.

We note that this theorem can be considered the only basis for a formal application of the method of point interpolation to an arbitrary function, since in the theorem $t_k$ and $x_k$ are arbitrary numbers. The question as to how satisfactory the approximation given by the polynomial is, is decided from the properties of the function by means of an estimate of the interpolational error. Sometimes, to justify the method, we sight the possibility of approximating a function by means of a partial sum of a power series, or Weierstrass' theorem on the possibility of approximating a continuous function by means of a polynomial with any desired degree of accuracy. However, neither of these has a direct bearing on the problem of point interpolation. No partial sum of a power series can exactly represent a function at all basic points, since, if the coefficients of the polynomial are determined by the process used in point interpolation, they will not be equal to the corresponding coefficients of the series.

To illustrate this assertion, let us suppose that a table of values of a periodic function is given and that the step in the table is equal to the period of the function. For example, suppose that a table for sin $t$ gives values for $t=0,\ 2\pi,\ 4\pi$, etc. Clearly, the interpolational polynomial that we would construct has a constant value, namely, zero. We would obtain the initial term of the series, but the approximation cannot be considered satisfactory. Thus, the possibility of constructing a power series for this function does not have a direct bearing on the problem of interpolation.

Weierstrass' theorem asserts that for a given function $x(t)$ and an arbitrary positive number $\varepsilon$, we may find a polynomial $P_n(t)$ satisfying the condition

$$|x(t)-P_n(t)|<\varepsilon$$

everywhere on the interval $a \leqslant t \leqslant b$, but the conditions of this theorem and its proof do not assume that $x(t_k) = P_n(t_k)$ for any sequence of values of the argument $t_k$ (for $k = 1, 2, \ldots, n$).

## 17. LAGRANGE'S INTERPOLATIONAL POLYNOMIAL

To find the interpolational polynomial, it is sufficient to solve in literal form the system of equations given in Section 14, which define the coefficients of the polynomial. If the system is solved by means of a determinant, every coefficient $a_s$ is determined by the formula

$$a_s = \frac{W_s}{W}, \tag{4.6}$$

where

$$W_s = \begin{vmatrix} 1 & t_0 & t_0^2 & \ldots & t_0^{s-1} & x_0 & t_0^{s+1} & \ldots & t_0^n \\ 1 & t_1 & t_1^2 & \ldots & t_1^{s-1} & x_1 & t_1^{s+1} & \ldots & t_1^n \\ \cdot & \cdot & \cdot & \cdot & \cdot & \cdot & \cdot & \cdot & \cdot \\ \cdot & \cdot & \cdot & \cdot & \cdot & \cdot & \cdot & \cdot & \cdot \\ 1 & t_n & t_n^2 & \ldots & t_n^{s-1} & x_n & t_1^{s+1} & \ldots & t_n^n \end{vmatrix}, \tag{4.7}$$

$$(s = 0, 1, 2, \ldots, n),$$

and $W$ is defined by (4.4).

If $W_s$ is expanded in terms of the elements of the column $(x_0, x_1, \ldots, x_n)$, then $W_s$ will be a linear expression of the form

$$W_s = \sum_{k=0}^{n} x_k b_k, \tag{4.8}$$

where the $b_k$ are numbers depending on all the basic points of the values of $t$ and on the number $s$. Then, the coefficients of the polynomial take the form

$$a_s = \sum_{k=0}^{n} x_k c_k, \tag{4.9}$$

where

$$c_k = \frac{b_k}{W}. \tag{4.10}$$

If we use (4.9) to substitute all the $a_s$ into the polynomial (4.1) and if we correct the terms containing $x_k$, we obtain

$$P(t) = \sum_{k=0}^{n} x_k L_k(t), \tag{4.11}$$

where the $L_k(t)$ are polynomials of degree $n$. Lagrange showed how one might obtain the values of $L_k(t)$ without solving the system of equations for the coefficient $a_0, a_1, a_2, \ldots, a_n$.

To satisfy the condition of point interpolation, the polynomials $L_k(t)$ must satisfy the conditions

$$P(t_k) = x_k \qquad (k = 0, 1, \ldots, n), \tag{4.12}$$

$$\left.\begin{aligned} &L_k(t_k) = 1, \\ &L_k(t_s) = 0, \quad \text{if} \quad k \neq s; \\ &k = 0, 1, 2, \ldots, n. \end{aligned}\right\} \tag{4.13}$$

The second of conditions (4.13) means that all the basic points of $t$ except $t_k$ are roots of $L_k(t)$. Therefore,

$$L_k(t) = A_k(t - t_0)(t - t_1) \ldots (t - t_{k-1})(t - t_{k+1}) \ldots (t - t_n),$$

where $A_k$ is an unknown coefficient. This coefficient is easily determined from the first of conditions (4.13):

$$A_k(t_k - t_0)(t_k - t_1) \ldots (t_k - t_{k-1})(t_k - t_{k+1}) \ldots (t_k - t_n) = 1.$$

Thus, finally,

$$L_k(t) = \frac{t - t_0}{t_k - t_0} \cdot \frac{t - t_1}{t_k - t_1} \cdots \frac{t - t_{k-1}}{t_k - t_{k-1}} \frac{t - t_{k+1}}{t_k - t_{k+1}} \cdots \frac{t - t_n}{t_k - t_n}.$$

We introduce the notation

$$L(t) = \prod_{s=0}^{n} (t - t_s).$$

If we differentiate $L(t)$ and substitute $t = t_k$ into the derivative, we shall obtain the denominator of the last expression for $L_k(t)$, since the derivative will consist of products only one of which fails to contain $t - t_k$. After the substitution, this term will give the denominator and the remaining products will vanish. Therefore,

$$L_k(t) = \frac{L(t)}{(t - t_k) L'(t_k)}. \tag{4.14}$$

Thus, Lagrange's interpolational polynomial, containing directly the basic points $(t_k, x_k)$, is of the form

$$P(t) = \sum_{k=1}^{n} x_k \frac{L(t)}{(t - t_k) L'(t_k)} \tag{4.15}$$

or, in expanded form,

$$P(t) = \sum_{k=1}^{n} x_k \frac{(t - t_0)(t - t_1) \ldots (t - t_{k-1})(t - t_{k+1}) \ldots (t - t_n)}{(t_k - t_0)(t_k - t_1) \ldots (t_k - t_{k-1})(t_k - t_{k+1}) \ldots (t_k - t_n)}. \tag{4.16}$$

Example 1. The function defined by the table

| $t$ | 0 | 1 | 2 |
|---|---|---|---|
| $x$ | 0 | 1 | 4. |

Let us give an approximation of this function for the intervals $0 \leqslant t \leqslant 1$ and $0 \leqslant t \leqslant 2$.

(a) On the interval $0 \leqslant t \leqslant 1$, we use the end points of this interval. From Lagrange's formula, we obtain

$$P_{\mathrm{I}}(t) = \frac{t-1}{0-1} \cdot 0 + \frac{t-0}{1-0} \cdot 1 = t.$$

(b) On the interval $0 \leqslant t \leqslant 2$, we have

$$P_{\mathrm{II}}(t) = \frac{t-2}{1-2} \cdot 1 + \frac{t-1}{2-1} \cdot 4 = 3t - 2.$$

Consequently,

$$P(t) = t, \quad \text{if} \quad 0 \leqslant t \leqslant 1,$$
$$P(t) = 3t - 2, \quad \text{if} \quad 1 \leqslant t \leqslant 2.$$

The table was constructed for the function $x = t^2$. Therefore, we may compare the piecewise-linear approximation that we have made with the exact expression $x = t^2$. On the interval [0, 1], the difference between the exact expression and $P_{\mathrm{I}}(t)$ is $\xi_{\mathrm{I}} = t^2 - t$.

It is easy to see that $\xi_{\mathrm{I}}$ has a minimum of $-0.25$ at $t = 0.5$. This means that $|\xi_{\mathrm{I}}| \leqslant 0.25$.

On the interval [1, 2], we have $\xi_{\mathrm{II}} = t^2 - 3t + 2$. $\xi_{\mathrm{II}}$ has a minimum of $-0.25$ at $t = 1.5$. We see that the approximation of the given function by a piecewise-linear function with two links ensures a limiting error of 0.25 throughout the interval of the table, namely, [0, 2].

Example 2. Construct an approximation of the function $x = \sin t$ by a linear function on the interval $0 \leqslant t \leqslant \frac{\pi}{4}$ from the basic points at the end points of the interval:

$$t: \quad 0 \quad \frac{\pi}{4},$$
$$x: \quad 0 \quad \frac{\sqrt{2}}{2}.$$

From Lagrange's formula, we obtain

$$P(t) = \frac{t - \frac{\pi}{4}}{0 - \frac{\pi}{4}} \cdot 0 + \frac{t-0}{\frac{\pi}{4} - 0} \cdot \frac{\sqrt{2}}{2} = \frac{2\sqrt{2}}{\pi} \cdot t$$

or

$$P(t) = 0.90031t.$$

If we use this approximation to interpolate the value for $t = \frac{\pi}{6}$, we obtain $P\left(\frac{\pi}{6}\right) = \frac{\sqrt{2}}{3} = 0.471$ instead of the exact value 0.5.

Here, we can also investigate the accuracy of the approximation in the general form. The difference between the function and the polynomial is

$$\xi = x - P(t) = \sin t - \frac{2\sqrt{2}}{\pi}\, t.$$

If we set the derivative equal to 0, we see that $\xi$ has a maximum of $0.43525 - 0.40542 = 0.02983$ at $t = 25^\circ\, 48'\, 05'' = 0.45031$ radians. We may take 0.03 as the limiting error of the approximation for the entire interval $[0, \frac{\pi}{4}]$.

Example 3. Construct an approximation of the function $x = \sin t$ from the following three basic points on the interval $[0, \frac{\pi}{4}]$:

| $t$ | $0$ | $\frac{\pi}{6}$ | $\frac{\pi}{4}$ |
|---|---|---|---|
| $x$ | $0$ | $0.5$ | $\frac{\sqrt{2}}{2}$. |

From Lagrange's formula,

$$P(t) = \frac{\left(t - \frac{\pi}{6}\right)\left(t - \frac{\pi}{4}\right)}{\left(0 - \frac{\pi}{6}\right)\left(0 - \frac{\pi}{4}\right)} \cdot 0 + \frac{t\left(t - \frac{\pi}{4}\right)}{\frac{\pi}{6}\cdot\left(\frac{\pi}{6} - \frac{\pi}{4}\right)} \cdot 0.5 + \frac{t\left(t - \frac{\pi}{6}\right)}{\frac{\pi}{4}\left(\frac{\pi}{4} - \frac{\pi}{6}\right)} \cdot \frac{\sqrt{2}}{2}.$$

Let us now consider this polynomial with argument $\tau$ where $\tau$ is defined by the equation $t = \frac{\pi}{4}\tau$. ($\tau$ will be a value of an angle if as a unit we take the angle $\frac{\pi}{4}$.) After some simplification, the polynomial takes the form

$$P(\tau) = \left(\frac{9}{4} - \sqrt{2}\right)\tau + \left(\frac{3\sqrt{2}}{2} - \frac{9}{4}\right)\tau^2.$$

We can see by direct verification that $P(\tau)$ passes exactly through all the basic points. If we use $P(\tau)$ to interpolate the value for $t = \frac{\pi}{12}$, corresponding to $\tau = {}^1/_3$, we obtain

$$P\left(\frac{1}{3}\right) = 0.5 - \frac{\sqrt{2}}{6} = 0.264.$$

The value of $\sin 15^\circ$, correct to three decimal places, is 0.259, so that the error in the interpolation is equal to $-0.005$.

## 18. ESTIMATE OF THE ERROR IN POINT INTERPOLATION

If the given function is not a polynomial, the interpolational polynomial will give values coinciding with the values of the function only at the basic points and, possibly, at certain other isolated points.*

*We note that this will be the case if the given function is a polynomial of higher degree than the interpolational polynomial.

In interpolating for given intermediary values of the argument, the polynomial only approximately represents the function. It is quite essential to determine the limiting error of the point interpolation, that is, the least upper bound of the absolute value of the error. This can be done in the following manner:

Suppose that an interpolational polynomial $P_n(t)$ of $n$th degree is constructed for a function $x(t)$ with basic points $(t_k, x_k)$ for $k=0, 1, 2, \ldots, n$. Let us construct an auxiliary function

$$F(z)=x(z)-P_n(z)-kL(z),$$

where $L(z)=(z-t_0)(z-t_1)\ldots(z-t_n)$ and $k$ is an as yet undetermined number. From the condition of point interpolation,

$$x(t_k)=P_n(t_k) \qquad (k=0, 1, 2, \ldots, n),$$

it follows by definition that

$$L(t_k)=0.$$

Therefore, $F(z)$ has $n+1$ roots $t_0, t_1, \ldots, t_n$. Since $k$ is at our disposal, we arrange for the function $F(z)$ to have one root $t \neq t_k$; that is, we impose the condition

$$x(t)-P_n(t)-kL(t)=0.$$

Note that we cannot immediately solve for $k$ from this equation because $x(t)$ is unknown. Let us now apply Rolle's theorem to the function $F(z)$. According to that theorem, if the function $f(z)$ vanishes at two consecutive values of the argument $t_r$ and $t_{r+1}$ and if the conditions of continuity and differentiability are satisfied, the derivative $\frac{df}{dz}$ will vanish at at least one value of $z$ between $t_r$ and $t_{r+1}$. Our function $F(z)$ has $n+1$ consecutive roots $t_k$ and an additional root $t$, which upon interpolation appears within one of the intervals between adjacent roots; that is, one of the intervals is divided into two parts. In making the interpolation, we obtain a total of $n+1$ intervals at whose end points $F(z)$ vanishes, so that $F(z)$ has $n+2$ roots.

Suppose that, instead of an interpolation, we are making an extrapolation. The function must then be defined outside the tabulated region of the argument and $t$ will be either less than $t_0$ or greater than $t_n$; that is, in addition to the $n$ intervals between the consecutive basic points, there will be yet another interval between $t$ and $t_0$ or between $t_n$ and $t$. If we apply Rolle's theorem to each of the $n+1$ intervals, we see that the derivative $\frac{dF}{dz}$ vanishes at least $n+1$ times. The points at which it vanishes will be within different intervals, that is, they cannot coincide. Let us suppose that $x(t)$ has derivatives up to the $(n+1)$st order throughout the entire tabulated region (and in the extended region if an extrapolation is being done). We now apply Rolle's theorem to the function $\frac{dF}{dz}$ in the intervals between the zeros. There are now $n$ of these intervals. Thus, we obtain $n$ values at which $\frac{d^2F}{dz^2}$ vanishes. If we continue this operation with the derivatives of successive orders, we conclude that the $(n+1)$st derivative of the function $F(z)$ vanishes for at least one value of $z$. We denote this value by $\tau$. (In the case of interpolation, $\tau$ lies within the tabulated region; in the case of extrapolation, it lies in the extended region.) It follows from the definition of $F(z)$ that

$$\frac{d^{n+1}F(z)}{dz^{n+1}} = \frac{d^{n+1}x(z)}{dz^{n+1}} - \frac{d^{n+1}P_n(z)}{dz^{n+1}} - k\frac{d^{n+1}L(z)}{dz^{n+1}}.$$

The second term on the right side of this equation is equal to 0 since the polynomial $P_n(z)$ of $n$th degree is differentiated $n+1$ times. The polynomial $L(z)$ of $(n+1)$st degree, when differentiated $n+1$ times, gives $(n+1)!$ since the coefficient of the highest power to appear in $L(z)$ is 1. Therefore,

$$\frac{d^{n+1}F(z)}{dz^{n+1}} = \frac{d^{n+1}x(z)}{dz^{n+1}} - k(n+1)!$$

If we set $z=\tau$, the left side will vanish and we obtain

$$k = \left(\frac{d^{n+1}x}{dz^{n+1}}\right)_{z=\tau} \cdot \frac{1}{(n+1)!}.$$

By hypothesis, $z=t$ is a root of $F(z)$. This means that if we substitute $z=t$ in the function $F(z)$, we obtain

$$0 = x(t) - P_n(t) - \frac{L(t)}{(n+1)!}\left(\frac{d^{n+1}x}{dt^{n+1}}\right)_{t=\tau}.$$

From this it is clear that the error of the interpolation $x - P_n$ is given by the formula

$$x(t) - P_n(t) = L(t)\frac{x^{(n+1)}(\tau)}{(n+1)!}, \tag{4.17}$$

where $x^{(n+1)}$ denotes the $(n+1)$st derivative and

$t_0 \leqslant \tau \leqslant t_n$ in the case of interpolation,

$\left.\begin{array}{l} t \leqslant \tau \leqslant t_n \\ t_0 \leqslant \tau \leqslant t \end{array}\right\}$ in the case of extrapolation.

These considerations do not enable us to determine $\tau$. Therefore, in practice we can find the limiting error only if it is possible to find an upper bound for the $(n+1)$st derivative of the given function. Let us denote by $M_{n+1}$ the maximum of the absolute value of the $(n+1)$st derivative in the region of the table or in the extended region.

Then, for every given value of $t$, we obtain

$$|x(t) - P_n(t)| \leqslant \frac{M_{n+1}}{(n+1)!} |L(t)|.$$

If we wish, we may set a uniform upper bound to the error of interpolation, that is, a bound not dependent on $t$. To do this, we need to find a number $N$ such that $|L(t)| \leqslant N$. Then,

$$|x(t) - P(t)| \leqslant \frac{NM_{n+1}}{(n+1)!}$$

for all values of $t$ in the tabulated or extended region.

Example 1. For $x = \sqrt{t}$, construct the interpolational polynomial from the two basic points

$$t_0 = 0.25 \qquad x_0 = 0.5$$
$$t_1 = 1, \qquad x_1 = 1.$$

By using Lagrange's formula, we obtain the linear interpolational formula

$$P(t) = \frac{t-1}{0.25-1} \cdot 0.5 + \frac{t-0.25}{1-0.25} \cdot 1 = \frac{2}{3}t + \frac{1}{3}.$$

To get an idea of the nature of the approximation, we note that

$$P(0.49) = \frac{1.98}{3} = 0.66, \text{ instead of } 0.70 \quad (\text{error} = +0.04);$$

$$P(0.81) = \frac{2.62}{3} = 0.87 \text{ instead of } 0.90 \quad (\text{error} = +0.03)$$

Let us find an estimate for the error in interpolation for all values of $t$ in this region. From the general formula, we have

$$x(t) - P_1(t) = (t-0.25)(t-1)\frac{x''(\tau)}{2!},$$

$$x'(t) = \frac{1}{2\sqrt{t}}, \qquad x''(t) = -\frac{1}{4\sqrt{t^3}},$$

where the primes denote the first and second derivatives. The quantity $|x''(t)|$ decreases monotonically in this region, and, therefore,

$$|x''(t)| \leqslant \frac{1}{4\sqrt{0.25^3}} = 2,$$

so that

$$|\sqrt{t} - P(t)| \leqslant |(t-0.25)(t-1)|.$$

When $t = 0.49$, the right side is equal to $0.12$. When $t = 0.81$, the right side is equal to $0.11$. Both these values are considerably greater than the actual error. The polynomial determining the estimate of the error is of the form

$$L(t) = (t-0.25)(t-1) = t^2 - 1.25t + 0.25.$$

$L(t)$ has an extremum at $t = 0.625$. Let us set $t = 0.625$ in $L(t)$ so as to obtain the maximum of the absolute value of $L(t)$:

$$|L(t)| \leqslant 0.375^2 \approx 0.14.$$

From this, we obtain an estimate of the error applicable to all values of $t$:

$$|\sqrt{t} - P_1(t)| \leqslant 0.14.$$

Example 2. For the function $x = \sin t$, let us construct the interpolational polynomial from the three basic points

| $t$ | $0$ | $\frac{\pi}{6}$ | $\frac{\pi}{2}$ |
|---|---|---|---|
| $x$ | $0$ | $0.5$ | $1$ |

From Lagrange's formula, we obtain

$$P(t) = \frac{\left(t-\frac{\pi}{6}\right)\left(t-\frac{\pi}{2}\right)}{\left(0-\frac{\pi}{6}\right)\left(0-\frac{\pi}{2}\right)} \cdot 0 + \frac{(t-0)\left(t-\frac{\pi}{2}\right)}{\left(\frac{\pi}{6}-0\right)\left(\frac{\pi}{6}-\frac{\pi}{2}\right)} \cdot 0.5 + \frac{(t-0)\left(t-\frac{\pi}{6}\right)}{\left(\frac{\pi}{2}-0\right)\left(\frac{\pi}{2}-\frac{\pi}{6}\right)} \cdot 1.$$

To simplify our work, let us set $t = \pi\alpha$. Then,

$$P(t) = -\frac{9}{2}\alpha(2\alpha-1) + \alpha(6\alpha-1) = \frac{7}{2}\alpha - 3\alpha^2.$$

Our control is

| $t$ | $\alpha$ | $P(\alpha)$ | $\sin t$ |
|---|---|---|---|
| $0$ | $0$ | $0$ | $0$ |
| $\frac{\pi}{6}$ | $\frac{1}{6}$ | $\frac{1}{2}$ | $\frac{1}{2}$ |
| $\frac{\pi}{2}$ | $\frac{1}{2}$ | $1$ | $1$ |

As a check on the quality of the approximation, we consider the special cases:

| $t$ | $\alpha$ | $P(\alpha)$ | $\sin t$ | Error |
|---|---|---|---|---|
| $\frac{\pi}{4}$ | $\frac{1}{4}$ | $\frac{11}{16} = 0.69$ | 0.71 | +0.02 |
| $\frac{\pi}{3}$ | $\frac{1}{3}$ | $\frac{5}{6} = 0.83$ | 0.87 | +0.04 |

Let us estimate the error in the interpolation. Here,

$$L(t) = t\left(t-\frac{\pi}{6}\right)\left(t-\frac{\pi}{2}\right),$$

$$|x'''(t)| = |\cos t| \leqslant 1,$$

$$|\sin t - P(t)| \leqslant \left|t\left(t-\frac{\pi}{6}\right)\left(t-\frac{\pi}{2}\right)\right| \cdot \frac{1}{6} = \frac{\pi^3}{72} \cdot \alpha(6\alpha-1)(2\alpha-1).$$

Let us compare the errors obtained from the estimate made by use of this formula with the actual errors in the particular cases given above:

| $t$ | $\mid L(t) \mid$ | Estimate of the error |
|---|---|---|
| $\frac{\pi}{4}$ | $\frac{\pi^3}{192} \approx 0.16$ | 0,03 |
| $\frac{\pi}{3}$ | $\frac{\pi^3}{108} \approx 0.30$ | 0,05 |

In both cases, the error obtained by using the estimate with the exact polynomial $L(t)$ is only slightly greater than the exact error.

Let us find a uniform estimate for all values of $t$. To do this, let us investigate the behavior of $L(t)$ throughout the entire interval from 0 to $\frac{\pi}{2}$. In the present case,

$$L(t) = \frac{\pi^3}{12} \alpha (2\alpha - 1)(6\alpha - 1).$$

Since $t = \pi\alpha$, $\alpha$ has values from 0 to $1/2$. Let us find the maximum of the absolute value of the polynomial

$$M(\alpha) = 12\alpha^3 - 8\alpha^2 + \alpha$$

in this interval. We find the derivatives

$$\frac{dM}{d\alpha} = 36\alpha^2 - 16\alpha + 1; \quad \frac{d^2M}{d\alpha^2} = 72\alpha - 16.$$

When we set the first derivative equal to 0,

$$36\alpha^2 - 16\alpha + 1 = 0,$$

we obtain the values of $\alpha$ at which $M(\alpha)$ has its maximum and minimum:

$$\alpha_{1,2} = \frac{4 \pm \sqrt{7}}{18}.$$

The plus sign gives the minimum and the minus sign gives the maximum. By a simple transformation, we can reduce the expressions for the extrema of $M(\alpha)$ to the form

$$M(\alpha_{1,2}) = -\frac{2}{27}(7\alpha_{1,2} - 1).$$

To do this, we need to eliminate $\alpha_{1,2}^2$ and $\alpha_{1,2}^3$ by using the equation defining $\alpha_{1,2}$. When we substitute the extreme values $\alpha_1$ and $\alpha_2$, we obtain

$$M(\alpha_1) = \frac{\sqrt{343} - 10}{243} = 0.0351; \qquad M(\alpha_2) = -\frac{\sqrt{343} + 10}{243} = -0.117.$$

The absolute value of the largest value of $M(\alpha)$ throughout the entire region is 0.117. The corresponding limiting value of the difference $|\sin t - P(t)|$ is equal to $\frac{\pi^3}{72} \cdot 0.117 =$ 0,0504, so that $|\sin t - P(t)| \leqslant 0.0504$. This value is attained at $\alpha = \frac{4 + \sqrt{7}}{18} = 0.37$ or $t = 0.37\pi \approx 67°$.*

*In the examples that we have been considering, the construction of the Lagrange polynomial caused no difficulties since only a few basic points were given and the values of the function and its arguments had few digits.

Chapter 5

# INTERPOLATION FROM A TABLE WITH A VARIABLE STEP

## 19. DIFFERENCE QUOTIENTS OF TABULATED FUNCTIONS

If a table of values of a function does not have a constant step (that is, if the intervals between adjacent values given for the argument are different in different parts of the table), the differences between adjacent values of the function cannot be used to denote the change in the function. For this, we use quantities known as difference quotients.

Suppose that we have a table of a function $x(t)$ as follows:

$$\begin{array}{c||ccccc} t & t_0 & t_1 & t_2 & \ldots & t_n, \\ x & x_0 & x_1 & x_2 & \ldots & x_n. \end{array}$$

The first or first-order difference quotient of two tabulated values of a function is the ratio of the difference between the values of the function to the corresponding difference between the values of the argument. This definition is applicable to any two values of the argument, but we will ordinarily be concerned only with adjacent values. The first difference quotients are indicated by placing the tabulated values of the argument in parentheses. Thus, we denote the difference quotients for the table shown above as follows:

$$x(t_1, t_0) = \frac{x_1 - x_0}{t_1 - t_0}, \quad x(t_2, t_1) = \frac{x_2 - x_1}{t_2 - t_1},$$
$$x(t_3, t_2) = \frac{x_3 - x_2}{t_3 - t_2} \qquad \text{etc.}$$

The difference quotient $x(t_r, t_s) = \frac{x_r - x_s}{t_r - t_s}$ can be written in a symmetric form:

$$x(t_r, t_s) = \frac{x_r}{t_r - t_s} + \frac{x_s}{t_s - t_r}.$$

It is clear from this that the order in which the tabulated values are taken is immaterial in computing difference quotients; that is,

$$x(t_r, t_s) = x(t_s, t_r)$$

The second difference quotient of three tabulated values is the ratio of the difference between two first-order difference quotients (that is, the difference quotient of the third and second of these values and that of the second and first) to the difference between the third and first values of the argument. Formally, the definition is applicable to any three tabulated values, but in practice, we usually take three adjacent values. Using notation analogous to that used for first-order difference quotients, let us write some second-order difference quotients:

$$x(t_2, t_1, t_0) = \frac{x(t_2, t_1) - x(t_1, t_0)}{t_2 - t_0},$$
$$x(t_3, t_2, t_1) = \frac{x(t_3, t_2) - x(t_2, t_1)}{t_3 - t_1},$$
$$x(t_4, t_3, t_2) = \frac{x(t_4, t_3) - x(t_3, t_2)}{t_4 - t_2} \quad \text{etc.}$$

If we use the symmetric expression for the first-order difference quotients, we obtain, for example,

$$x(t_3, t_2, t_1) = \frac{x_3}{(t_3 - t_2)(t_3 - t_1)} + \frac{x_3}{(t_2 - t_3)(t_3 - t_1)} - \\ - \frac{x_2}{(t_2 - t_1)(t_3 - t_1)} - \frac{x_1}{(t_1 - t_2)(t_3 - t_1)}.$$

After some simple manipulations, we obtain

$$x(t_3, t_2, t_1) = \frac{x_3}{(t_3 - t_2)(t_3 - t_1)} + \frac{x_2}{(t_2 - t_3)(t_2 - t_1)} + \frac{x_1}{(t_1 - t_3)(t_1 - t_2)}.$$

From this it is clear that second-order difference quotients are symmetric with respect to the tabulated values used; that is, changing the order in which they are taken does not change their values.

Difference quotients of arbitrary order are defined analogously. For example, consider the third-order quotients

$$x(t_3, t_2, t_1, t_0) = \frac{x(t_3, t_2, t_1) - x(t_2, t_1, t_0)}{t_3 - t_0},$$
$$x(t_4, t_3, t_2, t_1) = \frac{x(t_4, t_3, t_2) - x(t_3, t_2, t_1)}{t_4 - t_1},$$

etc.

The independence of the order in which the values are taken is a common property of difference quotients of all orders.

If $n+1$ values of a tabulated function are given, we can construct $n$ first-order difference quotients from that table, $n-1$ second-order difference quotients, ...., and only one $n$th-order difference quotient. A value in the table itself is sometimes called a difference quotient of order 0.

Example. Let us construct a table of the difference quotients of the function $x = \sin t$ in the interval from 0 to $\frac{\pi}{2}$ for the values

$$t = 0, \quad \frac{\pi}{6}, \quad \frac{\pi}{4}, \quad \frac{\pi}{3}, \quad \frac{\pi}{2}.$$

A complete table of the calculated difference quotients and the operations used in obtaining them is shown on page 63.

The column marked $x^{(1)}$ shows the differences of consecutive values of the function and the column marked $t^{(1)}$ shows the differences between the corresponding values of the argument. Division of the numbers in the $x^{(1)}$ column by the adjacent number in the $t^{(1)}$ column gives the first-order difference quotient. Their complete notations would be

$$x(t_1, t_0), \quad x(t_2, t_1) \ldots \text{ etc.}$$

The column marked $x^{(2)}$ contains the differences between successive first-order difference quotients and the column marked $t^{(2)}$ contains the differences $t_2 - t_0, t_3 - t_1$, and $t_4 - t_2$. Division of the numbers in the $x^{(2)}$ column by the adjacent number in the $t^{(2)}$ column gives the corresponding second-order difference quotient. The procedure for the remaining calculations is analogous. Since the numbers $x_k$ are given with three digits, we take three digits in the third-order difference quotients. This coincides with the number of digits to the right of the decimal. In the second third-order difference quotient, this gives four digits to the right of the decimal. Therefore, the first third-order difference quotient is also taken with four digits to the right of the decimal, which is not completely legitimate since this figure is obtained by dividing a three-digit dividend by a four-digit divisor.

## 20. THE CONSTRUCTION OF INTERPOLATIONAL FORMULAS REGARDING DIFFERENCES

Calculations by means of Lagrange's formula are rather tedious, at least for manual computations. If we have $n+1$ basic points, the formula contains $n+1$ terms. In each of these terms there are $n$ factors in the numerator and just as many in the denominator; besides, there is the tabular value of the function. In all, each term represents $2n$ calculations, namely $2(n-1)+1$ multiplications and one division. Considering multiplication and division as equivalent operations and addition and subtraction as equivalent operations, we have the following total number of operations:

Additions: $2n(n+1)+n = 2n^2+3n$,

Multiplications: $2n(n+1) = 2n^2+2n$.

| t | $x$ | $x^{(1)}$ | $t^{(1)}$ | First-Order Difference Quotient | $x^{(2)}$ | $t^{(2)}$ | Second-Order Difference Quotient | $x^{(3)}$ | $t^{(3)}$ | Third-Order Difference Quotient | $x^{(4)}$ | $t^{(4)}$ | Fourth-Order Difference Quotient |
|---|---|---|---|---|---|---|---|---|---|---|---|---|---|
| 0 | 0.000 | | | | | | | | | | | | |
| | | 0.500 | 0.524 | 0.954 | | | | | | | | | |
| $\frac{\pi}{6} = 0.524$ | 0.500 | | | | -0.161 | 0.785 | -0.205 | | | | | | |
| | | 0.207 | 0.261 | 0.793 | | | | -0.151 | 1.047 | -0.1442 | | | |
| $\frac{\pi}{4} = 0.785$ | 0.707 | | | | -0.186 | 0.523 | -0.356 | | | | +0.0573 | 1.571 | +0.0365 |
| | | 0.159 | 0.262 | 0.607 | | | | -0.091 | 1.047 | -0.0869 | | | |
| $\frac{\pi}{3} = 1.047$ | 0.866 | | | | -0.351 | 0.786 | -0.447 | | | | | | |
| | | 0.134 | 0.524 | 0.256 | | | | | | | | | |
| $\frac{\pi}{2} = 1.571$ | 1.000 | | | | | | | | | | | | |

If $n=4$, we have forty-four additions and forty multiplications. It is thus clear that a large number of additions can lead to too many errors. Furthermore, the organization of the calculations in accordance with Lagrange's formula is rather tedious.

Because of these defects, we turn now to an exposition of the method of difference interpolational formulas.

Suppose that we have a table for the function $x=f(t)$

| $t$ | $t_0$ | $t_1$ | $t_2$ | $\dots$ | $t_n$ |
|---|---|---|---|---|---|
| $x$ | $x_0$ | $x_1$ | $x_2$ | $\dots$ | $x_n$, |

and that we wish to derive an expression for the interpolational polynomial of $n$th degree (or of lower degree for certain special choices of the numbers $x_0, x_1, \dots, x_n$).

The condition of exact interpolation gives $n+1$ basic equations

$$x_0=P(t_0),\ x_1=P(t_1),\ \dots,\ x_n=P(t_n)$$

for determining the coefficients $a_0, a_1, \dots, a_n$ of the interpolational polynomial

$$P(t)=a_0+a_1t+\dots+a_nt^n.$$

It is clear from the basic equations that the values of the corresponding difference quotients of the tabulated function and the interpolational polynomial must be the same. When we equate these values, we obtain, for the coefficients of the interpolational polynomial, $n$ more equations containing first-order difference quotients, $n-1$ equations containing second-order difference quotients, etc., and finally one equation with an $n$th-order difference quotient.

The total number of equations of the system of equations that is expanded in this manner will be equal to the sum of natural numbers from 1 to $n+1$, that is, to $\frac{(n+1)(n+2)}{2}$.

In the derivation of Lagrange's formula (see Section 17) for determining the coefficients $a_0, a_1, \dots, a_n$, we used $n+1$ basic equations. However, these coefficients can be determined by choosing an arbitrary set of $n+1$ independent equations from the enlarged system above. Ordinarily, we take one of the basic equations and one equation each from the columns containing difference quotients of the same order.

The coefficients determined from this system will be expressed in terms of difference quotients from the zeroth to the $n$th order. Substituting these coefficients into the polynomial $P(t)$, we obtain a formula that we will call the formula for difference interpolation.

Let us consider the question of the choice of degree of the interpolational polynomial. To begin with, let us consider the case in which the tabular function is itself a polynomial $P(t)$ of degree $n$. Let us construct its difference quotients with a variable step. Let us call some particular value of the argument $t_0$. Then, for an arbitrary value of $t$ different from $t_0$, we have

$$x(t, t_0) = \frac{P(t) - P(t_0)}{t - t_0}.$$

By a theorem of Bézout, the division of a polynomial $P(t)$ by the difference $t - t_0$ gives a remainder of $P(t_0)$. Therefore, the expression $P(t) - P(t_0)$ is divided by $t - t_0$ without remainder and the result is a polynomial of degree $n - 1$. It then follows that a first-order difference quotient of an $n$th degree polynomial is a polynomial of degree $n - 1$. Analogously, we may show that a second-order difference quotient is a polynomial of degree $n - 2$, etc., and an $n$th-order difference quotient is a polynomial of zeroth degree; that is, it is a constant. It is easy to show that this constant is equal to the coefficient of the last term of the polynomial $P(t)$. The difference quotients of order greater than $n$ are equal to $0$.

This property of a polynomial is of great significance in the problem of interpolation. Only in unusual cases can the given tabulated function be an exact polynomial and, when this happens, we see after compiling the table of difference quotients that the difference quotients of some order are constants. In the general case, the given function is not a polynomial and the difference quotients are not quite constant. However, in a great many applied problems, the tabulated values of the function are such that they can be approximated by a polynomial of some degree. In the table of difference quotients of such functions, the differences of some order will be very nearly constant and the differences of the next higher order will be quite small. In this case, we may confidently use point interpolation and construct a polynomial whose degree is equal to the order of the almost-constant differences. Therefore, the compilation of a table of difference quotients is the only method of finding out what degree is necessary for the interpolational polynomial, that is, of finding out the number of basic points that are necessary for a satisfactory approximation.

Recently, there has been a tendency to prefer the use of Lagrange's formula in connection with machine calculation, but to solve the question of the necessary number of basic points we still must compile a table of difference quotients.

## 21. NEWTON'S INTERPOLATIONAL FORMULA FOR A TABLE WITH VARIABLE STEP

Newton and Gregory had already introduced a formula for difference interpolation that is different from Lagrange's formula (which was introduced later and which contains difference quotients). In this section, we shall give Newton's formula, confining ourselves in the derivation to the special case in which the number of basic points is equal to 4, that is, to the case in which $n = 3$.

For this case, the enlarged system of equations can be reduced to the form

| $t$ | $x$ | | | |
|---|---|---|---|---|
| $t_0$ | $x_0=a_0+a_1t_0+a_2t_0^2+a_3t_0^3$ | | | |
| | | $x_1(t_1,\ t_0)=a_1+a_2(t_1+t_0)+a_3\left(t_1^2+t_1t_0+t_0^2\right)$ | | |
| $t_1$ | $x_1=a_0+a_1t_1+a_2t_1^2+a_3t_1^3$ | | $x(t_2,\ t_1,\ t_0)=a_2+a_3(t_2+t_1+t_0)$ | |
| | | $x(t_2,\ t_1)=a_1+a_2(t_2+t_1)+a_3\left(t_2^2+t_2t_1+t_1^2\right)$ | | $x(t_3,\ t_2,\ t_1,\ t_0)=a_3$ |
| $t_2$ | $x_2=a_0+a_1t_2+a_2t_2^2+a_3t_2^3$ | | $x(t_3,\ t_2,\ t_1)=a_2+a_3(t_3+t_2+t_1)$ | |
| | | $x(t_3,\ t_2)=a_1+a_2(t_3+t_2)+a_3\left(t_3^2+t_3t_2+t_2^2\right)$ | | |
| $t_3$ | $x_3=a_0+a_1t_3+a_2t_3^2+a_3t_3^3$ | | | |

The first-order difference quotients of the polynomial, which appear on the right, are obtained after cancellation of $t_1-t_0$, $t_2-t_1$, $t_3-t_2$. All the second-order difference quotients of the polynomial are obtained in the form shown after the cancellation of $t_2-t_0$, $t_3-t_1$. The third-order difference quotient is obtained after cancelling by $t_3-t_0$.

From these ten equations, we may choose any four. Let us choose the equations written along the upper side of the hypothetical isosceles triangle that we would get if we replaced each equation with a point and connected the points with straight lines. These are the equations underlined in the design above. From them, we obtain the values of the coefficients:

$$a_3=x(t_3,\ t_2,\ t_1,\ t_0),$$
$$a_2=x(t_2,\ t_1,\ t_0)-(t_2+t_1+t_0)\,x(t_3,\ t_2,\ t_1,\ t_0),$$
$$a_1=x(t_1,\ t_0)-(t_1+t_0)\,x(t_2,\ t_1,\ t_0)+(t_2t_0+t_1t_0+t_2t_1)\,x(t_3,\ t_2,\ t_1,\ t_0),$$
$$a_0=x_0-t_0x(t_1,\ t_0)+t_1t_0x(t_2,\ t_1,\ t_0)-t_2t_1t_0x(t_3,\ t_2,\ t_1,\ t_0).$$

Substitution of the coefficients into the desired polynomial yields

$$P(t)=x_0-t_0x(t_1,\ t_0)+t_1t_0x(t_2,\ t_1,\ t_0)-$$
$$-t_2t_1t_0x(t_3,\ t_2,\ t_1,\ t_0)+tx(t_1,\ t_0)-$$
$$-t(t_1+t_0)\,x(t_2,\ t_1,\ t_0)+t(t_1+t_0)(t_2+t_1+t_0)\,x(t_3,\ t_2,\ t_1,\ t_0)+$$
$$+t^2x(t_2,\ t_1,\ t_0)-t^2(t_2+t_1+t_0)\,x(t_3,\ t_2,\ t_1,\ t_0)+$$
$$+t^3x(t_3,\ t_2,\ t_1,\ t_0).$$

We expand the polynomial obtained not in powers of $t$, but in difference quotients of successive orders. Here, we consider the given value as a difference quotient of zeroth order. The coefficients of these difference quotients are polynomials whose degrees are equal to the orders of the difference quotients. These coefficients are easily factored by grouping them properly. The interpolational polynomial then takes the form

$$P(t)=x_0+(t-t_0)\,x(t_1,\ t_0)+(t-t_1)(t-t_0)\,x(t_2,\ t_1,\ t_0)+$$
$$+(t-t_2)(t-t_1)(t-t_0)\,x(t_3,\ t_2,\ t_1,\ t_0).$$

The polynomial is constructed in an analogous manner for an arbitrary number of basic points.

For calculation, it is convenient to put $P(t)$ in the following form:

$$P(t) = x_0 + (t - t_0)\{x(t_1, t_0) + (t - t_1)[x(t_2, t_1, t_0) + \\ + (t - t_2)\,x(t_3, t_2, t_1, t_0)]\}.$$

The calculations are performed "from the end": the third-order difference quotient is multiplied by $t - t_2$; the second-order difference quotient is added to the resulting product; this sum is multiplied by $t - t_1$; the first-order difference quotient is added to this product; this sum is multiplied by $t - t_0$; and finally, the zeroth-order difference quotient is added to the product.

The formula and the method of calculation can easily be generalized for an arbitrary number of basic points. In working with a calculating machine, we hardly need to write anything besides the numbers $t - t_0, t - t_1, \ldots$ in compiling the table of difference quotients.

Example. Suppose that we have the following table of values of the sine:

| $t$ | $0$ | $\frac{\pi}{6}$ | $\frac{\pi}{4}$ | $\frac{\pi}{3}$ | $\frac{\pi}{2}$ |
|---|---|---|---|---|---|
| $\sin t$ | 0.000 | 0.500 | 0.707 | 0.866 | 1.000 |

We wish to construct an interpolational formula and compute from it the value of the sine for

$$t = 36° = \frac{\pi}{5} = 0.628.$$

We compile the table of difference quotients

| | $x = \sin t$ | 1st difference | 2nd difference | 3rd difference | 4th difference | $t - t_i$ |
|---|---|---|---|---|---|---|
| 0.000 | 0.000 | | | | | 0.628 |
| | | 0.954 | | | | |
| 0.524 | 0.500 | | −0.205 | | | 0.104 |
| | | 0.793 | | −0.1442 | | |
| 0.785 | 0.707 | | −0.356 | | +0.0365 | −0.157 |
| | | 0.607 | | −0.0869 | | |
| 1.047 | 0.866 | | −0.447 | | | −0.419 |
| | | 0.256 | | | | |
| 1.571 | 1.000 | | | | | |

The difference quotients used in the formula are underlined in the table. The last column contains the numbers $t - t_0$, $t - t_1$, $t - t_2$, and $t - t_3$. For arbitrary values of $t$, the formula is of the form

$$P(t) = t\{0.954 + (t - 0.524)[(-0.205) + \\ + (t - 0.785)(-0.1442 + (t - 1.047)(+0.0365))]\}.$$

For a given value of $t$, the following operations are carried out on a calculating machine:

(1) the number 0.0365 is multiplied by -0.419. To this product is added -0.1442000. The result is rounded off on the machine. We therefore obtain -0.1595.

(2) This number is transferred to the calculating machine. It is multiplied by -0.157 and to the product is added -0.2050000. After rounding off, we obtain -0.1800.

(3) This number is in turn fed into the machine and multiplied by 0.104. To the resulting product, we add 0.9540000. The sum is rounded off, yielding 0.9353.

(4) The number 0.9353 is fed into the machine and multiplied by 0.628. We do not need to add anything because the initial value is equal to 0. The resulting number is 0.5874. The fourth significant figure is a reserve figure, just as in the intervening calculations. From the table, we obtain 0.5878. Consequently, we know the first three digits for certain.

By means of the formulas of Section 19, Chapter 4, we can make an estimate of the interpolational error. In the present case, the absolute value of the derivative of any order does not exceed unity. Therefore,

$$|\sin t - P(t)| < \frac{|L(t)|}{5!},$$

where

$$L(t) = 0.628 \cdot 0.104 \cdot (-0.157) \cdot (-0.419)(-0.943).$$

We do not need to calculate $L(t)$. We may somewhat increase all the factors in order to make the estimate of the error simpler:

$$|L(t)| < 0.7 \cdot 0.1 \cdot 0.2 \cdot 0.5 \cdot 1.0 = 0.007.$$

Thus,

$$|\sin t - P(t)| < \frac{0.007}{5!} \approx 0.00006.$$

This error is considerably less than the actual error. The explanation is quite simple. The formula for determining the error does not contain values of the function and, consequently, does not allow for the exactness of the given values of the function. The formula only allows for the error inherent in the interpolation with the assumption that the given values of the function are exact.

In the present case, certain values of the function are given with three definitely known digits and therefore we cannot obtain a more precise interpolational result. The estimate that we have obtained shows that, for a given function, we cannot obtain an interpolation result more accurate than up to $0.5 \cdot 10^{-4}$, that is, with four digits to the right of the decimal. To ensure such accuracy, we would need to have the function tabulated with four digits to the right of the decimal.

Chapter 6

# INTERPOLATION FROM A TABLE WITH A CONSTANT STEP

## 22. ORDINARY AND CENTRAL DIFFERENCES OF A TABULATED FUNCTION WITH CONSTANT STEP

Let us suppose that a table has been compiled for a function and that at least in the part of the table in which we are interested the step of the table is constant:

| $t$ | $t_{-2}$ | $t_{-1}$ | $t_0$ | $t_1$ | $t_2$ | $\ldots$ |
|---|---|---|---|---|---|---|
| $x$ | $x_{-2}$ | $x_{-1}$ | $x_0$ | $x_1$ | $x_2$ | $\ldots,$ |

where $t_k = t_0 + hk$, the constant $h$ being the step, that is, the difference between two adjacent tabulated values of $t$. Three kinds of differences come up in connection with such a table:

(1) ordinary differences;
(2) central differences; and
(3) differences of negative orders.

### 1. *Ordinary differences*

Let us write the table in the form of two columns for $t$ and $x$ and let us leave a blank space between every pair of consecutive values. Both columns are placed near the left margin of the page. Let us perform the following operation on the entires appearing in the column for the function: from each number we subtract the preceding number and we write the difference in a third column (to the right) on the same level as the empty space between the two values whose difference we are taking:

$$
\begin{array}{cccccccc}
\cdots & \cdots & & & & & & \\
t_{-3} & x_{-3} & & & & & & \\
 & & x^1_{-5/2} & & & & & \\
t_{-2} & x_{-2} & & x^2_{-2} & & & & \\
 & & x^1_{-3/2} & & x^3_{-3/2} & & & \\
t_{-1} & x_{-1} & & x^2_{-1} & & x^4_{-1} & & \\
 & & x^1_{-1/2} & & x^3_{-1/2} & & x^5_{-1/2} & \\
t_0 & x_0 & & x^2_0 & & x^4_0 & & x^6_0 \\
 & & x^1_{+1/2} & & x^3_{+1/2} & & x^5_{1/2} & \\
t_1 & x_{+1} & & x^2_1 & & x^4_1 & & \\
 & & x^1_{3/2} & & x^3_{3/2} & & & \\
t_2 & x_{+2} & & x^2_2 & & & & \\
 & & x^1_{5/2} & & & & & \\
t_3 & x_{+3} & & & & & & \\
\cdots & \cdots & & & & & &
\end{array}
$$

This gives us a column of first-order differences. For these differences, we shall use the notations shown in the third column of the system:

$$x^1_{-5/2} = x_{-2} - x_{-3},$$

$$x^1_{-3/2} = x_{-1} - x_{-2} \qquad \text{etc.}$$

Here, the subscript is the arithmetic mean of the subscripts of those values of the function whose difference we have taken. The superscript 1 indicates a *first*-order difference. We now perform the same operation on these entries in the column of first-order differences. Thus we obtain a column of second-order differences, etc. For the entire table, we use a single system of notation: a difference of order $k$ is denoted by a superscript $k$. A subscript denotes the arithmetic mean of the subscripts of those $(k-1)$st-order differences from which the difference in question is formed. With such a system of notation, all the odd-order differences have fractional subscripts with denominator 2 and all even-order differences have integral subscripts. Differences of consecutive orders that appear in a single row have the same subscript. Differences of different orders, including the values of the function (which are zeroth-order differences), appear in the isosceles triangle with gaps (between the rows) in every row and in every column. Suppose that we have a difference denoted by $x^k_s$, where $k$ is a positive integer and $s$ is either an integer (for $k$ even) or a half-integer (for $k$ odd). From the definition of a difference, we have the following equation relating the difference $x^k_s$ with the differences of next lower order:

$$x^k_s = x^{k-1}_{s+1/2} - x^{k-1}_{s-1/2}.$$

If $n+1$ values of a function are given, this table will contain $n$ first-order differences, $n-1$ second-order differences, etc. The column for $n$th-order differences will contain only one number and with it the table of differences is completed.

The highest order of the differences in the table is one less than the number of values of the function that are tabulated.

## 2. Central differences.

In certain formulas, it is convenient to introduce the arithmetic means of adjacent ordinary differences that appear in a single column. These differences are called central or centered differences. We use the same system of subscripts and superscripts for them as for ordinary differences; that is, the subscript used with a central difference is equal to the arithmetic mean of the subscripts of those differences from which the central difference is formed:

$$x^k_{s+1/2} = (x^k_s + x^k_{s+1}) \cdot \frac{1}{2}.$$

Here, the central differences of odd order have integral subscripts and those of even order have fractional subscripts. This removes the danger of confusing central differences with ordinary differences because the situation is the reverse with ordinary differences; hence we can use the same notation for both without confusion. Central differences are written in the blank spaces between the ordinary differences from which they are formed.

It is easy to show that the formula giving the relationship between the $k$th-order difference and the differences of order $k-1$ remains valid for central differences of all orders. Suppose that $x^k_{s+1/2}$ is a $k$th-order central difference defined by the last formula given above. When we express the ordinary differences of $k$th order that appear in this formula in terms of the ordinary differences of $(k-1)$st order, we obtain

$$x^k_{s+1/2} = \frac{1}{2}\left[\left(x^{k+1}_{s+3/2} - x^{k-1}_{s+1/2}\right) + \left(x^{k-1}_{s+1/2} - x^{k-1}_{s-1/2}\right)\right].$$

If we regroup the terms within the square brackets and if we put the factor 1/2 inside, we obtain, from the definition of central differences,

$$\frac{1}{2}\left(x^{k-1}_{s+3/2} + x^{k-1}_{s+1/2}\right) = x^{k-1}_{s+1},$$

$$\frac{1}{2}\left(x^{k-1}_{s+1/2} + x^{k-1}_{s-1/2}\right) = x^{k-1}_{s}.$$

Therefore,

$$x^k_{s+1/2} = x^{k-1}_{s+1} - x^{k-1}_{s},$$

which is the desired relationship.

The number of central differences in each parenthetical expression is one less than the number of ordinary differences of the same order (since they appear in the spaces between the ordinary differences and since the number of spaces between $m$ points is $m-1$). Accordingly, if the column for the zeroth-order values of the function contains $n+1$ numbers, there will be $n$ zeroth-order central differences. The highest order of central differences will be $n-1$ (there will be one such central difference). If we include all the central differences in our table of differences, the isosceles triangle will be completely filled out.

We might note that other symbols and another system of notation can be used for indicating ordinary differences. For example,

$$\Delta x_0 = x_1 - x_0; \qquad \Delta x_1 = x_2 - x_1 \ldots \quad \text{etc.};$$
$$\Delta^2 x_0 = \Delta x_1 - \Delta x_0; \qquad \Delta^2 x_1 = \Delta x_2 - \Delta x_1 \quad \text{etc.}$$

When this notation is used, differences with the same subscripts are written in a single column and all differences are placed in a right triangle. This notation for ordinary differences cannot be extended to central differences because writing them in a right triangle with no blank spaces does not allow the inclusion of central differences in the diagram. Therefore, in using this notation in formulas containing central differences, we do not use special notation for the latter, but simply express them in terms of the ordinary differences. This complicates calculations.

## 3. *Differences of negative orders.*

Of any two adjacent columns in a table of differences of a function, the column on the right contains the first-order differences of the column on the left. If we consider only this relationship between two adjacent columns, it would be possible to add a number to all members of the column on the left (the same number in each case) without changing the column on the right. If we go from right to left across the table of differences, this relationship between two adjacent columns is interrupted at the column giving the values of the function (that is, the column of zeroth-order differences). In certain problems (for example, in the numerical solution of differential equations), it is convenient to construct other columns to the left of the zeroth-order column that contain the numbers for which the values of the function are differences. These numbers are called differences of the minus-first order. It follows from the definition that one of the differences of the minus-first order can be written arbitrarily, for example, the first one. It will appear in its column one row higher than the first value of the function. If we add this number to the first value of the function, we obtain the second value of the minus-first-order difference. Addition of this number to the second value of the function yields the third value of the minus-first-order difference, etc.

After the column of minus-first-order differences has been compiled, we may construct minus-second-order differences to the left of it, etc. These are denoted by the same system that we use for differences of positive order. If the first number in the zeroth-order column has subscript $s$, the first number in the minus-first-order column will have the subscript $s - {}^1/_2$; in the case of the minus-second-order differences, it will be $s - 1$, etc. The subscripts of the last numbers in each column on the left will exceed by ${}^1/_2$ the subscripts in the neighboring column on the right. After a choice has been made for the first number in each negative-order column, the remaining differences of this order are obtained by successive additions to the differences of the next higher order, and therefore the columns of negative-order differences are sometimes called columns of sums.

## 23. THE BASIC PROPERTIES OF ORDINARY DIFFERENCES

### 1. *The representation of differences of various orders in terms of tabulated values of a function*

Consider the table of ordinary differences:

$$
\begin{array}{cccccc}
\cdots & \cdots & & & & \\
t_{-1} & x_{-1} & & & & \\
 & & x^1_{-1/2} & & & \\
t_0 & x_0 & & x^2_0 & & \\
 & & x^1_{1/2} & & x^3_{1/2} & \\
t_1 & x_1 & & x^2_1 & & x^4_1 \\
 & & x^1_{3/2} & & x^3_{3/2} & \\
t_2 & x_2 & & x^2_2 & & \\
 & & x^1_{5/2} & & & \\
t_3 & x_3 & & & & \\
\cdots & \cdots & & & &
\end{array}
$$

This table can be continued both downward and upward—using negative subscripts for the values of the function and the differences in the latter case.

By definition, differences of a particular order are expressed in terms of the next-lower-order difference, but in some problems, we need to have a difference of arbitrary order directly expressed in terms of the tabulated values of the function. Such expressions are easily obtained by induction from an examination of particular cases.

For second-order differences, we have

$$x^2_0 = x^1_{1/2} - x^1_{-1/2} = (x_1 - x_0) - (x_0 - x_1) = x_1 - 2x_0 + x_1;$$

and analogously,

$$x_1^2 = x_2 - 2x_1 + x_0,$$
$$x_2^2 = x_3 - 2x_2 + x_1,$$
$$x_k^2 = x_{k+1} - 2x_k + x_{k-1},$$

where $k$ is an integer (positive, negative, or zero). Furthermore,

$$x_{1/2}^3 = x_1^2 - x_0^2 = x_2 - 2x_1 + x_0 - (x_1 - 2x_0 + x_1) =$$
$$= x_2 - 3x_1 + 3x_0 - x_{-1},$$
$$x_{3/2}^3 = x_2^2 - x_1^2 = x_3 - 2x_2 + x_1 - (x_2 - 2x_1 + x_0) =$$
$$= x_3 - 3x_2 + 3x_1 - x_0,$$
$$\cdots\cdots\cdots\cdots\cdots\cdots\cdots\cdots\cdots$$
$$x_{k+1/2}^3 = x_{k+2}^2 - 3x_{k+1} + 3x_k - x_{k-1}.$$

From these examples, it is clear that the relationship between the ordinary differences and the tabulated values of the function is expressed by formulas with the binomial coefficients:

$$x_k^{2p} = x_{k+p} - C_{2p}^1 x_{k+p+1} + C_{2p}^2 x_{k-p-2} - \dots$$
$$\dots + (-1)^p C_{2p}^p x_k + \dots + x_{k-p},$$
$$x_{k+1/2}^{2p+1} = x_{k+p+1} - C_{2p+1}^1 x_{k+p} + C_{2p+1}^2 x_{k+p-1} - \dots$$
$$\dots + (-1)^p C_{2p+1}^p (x_{k+1} - x_k) + \dots - x_{k-p}$$

(where $k$ is an integer and $p$ is a positive integer).

These formulas are suitable only for differences of positive order. For negative-order differences, we have no such formulas because these differences are defined only up to an arbitrary addend.

## 2. *The inversion of a table.*

Suppose that all the numbers in the table of values of a function are written in inverse order and that the differences of consecutive orders are defined according to the following principle: each number is subtracted from the preceding one. It is easy to see that all first-order differences will remain the same in absolute value but their signs will be reversed. The second-order differences change neither in absolute value nor in sign. This is true because the expression

$$x_k^2 = x_{k+1} - 2x_k + x_{k-1}$$

is symmetric with respect to $x_k$ and its value is not changed if we replace the three numbers $x_{k-1}$, $x_k$, and $x_{k+1}$ with $x_{k+1}$, $x_k$, and

$x_{k-1}$, respectively. It is clear from the common expressions for odd and even orders that all even-order differences remain unchanged and that odd-order differences change their sign. It follows from this that we must always keep to the chosen order of subtraction in calculating differences (that is, we must subtract each value from the preceding one), since violation of this order is equivalent to reversing the table with a resultant change in the sign of the differences.

## 3. *The sum of differences of a single order.*

If we write all the ordinary differences of a tabulated function with $n+1$ basic points according to the plan given above, we shall obtain an isosceles triangle intersected by straight lines parallel to the base. Each of these straight lines contains all the differences of a particular order. Let us consider the column of differences of order $s$. If the basic point with subscript $0$ appears at the beginning of the table, the first (upper) number of the column of differences will have the subscript $\frac{s}{2}$ and the last difference will have the subscript $n-\frac{s}{2}$. If we add all the differences of order $s$, replacing each of them with the difference between the differences of order $s-1$, we obtain

$$\sum_{k=\frac{s}{2}}^{n-\frac{s}{2}} x_k^s = \sum_{k=\frac{s}{2}}^{n-\frac{s}{2}} \left(x^{s-1}_{k+\frac{1}{2}} - x^{s-1}_{k-\frac{1}{2}}\right).$$

If we expand the right side, we obtain

$$\sum_{k=\frac{s}{2}}^{n-\frac{s}{2}} x_k^s = \left(x^{s-1}_{n-\frac{s-1}{2}} - x^{s-1}_{n-1-\frac{s-1}{2}}\right) + \left(x^{s-1}_{n-1-\frac{s-1}{2}} - x^{s-1}_{n-2-\frac{s-1}{2}}\right) + \dots$$

$$\dots + \left(x^{s-1}_{\frac{s+1}{2}+1} - x^{s-1}_{\frac{s+1}{2}}\right) + \left(x^{s-1}_{\frac{s+1}{2}} - x^{s-1}_{\frac{s-1}{2}}\right).$$

All the terms other than the first and the last cancel each other out, so that

$$\sum_{k=\frac{s}{2}}^{n-\frac{s}{2}} x_k^s = x^{s-1}_{n-\frac{s-1}{2}} - x^{s-1}_{\frac{s-1}{2}}.$$

The numbers on the right represent the first and last numbers in the column of differences of order $s-1$. Thus, the sum of all the differences of any order is equal to the difference between the last and the first numbers in the column of differences of the next-lower order. This property is used in certain applications and it is also used as a check in setting up a table of differences. Although the operations required in setting up these differences are extremely simple, nonetheless errors of carelessness are possible both with manual and with machine calculations. A check should then give exact equality between the sum of all the differences of order $s$ and the difference between the top and bottom numbers in the preceding column of differences.

## 4. Polynomial differences.

It is easy to show, in the same way as in Section 20, that the ordinary differences of $n$th order are constant for a polynomial of degree $n$ and that the differences of higher order are equal to 0. Just as in the case of a table with a variable step, this property can be used to find the degree of the interpolational polynomial for a table with constant step. This degree is equal to the order of those differences that are almost constant for the given tabulated function.

## 5. The effect of error on the differences in a table.

Let us suppose that an error $\varepsilon$ is made in the value of the "middle" number $x_0$ in the table of values of a function; that is, instead of $x_0$, the table reads $x_0+\varepsilon$. Let us show in a single diagram the differences that would appear in an exact table and the differences that appear in the table with the error:

| $t$ | $x$ | | | | | | |
|---|---|---|---|---|---|---|---|
| $t_0-3h$ | $x_{-3}$ | | | | | | |
| | | $x^1_{-5/2}$ | | | | | |
| $t_0-2h$ | $x_{-2}$ | | $x^2_{-2}$ | | | | |
| | | $x^1_{-3/2}$ | | $x^3_{-3/2}+\varepsilon$ | | | |
| $t_0-h$ | $x_{-1}$ | | $x^2_{-1}+\varepsilon$ | | $x^4_{-1}-4\varepsilon$ | | |
| | | $x^1_{-1/2}+\varepsilon$ | | $x^3_{-1/2}-3\varepsilon$ | | $x^5_{-1/2}+10\varepsilon$ | |
| $t_0$ | $x_0+\varepsilon$ | | $x^2_0-2\varepsilon$ | | $x^4_0+6\varepsilon$ | | $x^6_0-20\varepsilon$ |
| | | $x^1_{+1/2}-\varepsilon$ | | $x^3_{1/2}+3\varepsilon$ | | $x^5_{1/2}-10\varepsilon$ | |
| $t_1$ | $x_1$ | | $x^2_{+1}+\varepsilon$ | | $x^4_1-4\varepsilon$ | | |
| | | $x^1_{3/2}$ | | $x^3_{3/2}-\varepsilon$ | | | |
| $t_2$ | $x_2$ | | $x^2_2$ | | | | |
| | | $x^1_{5/2}$ | | | | | |
| $t_3$ | $x_3$ | | | | | | |

It is clear from this diagram that an error in one number in the table of values of the function has an effect on two first-order differences, on three second-order differences, etc. In the column of differences of a single order, these errors are multiples of the original error and their coefficients are the binomial coefficients with the degree of the binomial equal to the order of the difference. In even-order differences, the maximum error always appears on the same row as the original error, and in odd differences, the signs of the error alternate in consecutive differences on both sides of this row.

These differences are used in the following manner in detecting errors in a table: in the more common tables of functions that are used in the natural sciences, the differences of some order or other almost always become sufficiently small.* If there is a large error in one of the numbers listed in the table, this error is added (with the binomial coefficients and alternating signs) to small differences. This leads to wide fluctuations in the values of the differences with alternation of signs beginning with the difference of some particular order. In such cases, the differences are said to "jump." These jumps in the differences can serve to locate the error. It should then be sought on the line with the greatest jumps (or the line next to it). An approximation to the value of the error is obtained by dividing the jumps by the maximum binomial coefficient whose degree is equal to the order of the difference. For a jump, we may take the difference with the largest absolute value.

The problem of the influence of errors in the table on errors in the differences is rather complicated because in a table almost all numbers contain errors in rounding off; each of these errors in turn introduces errors in the differences of all orders, and these errors add up. An exact calculation of errors of this sort would be extremely tedious. Therefore, it is advisable to use the probability method.

Example. Consider a table of values of a third-degree polynomial. Let us compile a table of its differences:

| $t$ | $x$ | | | | | $x$ | | | | | |
|---|---|---|---|---|---|---|---|---|---|---|---|
| −2 | −22 | | | | | −22 | | | | | |
| | | 17 | | | | | 17 | | | | |
| −1 | −5 | | −12 | | | −5 | | −12 | | | |
| | | 5 | | +6 | | | 5 | | +7 | | |
| 0 | 0 | | −6 | | 0 | 0 | | −5 | | −4 | |
| | | −1 | | +6 | | | 0 | | +3 | | +10 |
| +1 | −1 | | 0 | | 0 | 0 | | −2 | | +6 | |
| | | −1 | | +6 | | | −2 | | +9 | | |
| +2 | −2 | | 6 | 6 | | −2 | | +7 | | | |
| | | +5 | | | | | 5 | | | | |
| +3 | +3 | | | | | +3 | | | | | |

Beside it, let us print almost exactly the same table except that we make an error of −1 for $t = +1$. A jump in the differences is likely in the third-order differences

*Strictly speaking, it is only to such functions that the principle of point interpolation is applicable. For greater detail, see Section 20 of Chapter 5.

(minimum) and becomes noticeable in the fourth-order difference. According to the preceding table, an error is possible on the row of the maximum jump, that is, the row corresponding to $t=+1$. In the fourth-order differences, the maximum binomial coefficient is equal to 6 and the error has the same sign as the original error. Assuming that those differences at which there are jumps would have to be approximately equal to 0, we see that the error in the fourth-order difference is equal to -6 and, consequently, that the error in the table is equal to -6/6 = -1.

Finally, it is usually more difficult to determine the error in a table than it was in this example, but its position and order can be determined in this manner.

## 24. THE METHOD OF CONSTRUCTING INTERPOLATIONAL FORMULAS FOR TABLES WITH A CONSTANT STEP

Suppose that a function is defined by a table with a constant step and that we wish to calculate the approximate value of the function at some intermediary value $t$ of the argument not listed in the table by means of an interpolational polynomial. We start with that listed value of the argument $t_0$ that is closest to the given number $t$. This means that $|t-t_0| \leqslant \frac{1}{2} h$, where $h$ is the step of the table. Here, $t$ may be greater than $t_0$. Since the values of the argument ordinarily increase from the initial value listed to the last value listed, we must, in such a case, interpolate forward, as it is called (from the initial value). If $t < t_0$, we interpolate backwards. Finally, if $|t-t_0| = \frac{1}{2} h$, we interpolate at the middle.

In such an interpolational problem, we thus have two parameters $t_0$ and $h$. The first depends on the given value of $t$ and on the step; the second (namely, the step $h$) is given by the table. It is natural to set up interpolational formulas in such a way that they do not contain these parameters explicitly. This is done quite simply by introducing the normalized argument

$$\tau = \frac{t-t_0}{h}.$$

Corresponding to the values of the argument

$$\ldots t_0-2h, \quad t_0-h, \quad t_0, \quad t_0+h, \quad t_0+2h$$

are the integral values of the normalized argument

$$\ldots -2, \quad -1, \quad 0, \quad +1, \quad +2, \ldots$$

For a table with argument $\tau$ and values of the function

$$\ldots x_{-2}, \quad x_{-1}, \quad x_0, \quad x_1, \quad x_2 \ldots,$$

we construct interpolational formulas that are applicable for all values of $t_0$ and $h$. For a normalized table, we shall construct an interpolational polynomial of the form

$$P(\tau) = a_0 + a_1\tau + a_2\tau^2 + \ldots,$$

that satisfies the conditions of point interpolation:

$$\ldots P(-2) = x_{-2}, \; P(-1) = x_{-1}; \; P(0) = x_0, \; P(1) = x_1, \; P(2) = x_2 \ldots$$

| $\tau$ | $x$ | | | | |
|---|---|---|---|---|---|
| $-3$ | $x_{-3}=a_0-3a_1+9a_2-27a_3+81a_4-\dots$ | | | | |
| | | $x^1_{-5/2}=a_1-5a_2+19a_3-65a_4\dots$ | | | |
| $-2$ | $x_{-2}=a_0-2a_1+4a_2-8a_3+16a_4-\dots$ | | $x^2_{-2}=2a_2-12a_3+50a_4\dots$ | | |
| | | $x^1_{-3/2}=a_1-3a_2+7a_3-15a_4\dots$ | | $x^3_{-3/2}=6a_3-36a_4\dots$ | |
| $-1$ | $x_{-1}=a_0-a_1+a_2-a_3+a_4-\dots$ | | $x^2_{-1}=2a_2-6a_3+14a_4\dots$ | | $x^4_{-1}=24a_4+\dots$ |
| | $x_{-1/2}=a_4-\frac{1}{2}a_1+\frac{1}{2}a_2-\frac{1}{2}a_3+\frac{1}{2}a_4\dots$ | $x^1_{-1/2}=a_1-a_2+a_3-a_4\dots$ | $x^2_{-1/2}=2a_2-3a_3+8a_4+\dots$ | $x^3_{-1/2}=6a_3-12a_4+\dots$ | |
| $0$ | $x_0=a_0$ | $x^1_0=a_1\quad+a_3$ | $x^2_0=2a_2\quad+2a_4+\dots$ | $x^3_0=6a_3+\dots$ | $x^4_0=24a_4+\dots$ |
| | $x_{1/2}=a_0+\frac{1}{2}a_1+\frac{1}{2}a_2+\frac{1}{2}a_3+\frac{1}{2}a_4\dots$ | $x^1_{1/2}=a_1+a_2+a_3+a_4+\dots$ | $x^2_{+1/2}=2a_2+3a_3+8a_4+\dots$ | $x^3_{1/2}=6a_3+12a_4\dots$ | |
| $+1$ | $x_1=a_0+a_1+a_2+a_3+a_4+\dots$ | | $x^2_1=2a_2+6a_3+14a_4+\dots$ | | $x^4_1=24a_4+\dots$ |
| | | $x^1_{3/2}=a_1+3a_2+7a_3+15a_4+\dots$ | | $a^3_{3/2}=6a_3+36a_4+\dots$ | |
| $+2$ | $x_2=a_0+2a_1+4a_2+8a_3+16a_4+\dots$ | | $x^2_2=2a_2+12a_3+50a_4+\dots$ | | |
| | | $x^1_{5/2}=a_1+5a_2+19a_3+65a_4+\dots$ | | | |
| $+3$ | $x_3=a_0+3a_1+9a_2+27a_3+81a_4+\dots$ | | | | |

These conditions lead to a system of equations for determining the unknown coefficients. We shall call these equations the basic equations. As was shown in the preceding chapter, a direct solution of the basic equations is a tedious operation. We shall set up supplementary equations that are consequences of the basic equations. To do this, let us write expressions for the differences of various orders for this polynomial in terms of its unknown coefficients. When we equate these expressions for the differences of the tabulated function, we shall obtain the extended system of simultaneous equations shown on page 79.

It is clear from the diagram that the first terms are the same in each of the columns of the differences of the polynomial. The diagram can be made more complete by adding the central differences in the spaces between the ordinary differences. We shall include only those that we shall use for deriving the formulas of greatest use in astronomy.

Various formulas for the given number of basic points can be obtained by choosing in different ways as many equations as there are basic points given. (The number of basic points is selected by starting with the criterion of near-constancy of differences explained above.)

It is convenient to take one equation from each column of differences, including the column of zeroth-order differences, that is, the list of values of the function. It should be noted that it is always advisable to arrange the interpolational difference polynomials according to increasing order of difference and not according to the degree of the argument.

## 25. NEWTON'S FORMULAS FOR INTERPOLATING FORWARD AND BACKWARD

### 1. *Newton's formula for interpolating forward.*

Suppose that we have a table of values of a function. Let us consider that part of it beginning with the particular value $x_0$ corresponding to the value $\tau = 0$. The differences formed from this portion of the table form an isosceles triangle in the diagram of the preceding section. To determine the coefficients of the interpolational polynomial, we take the equations along the upper side of this triangle. (These are underlined by solid lines on the diagram.) For definiteness, we shall confine ourselves to the case of the four basic points corresponding to four values of $\tau$, namely, 0, 1, 2, and 3. We then have the four equations

$$a_0 = x_0, \quad a_1 + a_2 + a_3 = \overset{1}{x}_{1/2},$$
$$2a_2 + 6a_3 = \overset{2}{x}_1, \quad 6a_3 = \overset{3}{x}_{3/2}.$$

Let us denote the interpolational polynomial by $N^+(\tau)$, where the superscript + denotes forward interpolation. In the present case,

$$N^+(\tau) = a_0 + a_1\tau + a_2\tau^2 + a_3\tau^3.$$

If we express the coefficients in terms of the differences, we obtain

$$N^{+}(\tau)=x_0+\tau\left(\overset{1}{x}_{1/2}-\frac{1}{2}\overset{2}{x}_{1}+\frac{1}{3}\overset{3}{x}_{3/2}\right)+$$
$$+\tau^2\left(\frac{1}{2}\overset{2}{x}_{1}-\frac{1}{2}\overset{3}{x}_{3/2}\right)+\tau^3\cdot\frac{1}{6}\overset{3}{x}_{3/2}.$$

If we group the right side according to differences of consecutive orders, we obtain Newton's interpolational polynomial in closed form:

$$N^{+}(\tau)=x_0+\tau\overset{1}{x}_{1/2}+\frac{\tau(\tau-1)}{2!}\overset{2}{x}_{1}+\frac{\tau(\tau-1)(\tau-2)}{3!}\overset{3}{x}_{3/2}.$$

This polynomial can be generalized in a natural manner to the case of an arbitrary number of basic points: consecutive terms contain differences of increasing orders with subscripts that increase by 1/2 from one term to the next. They are multiplied by consecutive coefficients of the binomial series. Thus, in the case of $n+1$ basic points, Newton's formula for forward interpolation takes the form

$$N^{+}(\tau)=x_0+\sum_{k=1}^{n}\frac{\tau(\tau-1)(\tau-2)\ldots(\tau-k+1)}{k!}\overset{k}{x}_{k/2}.$$

## 2. *Newton's formula for backward interpolation.*

Let us now consider a part of the table *ending* with the value of the argument $t_0$. That is, let us construct a formula for the table with basic points having the values $\ldots-3,\ -2,\ -1,\ 0$. For simplicity, we shall confine ourselves to four basic points. To determine the coefficients, we use the equations along the lower side of the isosceles triangle constituting the diagram on page 79. (These are underlined with the dotted line in the diagram.)

$$a_0=x_0,$$
$$a_1-a_2+a_3=\overset{1}{x}_{-1/2},$$
$$2a_2-6a_3=\overset{2}{x}_{1},$$
$$6a_3=\overset{3}{x}_{-3/2}.$$

The solution of these equations is

$$a_3=\frac{1}{6}\overset{3}{x}_{3/2},$$
$$a_2=\frac{1}{2}\overset{2}{x}_{-1}+\frac{1}{2}\overset{3}{x}_{-3/2},$$
$$a_1=\overset{1}{x}_{-1/2}+\frac{1}{2}\overset{2}{x}_{-1}+\frac{1}{3}\overset{3}{x}_{-3/2},$$
$$a_0=x_0.$$

Let us substitute these coefficients into the interpolational polynomial, which we shall denote by $N^{-}(\tau)$. (The superscript denotes backward interpolation.) If we arrange the polynomial first in powers of $\tau$ and then according to increasing order of the differences, we obtain

$$N^-(\tau) = x_0 + \tau x^1_{+1/2} + \frac{\tau(\tau+1)}{2!}x^2_{-1} + \frac{\tau(\tau+1)(\tau+2)}{3!}x^3_{-3/2}.$$

With backward interpolation, $\tau$ is always negative because $t < t_0$. Instead of $\tau$, let us use the absolute value of that number, which we denote by $u = -\tau$. We then have

$$N^-(u) = x_0 - ux^1_{-1/2} + \frac{u(u-1)}{2!}x^2_{-1} - \frac{u(u-1)(u-2)}{3!}x^3_{-3/2}.$$

In this form, the formula differs from the formula for $N^+(\tau)$ only by the alternation of signs in front of consecutive terms.

In the case of $n+1$ basic points, Newton's formula for interpolating backward is of the form

$$N^-(u) = x_0 + \sum_{k=1}^{n}(-1)^k \frac{u(u-1)\dots(u-k+1)}{k!}x^k_{-k/2}.$$

The formula for $N^-(\tau)$ is often called the formula with increasing differences and that for $N^+(\tau)$ is called the formula with decreasing differences. Let us note that neither of Newton's formulas changes its structure if the initial value of the part of the table that we are examining has a subscript $r$ different from 0. In that case, we would need to add $r$ to all the subscripts on the right side of the formula.

Example 1. Determine the right ascension of the moon on January 2, 1950 at 0630 universal time.

From the astronomical calendar for 1950, we write $\alpha_☾$ for $t = 2, 3, 4, 5, 6, 7$ (th day of January) and let us compile a table of the differences:

| $t$ | $\alpha_☾$ | | | | | | | |
|---|---|---|---|---|---|---|---|---|
| January 2 | $4^h\ 47^m\ 4^s$ | | | | | | | |
| | | $3376^s$ | | | | | | |
| 3 | 5 43 20 | | $+111^s$ | | | | | |
| | | 3487 | | $-99^s$ | | | | |
| 4 | 6 41 27 | | $+12$ | | $+7^s$ | | | |
| | | 3499 | | $-32$ | | $+27^s$ | | |
| 5 | 7 39 46 | | $-80$ | | $+34$ | | $-12^s$ | |
| | | 3419 | | $-58$ | | $+15$ | | $-11^s$ |
| 6 | 8 36 45 | | $-138$ | | $+49$ | | $-23$ | |
| | | 3281 | | $-9$ | | $-8$ | | |
| 7 | 9 31 26 | | $-147$ | | $+41$ | | | |
| | | 3134 | | $+32$ | | | | |
| 8 | 10 23 40 | | | | | | | |
| | | 3019 | $-115$ | | | | | |
| 9 | 11 13 59 | | | | | | | |

To see if six basic points are enough, let us make a crude estimate of the coefficient of the fifth difference in Newton's formula. We have $\tau \approx \frac{1}{4}$. Therefore, the coefficient of the fifth difference is equal to

$$\frac{\frac{1}{4}\left(-\frac{3}{4}\right)\cdot\left(-\frac{7}{4}\right)\cdot\left(-\frac{11}{4}\right)\cdot\left(-\frac{15}{4}\right)}{120} < \frac{3\cdot 2\cdot 3\cdot 4}{16\cdot 120} \approx 0{,}04.$$

We may take this coefficient as being approximately equal to 0.04, and, therefore, the term with the fifth difference gives a value greater than $1^s$.

Since the limiting error of the table is equal to $0.5^s$, six basic points are not sufficient because the term with the sixth-order difference can give a number that is greater than $0.5^s$. Therefore, let us extend the table to include seven and, as a check, eight basic points. The coefficient of the sixth difference is approximately equal to the product $0{,}04\cdot\frac{5}{6}$, which we may take as being roughly equal to 0,03. The term with the sixth difference gives a number of the order of 0,4, which is less than the error of the tables.

We arrange the calculations according to the following plan:

| | | Coefficients | Differences | Terms of the formula |
|---|---|---|---|---|
| $\tau = 0.27083$ | | $N_1 = 0.27083$ | $+3376^s$ | $\Delta_1 = +914^s.3$ |
| $\tau - 1 = -0.72917$ | $\frac{\tau-1}{2} = -0.3646$ | $N_2 = -0.0987$ | $+111$ | $\Delta_2 = -11.0$ |
| $\tau - 2 = -1.72917$ | $\frac{\tau-2}{3} = -0.5764$ | $N_3 = +0.0569$ | $-99$ | $\Delta_3 = -5.6$ |
| $\tau - 3 = -2.72917$ | $\frac{\tau-3}{4} = -0.682$ | $N_4 = -0.039$ | $+7$ | $\Delta_4 = -0.3$ |
| $\tau - 4 = -3.72917$ | $\frac{\tau-4}{5} = -0.747$ | $N_5 = +0.029$ | $-27$ | $\Delta_5 = +0.8$ |
| $\tau - 5 = -4.72917$ | $\frac{\tau-5}{6} = -0.788$ | $N_6 = -0.023$ | $-12^s$ | $\Delta_6 = +0^s.3$ |
| | | | | $\Delta = +898^s.5$ |
| | | | | $\Delta = 14^m58^s$ |
| | | | | $\alpha_0 = 4^h47^m4^s$ |
| | | | | $\alpha = 5^h\ 2^m2^s$ |

As an exercise, let us see if it is possible in the above calculations to stop at a fairly small descending fourth-order difference. An estimate of the coefficient gives

$$\left|\frac{\frac{1}{4}\cdot\left(-\frac{3}{4}\right)\cdot\left(-\frac{7}{4}\right)\cdot\left(-\frac{11}{4}\right)}{24}\right| < \frac{3}{16}\cdot\frac{2\cdot 3}{24} \approx 0{,}05.$$

The term with the fourth difference yields 0.35, which is less than the tabular error. This calculation shows that we may not always trust the original estimate. We must see whether the smallness of the difference is stable, since a small difference can arise from the fact that we happened on a sign change in the differences of the given order in the table. Therefore, when we have obtained a small difference of some particular order and have shown that it can have only a small effect on the result, we need to check the subsequent terms. In the example that we have been considering, we carried out our calculation up to the seventh-order difference. It is almost the same as the sixth-order difference. Therefore, we may stop at the term with the sixth-order difference.

It is useful to make the following clarifying remarks about the system of calculations. Suppose that we have a complete system of calculation that can be somewhat shortened by use of a calculating machine. The factors in the numerators of the coefficient are put in the first column. The factors of the entire coefficients appear in the following column; these are written in the form

$$N_1 = \tau,$$

$$N_2 = N_1 \frac{\tau - 1}{2};$$

$$N_3 = N_2 \frac{\tau - 2}{3} \quad \text{etc.}$$

From these formulas, we obtain the successive coefficients of the formula: $N_1, N_2, \ldots, N_6$. The coefficients are multiplied by the differences of the same order. We thus obtain successive terms (beginning with the second) of the formula, which we denote by $\Delta_1$, $\Delta_2, \ldots, \Delta_6$.

The calculations are carried out with a reserve digit (the tenth parts of a second) in order to decrease the accumulation of errors from the individual terms of the formula. Therefore, we calculate $\tau = N_1$ with five digits to the right of the decimal in order that we may vouch for the tenth parts of a second after we multiply by the four-digit value of the first difference. This operation is legitimate since $\tau$ is given and, consequently, this number can be treated as exact. Since the second-order difference has three digits and the third-order difference differs only slightly from it, the coefficients of these are calculated to four decimal places (with conservation of accuracy). The differences of the remaining orders are two-digit. Therefore, it is sufficient to take their coefficients with three decimal places. In the fourth column, the successive differences are written for convenience. We do not have to complete this column if the table of differences is placed close to the diagram. (If the calculation is done by a technician, it is best to write out this column because the column of second factors in the interpolational formula is situated along a diagonal line and the column of first factors along a vertical line, which can be a source of errors.) The last column contains successive terms of the formula. When they are added with the tenth parts kept and the sum is rounded off to the nearest second, we obtain a number that must be added to the original value. The individual terms do not have to be calculated in those problems in which a sufficient number of basic points are known from the preceding experiment to ensure the necessary accuracy. If this number is not known, the last column is necessary since we need to know the individual consecutive terms of the formula in order to know the greatest order of the differences that have an effect on the result of the interpolation. As was stated above, this determines the degree of the polynomial, that is, the number of basic points. In the present case, the term with the fourth-order difference does not have an effect on the result, but the following term yields almost a unit. Therefore, we still need to take the sixth-order difference and consequently seven basic points.

Example 2. Determine the declination of the moon on December 29, 1950 at 1745 universal time. For the initial value of the argument, we take the first instant of December 30th, which is close to the given instant. In this case, we need to interpolate backwards. From the astronomical calendar, we copy the table of values of $t$ and δ☾, and we form a table of the differences as follows:

| $t$ | δ☾ | | | | | | |
|---|---|---|---|---|---|---|---|
| December 24 | +28°23′.0 | | | | | | |
| | | −27′.1 | | | | | |
| 25 | 27 55.9 | | −80′.0 | | | | |
| | | −107.1 | | +6′.0 | | | |
| 26 | 26 8.8 | | −74.0 | | +3′.6 | | |
| | | −181.1 | | +9.6 | | −1′.5 | |
| 27 | 23 7.7 | | −64,4 | | +2.1 | | +0′.2 |
| | | −245.5 | | +11.7 | | −1′.3 | |
| 28 | 19 2,2 | | −52.7 | | +0′.8 | | |
| | | −298.2 | | +12′.5 | | | |
| 29 | 14 4.0 | | −40′.2 | | | | |
| | | −338′.4 | | | | | |
| 30 | 8°25′.6 | | | | | | |

The sixth-order difference is sufficiently small, and we may therefore confine ourselves to seven basic points.

In this case, $t - t_0 = -6^h15^m$ and $\tau = -0.26042$. We follow the calculating procedure as indicated in example 1:

| | | Coefficients | Differences | Terms of the formula |
|---|---|---|---|---|
| $\tau = -0.26042$ | | $N_1 = -0.26042$ | $-338.4$; | $\Delta_1 = +88'.13$ |
| $\tau + 1 = 0.7396$; | $\frac{\tau+1}{2} = 0.3698$; | $N_2 = -0.0963$ | $-40.2$; | $\Delta_2 = +\ 3.87$ |
| $\tau + 2 = 1.7396$; | $\frac{\tau+2}{3} = 0.580$; | $N_3 = -0.0559$ | $+12.5$; | $\Delta_3 = -\ 0.70$ |
| $\tau + 3 = 2.7396$; | $\frac{\tau+3}{4} = 0.68$; | $N_4 = -0.04$ | $+0.8$; | $\Delta_4 = +\ 0.03$ |
| $\tau + 4 = 3.7396$; | $\frac{\tau+4}{5} = 0.75$; | $N_5 = -0.03$ | $-1.3$; | $\Delta_5 = +\ 0.04$ |
| $\tau + 5 = 4.7396$; | $\frac{\tau+5}{6} = 0.79$; | $N_6 = -0.02$ | $+0.2$; | $\Delta_6 = -\ 0.00$ |
| | | | | $\Delta = +91'.3$ |

$\delta_0 = 8°25'.6$

$\Delta = 1\ 31.3$

$\delta = 9°56'.9$

## 26. STIRLING'S FORMULA

The line containing the initial value and the ordinary differences of even order with subscript 0 will be designated as the central line of the table. Let us fill out the table with the central differences of odd order that appear on the same line and let us take the equations located on the central line. If we confine ourselves to five basic points, that is, if we consider only the fourth-order differences, we obtain the following system of equations for determining the coefficients of the polynomial:

$$a_0 = x_0,$$
$$a_1 + a_3 = x_0^1,$$
$$2a_2 + 2a_4 = x_0^2,$$
$$6a_3 = x_0^3,$$
$$24a_4 = x_0^4.$$

Solution of this system gives the following values for the coefficients:

$$a_0 = x_0,$$
$$a_1 = x_0^1 - \frac{1}{6}\, x_0^3,$$
$$a_2 = \frac{1}{2}\, x_0^2 - \frac{1}{24}\, x_0^4,$$
$$a_3 = \frac{1}{6}\, x_0^3, \qquad a_4 = \frac{1}{24}\, x_0^4.$$

The interpolational polynomial is of the form

$$S(\tau) = x_0 + \tau\left(x_0^1 - \frac{1}{6}\, x_0^3\right) + \tau^2\left(\frac{1}{2}\, x_0^2 - \frac{1}{24}\, x_0^4\right) + \tau^3\, \frac{1}{6}\, x_0^3 + \tau^4 \frac{1}{24}\, x_0^4.$$

If we expand it in differences of consecutive orders, we obtain Stirling's formula in its usual form:

$$S(\tau) = x_0 + \frac{\tau}{1!} x_0^1 + \frac{\tau^2}{2!} x_0^2 + \frac{\tau(\tau^2-1)}{3!} x_0^3 + \frac{\tau^2(\tau^2-1)}{4!} x_0^4.$$

When a complete study of the principle of point interpolation is made, an odd number of basic points is always chosen for Stirling's formula, namely, the initial basic point and the basic points that are symmetric to it preceding and following it. Therefore, Stirling's polynomial always is of even degree. The law of formation of the consecutive terms of the polynomial, beginning with the third, is as follows: a coefficient of an even-order difference is obtained from the preceding coefficient (of an odd-order difference) by adding 1 to the argument of the factorial in the denominator and by multiplying the numerator by $\tau$. The coefficient of a difference of odd order, let us say of order $2k+1$, is obtained from the preceding difference of odd order by adding 2 to the argument of the factorial in the denominator and by multiplying the numerator by the factor $\tau^2 - k^2$. For example, the fifth- and sixth-order differences are of the form

$$\frac{\tau(\tau^2-1)}{(3+2)!} \cdot (\tau^2 - 2^2)\, x_0^{3+2} = \frac{\tau(\tau^2-1)(\tau^2-2^2)}{5!} x_0^5,$$

$$\frac{\tau(\tau^2-1)(\tau^2-2^2)\tau}{(5+1)!} x_0^{5+1} = \frac{\tau^2(\tau^2-1)(\tau^2-2^2)}{6!} x_0^6.$$

The law of formation of the coefficients in Stirling's formula is such that the coefficients do not change uniformly. For example, for $\tau = \frac{1}{2}$, the consecutive coefficients are equal to

$$\frac{1}{2},\ \frac{1}{8},\ -\frac{1}{16},\ -\frac{1}{128},\ \frac{3}{256},\ \frac{1}{1024},\ \ldots$$

The signs of the coefficients alternate in pairs; that is, there are two positive terms, two negative, two positive, etc. Each coefficient of an odd-order difference, beginning with the fifth, is greater than the preceding coefficient of an even-order difference. Therefore, in using Stirling's formula one should not stop at an odd-order difference since the corresponding terms can be greater than the preceding one if the differences decrease slowly.

Furthermore, if Stirling's formula is cut off at an odd difference, it will not represent exactly the highest or lowest of the basic points used.

In practice, however, the formula is often cut off at an odd difference since an arbitrary coefficient of an even difference is much less than the preceding coefficient of an odd difference. For example, if the term with the fifth difference gives five units of the last digit, then, for $\tau = \frac{1}{2}$, the term with the sixth difference yields less than one half a unit of the last difference and, consequently, it can have an effect only on the reserve digit and cannot change the result by more than a unit of the last digit (if the reserve digit is considered in all terms).

Because of the symmetry of Stirling's formula about the line passing through the initial basic point, this formula can be applied without change in forward interpolation ($\tau > 0$) and backward interpolation ($\tau < 0$).

Example. Determine the right ascension of the moon on December 13, 1950 at 0936 universal time.

For the initial instant, we take December 13 at 0000 universal time. Let us write the value of $\alpha$ at three preceding and three succeeding instants and let us draw up a table of the ordinary differences:

| $t$ | $\alpha$ | | | | | | |
|---|---|---|---|---|---|---|---|
| December 10 | $17^h41^m57^s$ | | | | | | |
| | | $4111^s$ | | | | | |
| 11 | 18 50 28 | | $-205^s$ | | | | |
| | | 3906 | | $-111^s$ | | | |
| 12 | 19 55 34 | | $-316$ | | $+97^s$ | | |
| | | 3590 | | $-14$ | | $-30^s$ | |
| 13 | 20 55 24 | $+3425$ | $-330$ | $+20$ | $+67$ | $-38$ | $-15$ |
| | | 3260 | | $+53$ | | $-45$ | |
| 14 | 21 49 44 | | $-277$ | | $+22$ | | |
| | | 2983 | | $+75$ | | | |
| 15 | 22 39 27 | | $-202$ | | | | |
| | | 2781 | | | | | |
| 16 | 23 25 48 | | | | | | |

Let us now write the central differences of odd order on the line passing through the origin. We carry out the calculation of the coefficients in Stirling's formula

$$S(\tau) = x_0 + S_1 x_0^1 + S_2 x_0^2 + S_3 x_0^3 + S_4 x_0^4 + S_5 x_0^5 + S_6 x_0^6$$

by use of the equations

$$S_1 = \tau, \qquad S_2 = S_1 \frac{\tau}{2}, \qquad S_3 = S_1 \frac{\tau^2 - 1}{6}, \qquad S_4 = S_3 \frac{\tau}{4},$$

$$S_5 = S_3 \frac{\tau^2 - 4}{20}, \qquad S_6 = S_5 \frac{\tau}{6}$$

We indicate the calculations that we must do for the interpolation in the following table:

| | | Coefficients | Differences | Terms of the formula |
|---|---|---|---|---|
| $\tau = 0.40000$ | $\frac{\tau}{4} = 0.1000$ | $S_1 = 0.40000$ | $+3425^s$ | $+1370.0^s$ |
| $\tau^2 = 0.1600$ | $\frac{\tau}{2} = 0.2000$ | $S_2 = 0.0800$ | $-330$ | $-26.4$ |
| $\tau^2 - 1 = -0.8400$ | $(\tau^2 - 1) : 6 = -0.1400$ | $S_3 = -0.056$ | $+20$ | $-1.1$ |
| $\tau^2 - 4 = -3.8400$ | $(\tau^2 - 4) : 20 = -0.192$ | $S_4 = -0.006$ | $+67$ | $-0.4$ |
| | $\tau : 6 = 0.067$ | $S_5 = +0.001$ | $-38$ | $-0.4$ |
| | | $S_6 = +0.001$ | $-15^s$ | $-0.0^s$ |
| $\alpha_0 = 20^h55^m24^s$ | | | | |
| $\Delta = 22^m22^s$; $\alpha = 21^h17^m46^s$ | | | | $\Delta = +1342^s$ |

Here, $\Delta$ denotes the sum of the terms in Stirling's formula that contain differences from the first to the sixth order. This number must be added to the initial value $\alpha_0$ to obtain the desired value of the right ascension.

## 27. BESSEL'S FORMULA (TWO VARIANTS)

### 1. The first variant.

The value of the argument that is given for interpolation is included between two tabulated values that are denoted by $t_0$ and $t_0+h=t_1$ in the diagram of Section 24. Let us take as a starting point for the calculation the average value of the argument $\frac{1}{2}(t_0+t_1)$. Accordingly, we introduce the argument

$$\tau' = \frac{t-t_0}{h} - \frac{1}{2},$$

which takes the values

| | |
|---|---|
| $\tau'$ | $\ldots -\frac{5}{2},\ -\frac{3}{2},\ -\frac{1}{2},\ +\frac{1}{2},\ +\frac{3}{2},\ \ldots,$ |
| $t$ | $\ldots\ t_{-2},\ t_{-1},\ t_0,\ t_1,\ t_2,\ \ldots$ |

at the basic points. Here, $t_k=t_0+kh$, where the $k$ are negative and positive integers.

We limit ourselves to the four basic points $t_{-1}$, $t_0$, $t_1$, and $t_2$; that is, we shall construct a third-degree interpolational polynomial of the form

$$B(\tau') = b_0 + b_1\tau' + b_2\tau'^2 + b_3\tau'^3$$

Let us set up a system of equations analogous to that used in Section 19, but with argument $\tau'$ (see page 89).

Let us take the equations situated on the middle line between the basic points $t_1$ and $t_0$:

$$b_0 + \frac{1}{4}b_2 = x_{1/2},\quad b_1 + \frac{1}{4}b_3 = x^1_{1/2},\quad 2b_2 = x^2_{1/2},\quad 6b_3 = x^3_{1/2}.$$

Solution of this system yields

$$b_3 = \frac{1}{6}x^3_{1/2},\quad b_2 = \frac{1}{2}x^2_{1/2},\quad b_1 = x^1_{1/2} - \frac{1}{24}x^3_{1/2},\quad b_0 = x_{1/2} - \frac{1}{8}x^2_{1/2}$$

When we substitute these coefficients into the polynomial

$$B(\tau') = b_0 + b_1\tau' + b_2\tau'^2 + b_3\tau'^3$$

| $\tau'$ | | | | |
|---|---|---|---|---|
| $-1.5$ | $x_{-1} = b_0 - \frac{3}{2} b_1 + \frac{9}{4} b_2 - \frac{27}{8} b_3$ | | | |
| | | $x^1_{1/2} = b_1 - 2b_2 + \frac{13}{4} b_3$ | | |
| $-0.5$ | $x_0 = b_0 - \frac{1}{2} b_1 + \frac{1}{4} b_2 - \frac{1}{8} b_3$ | | $x^2_0 = 2b_2 - 3b_3$ | |
| | $x_{1/2} = b_0 + \frac{1}{4} b_2$ | $x^1_{1/2} = b_1 + \frac{1}{4} b_3$ | $x^2_{1/2} = 2b_2$ | $x^3_{1/2} = 6b_3$ |
| $+0.5$ | $x_1 = b_0 + \frac{1}{2} b_1 + \frac{1}{4} b_2 + \frac{1}{8} b_3$ | | $x^2_1 = 2b_2 + 3b_3$ | |
| | | $x^1_{3/2} = b_1 + 2b_2 + \frac{13}{4} b_3$ | | |
| $+1.5$ | $x_2 = b_0 + \frac{3}{2} b_1 + \frac{9}{4} b_2 + \frac{27}{8} b_3$ | | | |

and then expand it in differences of increasing orders, we obtain Bessel's formula

$$B(\tau') = x_{1/2} + \tau' x^1_{1/2} + \frac{\tau'^2 - \frac{1}{4}}{2!} x^2_{1/2} + \frac{\tau'\left(\tau'^2 - \frac{1}{4}\right)}{3!} x^3_{1/2}.$$

This formula can quite easily be generalized to the case of an arbitrary even number of basic points. For example, a fifth-degree interpolational polynomial is of the form

$$B(\tau') = x_{1/2} + \tau' x^1_{1/2} + \frac{\tau'^2 - 0{,}25}{2!} x^2_{1/2} + \frac{\tau'(\tau'^2 - 0{,}25)}{3!} x^3_{1/2} + \frac{(\tau'^2 - 0{,}25)(\tau'^2 - 2{,}25)}{4!} x^4_{1/2} + \frac{\tau'(\tau'^2 - 0{,}25)(\tau'^2 - 2{,}25)}{5!} x^5_{1/2}.$$

The law of formation of the coefficients is quite simple: a coefficient of an odd-order difference is obtained from the preceding even-order difference by adding 1 to the argument of the factorial in the denominator and multiplying the numerator by $\tau'$. The coefficient of an even-order difference, let us say of order $2k$, is obtained from the coefficient of the preceding even-order difference by adding 2 to the argument of the factorial in the denominator and multiplying the numerator by

$$\tau'^2 - \frac{(2k-1)^2}{4}$$

We note that, in the general formula, the free terms of the binomials in the numerator are of the form

$$\frac{1}{4}, \ \frac{3^2}{4} = \frac{9}{4}, \ \frac{5^2}{4} = \frac{25}{4}, \ \frac{7^2}{4} = \frac{49}{4} \ \text{etc.}$$

It is easy to write the general expression for the terms with even- and odd-order differences. The coefficient of $x^{2k}_{1/2}$ is equal to

$$\frac{\left(\tau'^2 - \frac{1}{4}\right)\left(\tau'^2 - \frac{9}{4}\right)\cdots\left[\tau'^2 - \frac{(2k-1)^2}{4}\right]}{(2k)!};$$

the coefficient of $x^{2k+1}_{1/2}$ is equal to

$$\frac{\tau'\left(\tau'^2 - \frac{1}{4}\right)\left(\tau'^2 - \frac{9}{4}\right)\cdots\left[\tau'^2 - \frac{(2k-1)^2}{4}\right]}{(2k+1)!}.$$

It is clear from these formulas that Bessel's formula is especially convenient for $\tau' = 0$, that is, for $t = \frac{t_0 + t_1}{2}$. In this case, the interpolation is known as "interpolation on an average." The coefficients of all odd-order differences in Bessel's formula then vanish and the number of remaining terms is halved, with the result that the number of computations and the resulting error are decreased. The formula can be applied without change for $t$ close to $t_0 (\tau' < 0)$ and for $t$ close to $t_1 (\tau' > 0)$. For example, if $t = t_0 + 0.25h$, we shall have $\tau' = -0.25$, and if $t = t_1 - 0.25h = t_0 + 0.75h$, we shall have $\tau' = +0.25$.

## 2. *The second variant*

Let us substitute $\tau - 0.5$ for $\tau'$ in Bessel's formula; that is, let us measure the normalized argument from the initial basic point. In the coefficients of the differences of successive orders (other than the first) there are factors of the form

$$\tau'^2 - \frac{(2m-1)^2}{4}.$$

Rewriting these factors in terms of the argument $\tau$, we obtain

$$\tau'^2 - \frac{(2m-1)^2}{4} = \tau^2 - \tau - m^2 + m = (\tau - m)(\tau + m - 1).$$

Bessel's formula with the new argument is written as

$$B(\tau) = x_{1/2} + \left(\tau - \frac{1}{2}\right) x^1_{1/2} + \frac{\tau(\tau-1)}{2!} x^2_{1/2} + \\ + \frac{\tau(\tau-1)\left(\tau - \frac{1}{2}\right)}{3!} x^3_{1/2} + \frac{(\tau+1)\tau(\tau-1)(\tau-2)}{4!} x^4_{1/2} + \\ + \frac{(\tau+1)\tau(\tau-1)(\tau-2)\left(\tau-\frac{1}{2}\right)}{5!} x^5_{1/2}.$$

This formula can also be obtained from the diagram of Section 19 if we delete the equations situated on the middle line between the initial basic point and the subsequent basic point. It is suggested that the reader do this himself and thus check the formula just given.

We note a modification of the second variant of Bessel's formula that is often used in practice. Let us make the simple transformations

$$x_{1/2} = \frac{x_0 + x_1}{2} = \frac{x_0 + x_0 + x^1_{1/2}}{2} = x_0 + \frac{1}{2} x^1_{1/2}.$$

If we replace the first term in Bessel's polynomial with its value given by this equation and if we reduce the terms, we obtain the following formula, which differs from the above only in the first two terms:

$$B(\tau) = x_0 + \tau \cdot x^1_{1/2} + \frac{\tau(\tau-1)}{2!} x^2_{1/2} + \dots$$

Example. Determine the right ascension of the moon on December 13, 1950 at 0936 universal time. This instant of time lies between the tabulated instants 1300 and 1400. Let us write the tabulated values symmetrically about the middle line and let us calculate the differences that we need for interpolation:

| $t$ | $\alpha$ | | | | | |
|---|---|---|---|---|---|---|
| December 11 | $18^h50^m28^s$ | | | | | |
| | | $3906^s$ | | | | |
| 12 | 19 55 34 | | $-316^s$ | | | |
| | | 3590 | | $-14^s$ | | |
| 13 | 20 55 24 | | $-330$ | | $+67^s$ | |
| | 21 22 34 | $3260^s$ | $-304^s$ | $+53^s$ | $+44^s$ | $-45^s$ |
| 14 | 21 49 44 | | $-277$ | | $+22^s$ | |
| | | 2983 | | $+75^s$ | | |
| 15 | 22 39 27 | | $-202^s$ | | | |
| | | $2781^s$ | | | | |
| 16 | 23 25 48 | | | | | |

When we determine $\tau$ and $\tau'$, we get $\tau = 0.4$ and $\tau' = 0.4 - 0.5 = -0.1$. The calculations can be made as indicated below:

| | Coefficients | Differences | Terms of the formula |
|---|---|---|---|
| $\tau' = -0.1$ | $B_1 = -0.1$ | $+3260^s$ | $\Delta_1 = -326.0^s$ |
| $\tau'^2 - 0{,}25 = -0{,}24$ | $B_2 = -0{,}1200$ | $-304$ | $\Delta_2 = +36.5$ |
| $\tau' : 3 = -0{,}0333$ | $B_3 = +0{,}004$ | $+53$ | $\Delta_3 = +0.2$ |
| $\tau'^2 - 2{,}25 = -2.24$ | $B_4 = +0.022$ | $+44$ | $\Delta_4 = +1.0$ |
| $(\tau'^2 - 2.25) : 12 = -0.187$ | $B_5 = -0.0004$ | $-45^s$ | $\Delta_5 = +0.0$ |
| $\tau' : 5 = -0.02$ | | | $\Delta = -288^s = -4^m48^s$ |
| $\alpha = 21^h17^m46^s$ | | | $\alpha_0 = 21^h22^m34^s$ |

In this example, calculations by using Bessel's formula turned out to be somewhat simpler than those using Stirling's formula.

It should be noted here that the coefficient $B_2$ is somewhat greater than $B_1$ and that the coefficient $B_4$ is five times as great as $B_3$. It can be shown that the coefficients of odd-order differences are always much smaller than the coefficients of the immediately preceding even-order differences. From Bessel's general formula (first variant), we have

$$\frac{B_{2m+1}}{B_{2m}} = \frac{\tau'}{2m+1},$$

so that

$$\left|\frac{B_{2m+1}}{B_{2m}}\right| < \frac{1}{2(2m+1)},$$

since $|\tau'| < 0{,}5$. (We cannot have equality because $\tau' = 0{,}5$ indicates that the tabulated value of the argument is taken.) Furthermore,

$$\frac{B_{2m}}{B_{2m-1}} = \frac{\tau'^2 - \frac{(2m-1)^2}{4}}{2m\tau'}$$

Let us denote this ratio by the letter $u$. It is a function of $\tau'$ and depends on the parameter $m$. Since

$$\frac{du}{d\tau'} = \frac{\tau'^2 + \frac{(2m-1)^2}{4}}{2m\tau'^2} > 0$$

for all values of $\tau'$, the ratio $u$ increases monotonically for all values of $\tau'$. If $\tau'$ is nonpositive, it takes values from -0.5 to 0. Therefore, at $\tau' = -0{,}5$, we have the minimum value of $u$:

$$u_{\min} = \frac{\frac{1}{4} - \frac{(2m-1)^2}{4}}{-m} = m - 1; \quad \text{for} \quad \tau' = 0 \quad u = \infty.$$

If $\tau'$ is nonnegative, $u$ will be negative and will take values from $-\infty$ to minus $|m-1|$. Consequently, the ratio of the coefficient of an even-order difference to the preceding coefficient exceeds $m-1$ independent of the value of $\tau'$.

## 28. GENERAL REMARKS ABOUT THE APPLICATION OF THE INTERPOLATIONAL DIFFERENCE FORMULAS

If the given value of the argument is close to the lowest value tabulated, we may take only Newton's formula for interpolating forward since use of the other formulas requires knowledge of basic points preceding the one taken as the initial basic point. For the same reason, we can use only Newton's formula for interpolating backward if the given value of the argument is close to the highest tabulated value. However, if the given value is such that the value taken as initial lies in the interior of the table, we may choose any of the difference formulas.

We mention two criteria that are used in regard to this. The simplest criterion has to do with the values of the coefficients of differences of successive orders in the different formulas. For a given value of $t$ and the corresponding value of $\tau$, the most suitable formula is the one with the smallest coefficients of the differences, since the unavoidable errors that occur on rounding off the table and the differences are thus decreased. For use in connection with this criterion, we give a table for the different interpolational formulas:

| Order of difference | $\tau$ | Interpolational formula | | |
|---|---|---|---|---|
| | | Newton's (forward interpolation) | Stirling's | Bessel's (first variant) |
| 2nd | 0.1 | −0.045 | +0.005 | −0.045 |
| | 0.2 | −0.080 | +0.020 | −0.080 |
| | 0.3 | −0.105 | +0.045 | −0.105 |
| | 0.4 | −0.120 | +0.080 | −0.120 |
| | 0.5 | −0.125 | +0.125 | −0.125 |
| 3rd | 0.1 | +0.0285 | −0.0165 | +0.006 |
| | 0.2 | +0.0480 | −0.0320 | +0.008 |
| | 0.3 | +0.595 | −0.0455 | +0.007 |
| | 0.4 | +0.0640 | −0.0560 | +0.004 |
| | 0.5 | +0.0625 | −0.0625 | +0.000 |
| 4th | 0.1 | −0.0207 | −0.0004 | +0.0078 |
| | 0.2 | −0.0336 | −0.0016 | +0.0144 |
| | 0.3 | −0.0402 | −0.0034 | +0.0193 |
| | 0.4 | −0.0416 | −0.0056 | +0.0224 |
| | 0.5 | −0.0391 | −0.0078 | +0.0234 |

As was stated above, it is sufficient to have values of $\tau$ given from 0 to 0.5 since, for values of $\tau$ exceeding 0.5, we need only take the opposite initial value. Only the absolute values of the coefficients are necessary, though we included the signs as well. Comparison of the coefficients shows that, in all cases, the coefficients in Newton's formula are at least as great as the coefficients in the other two formulas and in several cases they are greater.

Another criterion as to the relative values of the interpolational formulas is the estimate of interpolational error. This estimate depends on the properties of the functions being interpolated, on the number of basic points, and on the values of the argument. The combinations of basic points are different for the different formulas used. The maximum absolute value of a derivative of order $n+1$ is obtained in different regions of the argument. Therefore, somewhat different estimates of the interpolational error are obtained from the different formulas. If it is possible to make a comparison of the estimates of the interpolational errors obtained from the different formulas, the formula with the smallest estimate should be chosen.

In conclusion, we shall give a brief summary of the rules for applying the formulas given in this chapter for point interpolation.

1. We choose an initial value $t_0$ such that $|t-t_0| \leqslant \frac{1}{2}h$. If $t > t_0$, we interpolate forward; if $t < t_0$, we interpolate backward.

2. We compile a table of differences and determine the degree of the interpolational polynomial from the order of the differences that remain approximately constant.

3. We calculate the argument $\tau = \frac{t-t_0}{h}$ if we are using the formulas of Newton or Stirling or the second variant of Bessel's formula and $\tau' = \tau - \frac{1}{2}$ if we are using the first variant of Bessel's formula.

4. We then calculate the consecutive terms of the chosen formula until we reach the terms that no longer have an effect on the result. If the table contains $m$ digits to the right of the decimal, the consecutive terms are often counted with $m+1$ digits. The extra term is kept while we are adding but is discarded when we round the figure off after the addition is performed.

# Part III

# PROBABILITY THEORY

Chapter 7

# RANDOM EVENTS; BASIC CONCEPTS

## 29. RANDOM EXPERIMENTS

The concept of probability is introduced in order to study those experiments for which it is impossible to accurately predict the results of future observations, even when the conditions under which the experiment will take place are known.

Examples. (a) Because of the imperfections of our instruments and various other random causes, random errors appear in all types of measurements. When we begin to take measurements, we cannot tell in advance how great the errors will be, nor can we give sufficiently narrow bounds within which the error will lie.

(b) The owner of a lottery ticket cannot predict his winnings before the drawing.

(c) If a star is chosen at random from a list of stars, one cannot predict its basic characteristics.

(d) If a person is chosen at random from a group, for example, a group of recruits, we cannot say in advance what the color of his eyes will be.

(e) If a box contains white and black balls and one of them is drawn, we cannot say without looking what color this ball will be.

Experiments such as these are said to be random.

When we consider the results that can be expected in a random experiment, it often happens that there will be not one definite result but several that can occur. Here, the a priori considerations (based on experience) depend to some extent on the conditions under which the experiment will take place.

Examples. (a) If it is known that the absolute value of the random error incurred when a measurement is made with an angle-measuring instrument does not exceed 10', the question as to the magnitude of the error that will be made in a future observation may be answered, for example, as follows: errors with absolute values from 0' to 2' or from 2' to 4', or from 4' to 6', etc. are possible.

(b) If a star of a certain spectral class is picked from a list, we may give approximate possible bounds for its absolute value that are narrower than they would be if we had no information on the spectral type.

(c) If a box contains three white balls and two black ones, when a ball is drawn, we may say that the possible results are (1) a white ball or (2) a black one.

(d) If a coin is tossed, we may get either heads or tails.

(e) If a die is thrown, the following results are possible:

1, 2, 3, 4, 5, 6.

Multiple observations of random experiments give certain practical criteria by means of which (in view of the known conditions)

H

we may expect some of the possible results to be more likely than others.

Experience with measurements indicates that small random errors are encountered more often than large ones. Because of this, we feel that it is more likely that we shall get a small error in our measurements than a large one (provided all the necessary technological conditions are met). In all such cases, the words "possible," "probable," "almost certain," etc., are used in practice to give a *qualitative* idea of the degree of certainty of some result of a future observation.

When we characterize the "degree of certainty" quantitatively, we agree in advance to consider only those random experiments that satisfy the following conditions:

(1) The number $n$ of possible results of an observation is *finite*. Let us denote these results by the letters

$$A_1, A_2, \ldots, A_k, A_{k+1}, \ldots, A_n$$

We shall call any possible result of a random experiment an *outcome*. In particular, the results $A_k$ are outcomes.

The word "outcome" should be understood in a rather broad sense. If we are considering various forms of precipitation, rain will be an "outcome" and the absence of any precipitation at all will also be an "outcome." If we are considering the possible physical characteristics of a randomly chosen star, its belonging to any one particular spectral class is an outcome. The various possible wave lengths are also outcomes. To understand this last example properly, it should be borne in mind that we are speaking of the possible physical characteristics *before* the star is investigated (i.e., the "experiment" is the act of investigating).

(2) The outcomes listed (that is, the outcomes $A_1, \ldots, A_n$) constitute a complete set of outcomes; that is, at least one of them is certain to happen.*

(3) The outcomes $A_1, \ldots, A_k$ are mutually exclusive; that is, if one of them happens, the others cannot happen. (The term "pairwise exclusive" is also used.)

If the answer to the question in example (a) above as to the magnitude of the absolute value of the error is that an error with absolute value from 0' to 5' or an error from 5' to 10' are possible, these outcomes are mutually exclusive if we make an agreement as to which of these possibilities represents the case in which the absolute value is exactly 5'.

(4) The outcomes $A_1, \ldots, A_n$ are equally likely. We shall consider the concept of equally likely outcomes as basic, that is, reflecting the properties of the experiment. The use of this concept in various problems is motivated primarily by the symmetry of an experiment with respect to the outcomes. In certain problems, the assumption of equal likelihood is a *hypothesis* concerning the properties of the experiment, which can be subject to verification by

*The phrase "these outcomes are the only ones possible" is also used in the literature to indicate that the set is complete.

observation. It is only in the very simplest cases that we can easily show whether the assumption of equal likelihood of the enumerated outcomes in a list similar to that given in paragraph 1 is admissible.

To illustrate, let us suppose that a die is thrown. Any one of the six faces from 1 to 6 can appear. If the die is a perfect homogeneous cube, then throwing the die is a random experiment. The entire set of outcomes consists of the appearance of faces with 1, 2, 3, 4, 5, and 6 spots. These outcomes are mutually exclusive and, because of the symmetry of the faces with respect to the center of gravity about which the die rotates when it is thrown, these outcomes are equally likely. If the die consisted of a wooden part and an iron part, the center of gravity would be displaced toward the iron part, and if the die were to be thrown, it would naturally be more likely that a number on a wooden face would appear. The assertion of equal likelihood of the faces would not be justified once we know the composition of the die, since there is no symmetry about the center of gravity. If we had no such information, we could initially make the hypothesis of equal likelihood for the numbers 1, 2, ....., 6. For definiteness, let us suppose that the single dot is placed on an iron face and that the 6 is on a wooden face. If the die is thrown many times, the 6 will be thrown many more times than the 1. And we should have to reconsider our hypothesis of equality of likelihood of all the numbers from 1 to 6.

Let us consider a second example, which we shall frequently encounter in what follows. A coin is tossed. The question is which side will appear on top. There are only two possible results—heads and tails—and they are mutually exclusive. If we assume that the coin is an ideal thin homogeneous disc, we can consider these two outcomes as being equally likely, since there is no reason to suppose that one side is in any way different from the other or that one has a better chance of appearing on top.

It is much more difficult to establish the equality of likelihood of natural phenonema. From a formal point of view, in considering certain outcomes equally likely, we introduce supplementary assumptions into the problem that are not always strictly justifiable from a physical point of view.

Let us consider another example. Three white balls and two black ones are in a box. Let us suppose that these five balls are indistinguishable to the touch and that they have been thoroughly mixed. Without looking into the box, we take out the first ball that we touch. Before looking to see, we ask what is the color of the ball that has been drawn. There are two possible answers—white and black. These two outcomes are mutually exclusive since, by hypothesis, we take out only one ball. We cannot, however, call these outcomes equally likely since there are more white balls than black ones. To get equally likely outcomes, let us number the balls so that numbers 1, 2, and 3 are white and 4 and 5 are black. We can now list the outcomes differently: Outcome (1) corresponds to ball number 1, which is white; outcome (2) to ball 2, which is white; (3) to ball 3, which is white; (4) to ball 4, which is black; and (5) to ball 5, which is black. These five outcomes are the only possible outcomes; they are mutually exclusive; and they are equally likely since the balls are assumed to be all just alike.

## 30. THE CLASSICAL DEFINITION OF PROBABILITY

The first problem in probability theory is that of explaining the concept of probability, that is, of a number characterizing the degree of likelihood of a particular result of a future observation.

Let us suppose that the outcomes representing the possible outcomes of an observation are

$$A_1, A_2, \ldots, A_k, A_{k+1}, \ldots, A_n.$$

Suppose that these are the only possible outcomes, that they are mutually exclusive, and that they are equally likely. The result whose probability we are seeking to determine we shall call an *event*.

Suppose that $C$ is an event that may or may not take place in future observations. Suppose also that, among the enumerated possible outcomes $A_1, A_2, \ldots, A_n$, we single out those outcomes under which the event will take place. Suppose that these are the outcomes $A_1, \ldots, A_k$, where $k \leqslant n$. We shall call these outcomes *favorable* for the event $C$.

We give the following definition:

The ratio of the number of outcomes that are favorable for a given event $C$ to the number of equally possible mutually exclusive outcomes representing the only possible outcomes is called the *probability* of a random event:

$$p = P(C) = \frac{k}{n}. \tag{7.1}$$

To calculate the probability, we must first enumerate all the possible outcomes and then single out those that are favorable for the event. Let us note that in certain problems all the possible equally likely, mutually exclusive outcomes can be listed differently. For example, the list of outcomes that may occur when a die is thrown can be given in the following two forms:

(a) An odd number (1, 3, 5); an even number (2, 4, 6).

(b) The numbers 1, 2, 3, 4, 5, 6.

We now give some consequences of the definition of probability.

1. Suppose that $k = 0$. Then, by definition, $p = 0$. Since there are no outcomes that are favorable for this event, the event is impossible. Thus, the probability of an impossible event is 0.

2. Suppose that $k = n$. On the basis of the definition, we have $p = 1$. Since all the outcomes are favorable for the event, it will certainly take place. Such an event is said to be *certain*. Thus, the probability of a certain event is unity.

3. In the general case, $0 \leqslant k \leqslant n$. Consequently, $0 \leqslant p \leqslant 1$. The probability can assume values from 0 to 1. According to the classical definition, $p$ can take only rational values.

4. If $k$ is the number of outcomes that are favorable for an event, the number of unfavorable events is $n - k$. If we denote by $q$ the probability of the event not taking place, we obtain from the definition

$$q = \frac{n-k}{n}, \tag{7.2}$$

since the unfavorable outcome are favorable for the non-occurrence of the event. Adding equations (7.1) and (7.2), we obtain

$$p + q = 1. \tag{7.3}$$

## 31. EXAMPLES OF THE CALCULATION OF A PROBABILITY

Example 1. A coin is tossed. Determine the probability of its falling heads.

The list of the only possible, equally likely, and mutually exclusive cases is (1) heads or (2) tails; that is, $n = 2$. Of these two possibilities, the favorable outcome is heads; that is, $k = 1$. Therefore, the probability $p = 1/2$.

Example 2. A die is thrown. Determine the probability of getting a five. The only possible, equally likely, and mutually exclusive cases are 1, 2, 3, 4, 5, and 6. Only the single outcome of the die falling on five is favorable. Consequently, $p = 1/6$.

Example 3. A die is thrown. Calculate the probability of getting an odd number.

Method 1. The only possible, equally likely, and mutually exclusive outcomes are 1, 2, 3, 4, 5, 6. Of these, the outcomes 1, 3, and 5 are favorable. Therefore, $p = 3/6 = 1/2$.

Method 2. The two outcomes of an even number being thrown and an odd number being thrown are exhaustive, equally possible, and mutually exclusive. Only the second case of the odd number is favorable. Consequently, $p = 1/2$.

Example 4. Two coins are tossed. Determine the probability of getting heads on each. We make up the table

| | | | | |
|---|---|---|---|---|
| 1st coin | heads | heads | tails | tails |
| 2nd coin | heads | tails | heads | tails |

It is clear from the table that $k = 1$ and $n = 4$. Therefore, $p = 1/4$.

Example 5. A box contains three white and five black balls. The balls are mixed up and they are indistinguishable to the touch. Without looking into the box, we take out two balls at random. Calculate the probability that both of them will be black.

The number of all possible outcomes is the number of ways in which we can take two balls out of a set of eight; that is, $n = C_8^2$. The number of favorable events is the number of ways in which we can take two black balls from a set of five black balls; that is, $k = C_5^2$. Therefore, we obtain

$$k = 10; \qquad n = 28; \qquad p = \frac{10}{28} = \frac{5}{14}.$$

Example 6. There are twelve white and eighteen black balls in a box. We take out ten balls. Calculate the probability of taking out exactly four white and six black balls.

The total number of cases is the number of ways in which it is possible to take ten balls out of a set of thirty; that is, $n = C_{30}^{10}$. The number of favorable outcomes is determined as follows: the number of ways in which it is possible to take four white balls out of a set of twelve is $C_{12}^4$. To each set of four white balls, there corresponds $C_{18}^6$ sextuples of black balls. Therefore, the number of favorable outcomes is $C_{12}^4 \cdot C_{18}^6$. The probability of taking four white and six black balls is

$$p = \frac{C_{12}^4 \cdot C_{18}^6}{C_{30}^{10}} = \frac{495 \cdot 18{,}564}{30{,}045{,}015} \approx 0.306$$

This problem is an example from sampling theory. In various fields, we have occasion to deal with the following problem. Suppose that we have a complete set of objects (the "general set"). We wish to find the characteristics that can describe it to some degree.

Examples: (a) For the set of all stars, assorted according to spectral class, find the percentage of spectrally double stars.

(b) For the set of small planets, determine the average declination.

(c) Determine the percentage of rejects in an order of identical wares.

To solve the problem completely, we would have to examine the entire set, which could be an extremely tedious procedure and sometimes impossible (for example, determining the percentage of unexploded artillery shells). In such cases, we take some portion of the entire set and determine the desired numerical characteristics of it. The problem then arises as to what the probability is of getting from this sample a value of the characteristic that is close to the characteristic of the entire set. This example is one of the problems of sampling theory. The general set is the collection of balls in a full box in which the ratio of the number of white balls to the number of black balls is two to three. The question then is what is the probability of making a sampling of ten balls and obtaining the same ratio, that is, of judging the composition of the full box from the sample.

It is clear from examples 4, 5, and 6 that the determination of the total number of events and the number of favorable events is not always so simple as in the first three examples. In particular, if in the fourth example there were five coins instead of two, the total number of events would be thirty-two and the direct listing of them would be tedious. Therefore, one of the problems of probability theory is to derive rules for calculating probabilities of certain events from the known probabilities of other events. Such rules will be given in the following two sections. Another, extremely important, example is the problem of establishing the conditions under which the probability will be close to 1 or to 0.

This problem is connected with the assumptions, since the event can be considered almost certain if its probability differs only slightly from unity and almost impossible if its probability is close to zero.

## 32. A THEOREM ON THE ADDITION OF PROBABILITIES

THEOREM. *The probability that one or the other of two mutually exclusive events C and D will take place is equal to the sum of the individual probabilities of these events.*

Proof: Suppose that the list of exhaustive, equally likely, and mutually exclusive events is of the form

$$A_1, A_2, \ldots, A_k, A_{k+1}, \ldots, A_{k+l}, A_{k+l+1}, \ldots, A_n.$$

Suppose that

$$A_1, A_2, \ldots, A_k$$

are the only cases that are favorable for the event $C$. Since the events $C$ and $D$ are mutually exclusive, none of these $k$ cases can be favorable for the event $D$. Let us suppose that $A_{k+1}, A_{k+2}, \ldots,$ $A_{k+l}$ are all outcomes that are favorable for the event $D$. We denote the probabilities of the events $C$ and $D$ by $P(C)$ and $P(D)$. Of all $n$ outcomes, $k$ are favorable to $C$ and $l$ are favorable for $D$. Therefore,

$$P(C)=\frac{k}{n}, \quad P(D)=\frac{l}{n}.$$

The cases $A_1, A_2, \ldots, A_k, A_{k+1}, \ldots, A_{k+l}$, taken together are favorable for either the event $C$ or the event $D$. Therefore,

$$P(C \text{ or } D)=\frac{k+l}{n}.$$

When we compare this last equation with the preceding two equations, we obtain*

$$P(C \text{ or } D)=\frac{k}{n}+\frac{l}{n}.$$

*In some text books, the occurrence of the event $C$ or the event $D$ is denoted by $C+D$ (symbolic addition), and the theorem on the addition of probabilities is written in the form

$$P(C+D)=P(C)+P(D)$$

if $C$ and $D$ are mutually exclusive.

or

$$P(C \text{ or } D) = P(C) + P(D). \tag{7.4}$$

COROLLARY 1. *If the events* $C_1, C_2, \ldots, C_s$ *are mutually exclusive and their probabilities are* $p_1, p_2, \ldots, p_s$, *then*

$$P(C_1 \text{ or } C_2, \ldots, \text{ or } C_s) = p_1 + p_2 + \cdots + p_s. \tag{7.5}$$

COROLLARY 2. Let $C$ denote the occurrence of any one of a set of mutually exclusive events $C_1, C_2, \ldots, C_s$. Let us agree to call the individual events $C_1, \ldots, C_s$ mutually exclusive ways in which the event $C$ can happen. Then, the theorem of addition for $s$ events can be formulated in the following manner:

*The probability of the event C, which can happen in the different ways* $C_1, \ldots, C_s$, *is equal to the sum of the individual probabilities of each of these ways.*

COROLLARY 3. *Suppose that in a certain experiment, some one of the mutually exclusive events* $C_1, C_2, \ldots, C_n$ *must necessarily occur. Suppose that their probabilities are respectively equal to* $p_1, p_2, \ldots, p_n$. *Then,*

$$p_1 + p_2 + \cdots + p_n = 1. \tag{7.6}$$

Proof: From the addition theorem, the probability of any one of the mutually exclusive events $C_1, C_2, \ldots, C_n$ is equal to the sum of the probabilities of these events and, by hypothesis, one of these events must certainly take place.

Formula (7.3) is a special case of formula (7.6). For the event either will take place (we denote the probability of this by $p$) or it will not take place (we denote the probability of this by $q$). These results are mutually exclusive. Therefore, if we apply formula (7.6), we can write $p + q = 1$.

Example 1. A box contains five white, seven green, and eight red balls. Determine the probability of taking a ball at random and getting either a green or a red one.

The probability of getting a green ball is

$$P(\text{green}) = 7/20$$

The probability of getting a red ball is

$$P(\text{red}) = 8/20$$

From the addition theorem, we have

$$P(\text{green or red}) = 7/20 + 8/20 = 15/20 = 3/4$$

This result can be derived by a simple calculation. Since we are determining the probability of the event "getting either a green or a red ball," the number of favorable events is $k = 7 + 8 = 15$ and $n = 20$. Therefore,

$$P(\text{green or red}) = 15/20 = 3/4$$

In this example, it would have been possible not to give the number of balls: the probabilities would have been sufficient.

Example 2. A die is thrown. Determine the probability of getting either a five or an even number.

From the results of example 2 of the preceding section, we have

$$P(5) = 1/6$$

It is easy to see that

$$P(\text{even number}) = 1/2$$

Since getting a five and getting an even number are mutually exclusive events,

$$P(\text{five or even number}) = 1/2 + 1/6 = 2/3$$

Example 3. A die is thrown. Determine the probability of getting either a five or an odd number.

The addition theorem is not applicable here because these events are not mutually exclusive. However, since the first event is a particular way of getting the second, we have

$$P(\text{five or odd number}) = P(\text{odd number}) = 1/2$$

## 33. THE THEOREM ON THE MULTIPLICATION OF PROBABILITIES

Definition 1. An event is said to be *composite* if it consists of the occurrence of two or more events. These events are called the *components* of the composite event. It is sometimes said that "a composite event is a combination of events." (The word "combination" is used somewhat broadly; the events referred to may take place at different times or in different places.)

Definition 2. The probability of an event $C$ calculated with the assumption that an event $D$ has taken place is called the *conditional probability* of the event $C$ given $D$ and is denoted by $P(C|D)$. Probabilities of the form $P(C)$ are sometimes called unconditional.

THEOREM. *The probability of a composite event representing a combination of two events is equal to the product of the probability of one of them multiplied by the conditional probability of the other given the first.*

Proof: Suppose that the entire set of equally likely and mutually exclusive outcomes is of the form

$$A_1,\ A_2,\ \ldots,\ A_k,\ A_{k+1},\ \ldots,\ A_{k+l+1},\ \ldots,\ A_n.$$

Let us suppose that only the first $k$ of these outcomes are favorable to both the components $C$ and $D$ of the composite event in question. Suppose that the outcomes $A_1, A_2, \ldots, A_{k+l}$ represent all the outcomes that are favorable for the event $C$. Among the outcomes $A_{k+l+1}, \ldots, A_n$ there may be events favorable for $D$ and unfavorable for $C$, but we are not concerned with them.

Let us write the decomposition in the following manner:

$$\overbrace{\underbrace{A_1,\ A_2,\ \ldots,\ A_k}_{\text{Favorable for both } C \text{ and } D}\quad \underbrace{A_{k+1},\ \ldots,\ A_{k+l}}_{\text{Unfavorable for } D}}^{\text{Favorable for } C}\quad \underbrace{A_{k+l+1},\ \ldots,\ A_n}_{\text{Unfavorable for } C}$$

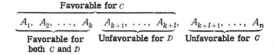

By the definition of probability, we have

$$P(C) = \frac{k+l}{n}, \quad P(C \text{ and } D) = \frac{k}{n}.$$

To calculate the probability of $D$ given $C$, we reason as follows.

If the event $C$ has taken place, this means that one of the outcomes $A_1, A_2, \ldots, A_{k+l}$ has taken place; therefore, the number of all the outcomes is equal to $k+l$. Among these, the outcomes $A_1, A_2, \ldots, A_k$ are favorable for the event $D$. Consequently,

$$P(D|C) = \frac{k}{k+l}. \tag{7.7}$$

It is now easy to verify the theorem:*

$$P(C)P(D|C) = \frac{k+l}{n}\frac{k}{k+l} = \frac{k}{n} = P(C \text{ and } D), \tag{7.8}$$

$$P(C \text{ and } D) = P(C)P(D|C). \tag{7.9}$$

COROLLARY 1. *If we switch the notations for the events, we obtain*

$$P(D \text{ and } C) = P(D)P(C|D); \tag{7.10}$$

Since $P(D \text{ and } C) = P(C \text{ and } D)$, we have

$$P(C)P(D|C) = P(D)P(C|D). \tag{7.11}$$

This formula establishes a relationship between two unconditional probabilities ($P(C)$ and $P(D)$ and two conditional probabilities of two events. We see that only three of these can be given arbitrarily. The fourth is determined from the formula. However, even the three probabilities cannot be given altogether arbitrarily since their values must not be such as to make the value of the fourth greater than unity.

COROLLARY 2. *The multiplication theorem for several events can be written in the following form:*

$$\begin{aligned} &P(C_1 \text{ and } C_2 \text{ and} \ldots \text{and } C_s) = \\ &= P(C_1)P(C_2|C_1)P(C_3|C_1, C_2) \ldots P(C_s|C_1, C_2 \ldots \text{and } C_{s-1}), \end{aligned} \tag{7.12}$$

*where $P(C_3| C_1$ and $C_2)$ denotes the probability of the event $C_3$ given $C_1$ and $C_2$, etc.*

COROLLARY 3 (division of probabilities). From the formula

$$P(C \text{ and } D) = P(C)P(D|C) = P(D)P(C|D)$$

---

*A composite event (combination of events) is often denoted symbolically by a multiplication sign; that is, instead of writing "C and D," we write C x D.

it follows that

$$P(D|C)=\frac{P(C \text{ and } D)}{P(C)}, \quad P(C|D)=\frac{P(C \text{ and } D)}{P(D)}, \tag{7.13}$$

*that is, the conditional probability of one event given another event is equal to the quotient obtained by dividing the probability of the composite event by the probability of the second event.*

Definition 3. Events are said to be *independent* if the probability of each of them does not depend on whether the remaining events have taken place or not.

If this condition is not satisfied, the events are said to be *dependent*. Formally, the condition of independence of two events can be written in the form

$$P(C|D)=P(C), \; P(D|C)=P(D)$$

Here, it follows from the definition of conditional probability that the second of these equations is a consequence of the first.

The multiplication theorem proven above is applicable to dependent events. In the case of independent events, the multiplication theorem can be worded more simply:

The probability of a composite event is equal to the product of the probabilities of the components of that composite event:

$$P(C_1 \text{ and } C_2 \text{ and} \ldots \text{and } C_s)=P(C_1)\,P(C_2)\ldots P(C_s). \tag{7.14}$$

The validity of the theorem is clear from the fact that, from the definition of independence, the probability of the event $C_2$ does not depend on the occurrence or non-occurrence of the event $C_1$. Therefore,

$$P(C_1 \text{ and } C_2)=P(C_1)\,P(C_2|C_1)=P(C_1)\,P(C_2). \tag{7.15}$$

The proof for an arbitrary number of component events proceeds analogously.

Example 1. Two coins are tossed. Determine the probability of getting heads both times.

Getting heads on an individual coin is an independent event since the probability of getting heads on the second coin obviously does not depend on whether the first coin fell heads or tails. In each case, the probability of getting heads is 1/2. By the multiplication theorem, the probability of getting heads both times, that is, the probability of an event representing a combination of two events, can be written in the form

$$P(\text{heads and heads}) = P(\text{heads}) \cdot P(\text{heads}) = 1/2 \cdot 1/2 = 1/4$$

Example 2. A box contains five white and four black balls. Suppose that you plan to take out one ball, look to see what color it is, put it back, mix the balls up again, and again take out a ball. What is the probability (before the experiment) of getting black balls both times.

The two events of getting a black ball the first time and getting a black ball the second time are, because of the way in which the experiment is conducted, independent. Therefore,

$$P(\text{black and black}) = P(\text{black}) \cdot P(\text{black}) = 4/9 \cdot 4/9 = 16/81$$

Example 3. A box contains five white and four black balls. This time, the plan is to take out two balls one after the other without putting the first one back. Determine the probability of getting black balls both times.

Here, the probability of getting a black ball the second time depends on whether the first ball was white or black. In the first case, this probability is equal to 3/8, and in the second, it is equal to 1/2. Our two events are dependent, and therefore,

$$P(\text{first black and second black}) = P(\text{first black}) \cdot P(\text{second black}|\text{first black})$$

or

$$P(\text{first black and second black}) = 4/9 \cdot 3/8 = 1/6$$

Here, $P(\text{second black}|\text{first black})$ denotes the probability of getting a black ball the second time, given that the first ball was black.

## 34. TOTAL PROBABILITY HYPOTHESES

Suppose that an event $C$ can occur when one or several of the mutually exclusive random conditions $H_1, H_2, \ldots, H_n$ are satisfied. These conditions are called *hypotheses*. Since the hypotheses are random, we must give their probabilities $P_1, P_2, \ldots, P_n$. The list of hypotheses must be complete. Therefore, from the addition theorem,

$$\sum_{k=1}^{n} P_k = 1.$$

Let us suppose also that the conditional probabilities of an event are given for each of the hypotheses. We denote them by $p_k = P(C|H_k)$, for $k = 1, 2, \ldots, n$.

The *total probability* of an event $C$ under the stated conditions is the probability that the event will take place, computed under the assumption that first a particular one of the hypotheses is satisfied.

To calculate the total probability, we reason as follows: the event $C$ can take place in any of the ways $H_k \times C$ for $k = 1, 2, \ldots, n$, that is, the composite of the hypothesis $H_k$ and the event $C$. The probability of each way in which $C$ can happen can be calculated from the multiplication theorem for dependent events since the probability of the event $C$ depends on which of the hypotheses is satisfied. We obtain

$$P(H_k \times C) = P(H_k) P(C|H_k) = P_k p_k.$$

The ways $H_k \times C$ in which $C$ can occur are mutually exclusive. Therefore, from the addition theorem,

$$P(C) = \sum_{k=1}^{n} P(H_k \times C).$$

The total probability can be calculated from the formula

$$P(C) = \sum_{k=1}^{n} P_k p_k. \tag{7.16}$$

To make clear the derivation of the general formula, we repeat this reasoning for a particular case.

Example. Suppose that we have three red boxes, each containing four white and five black balls, and seven green boxes, each containing two white and three black balls. All the boxes are just alike except for color and so are all the balls. The balls are thoroughly mixed up. We take a ball out of the first box we put our hands on. The conditions of the experiment are such that we cannot say which of the boxes this will be. Determine the probability of getting a white ball.

To solve this problem, we should first note that the event in question, getting a white ball, can happen in two mutually exclusive ways since a white ball can be taken from any of the green boxes and from any of the red boxes. Therefore, from the addition theorem,

$$P(\text{white ball}) = P(\text{white ball from green box}) + P(\text{white ball from red box}).$$

Getting a white ball from any of the green boxes is a composite event consisting of two events since for it to happen it is necessary that (1) we choose a green box and (2) we take a white ball from it. The same is true with regard to getting a white ball from a red box. From the theorem on multiplication (for dependent events), we obtain

$$P(\text{white ball from green box}) = P(\text{green box})\, P(\text{white ball} \mid \text{green box}),$$

$$P(\text{white ball from red box}) = P(\text{red box})\, P(\text{white ball} \mid \text{red box}).$$

Here, $P(\text{green box})$ is 7/10 and $P(\text{red box})$ is 3/10. $P(\text{white ball} \mid \text{green box})$ is the probability of taking a white ball given that we have chosen a green box, and $P(\text{white ball} \mid \text{red box})$ is the probability of getting a white ball given that we have chosen a red box. Since

$$P(\text{white ball} \mid \text{green box}) = 2/5$$

and

$$P(\text{white ball} \mid \text{red box}) = 4/9$$

the desired probability of getting a white ball is equal to

$$P(\text{white ball}) = 7/10 \cdot 2/5 + 3/10 \cdot 4/9 = 31/75$$

The solution can be written in the following table:

| | Number of boxes | Number of black balls | Number of white balls | Number of balls | Conditional probability of getting a white ball | Probability of choosing such a box |
|---|---|---|---|---|---|---|
| Green | 7 | 3 | 2 | 5 | 2/5 | 7/10 |
| Red | 3 | 5 | 4 | 9 | 4/9 | 3/10 |
| Sum | 10 | 8 | 6 | 14 | 6/14 | 1 |

To solve this problem, we did not actually need to know the composition of the boxes. It would have been sufficient to know the probability of drawing a white ball given that we have chosen a red box (or a green one). Also, instead of knowing the number of boxes, it would have been sufficient to know the percentage that were red and the percentage that were green. We note that it would not have been correct to calculate the overall number of white or black balls in all the boxes and then divide the number of white balls or black balls in all the boxes and then divide the number of white balls by the number of balls of both colors, that is, to use the definition of probability directly. This can be done only when we are equally likely to draw one ball as another. In the present case, the proportion of white balls is somewhat greater in the red boxes than in the green boxes. Therefore, we cannot assume that the balls are evenly mixed or that we have an equal chance of getting each of the balls.

## 35. A PRIORI AND A POSTERIORI PROBABILITIES OF THE HYPOTHESES

Suppose that the occurrence or non-occurrence of an event is connected with certain assumptions as to the causes of that event or as to the conditions under which it will take place. To each of these assumptions there corresponds a definite probability of the event. Furthermore, the assumptions (hypotheses) are also considered random. Consequently, for the problem to be defined, the probabilities of the hypotheses must be given. For example, if we take a ball out of a box containing five balls and if we know only that there are white and black balls in the box, there are numerous assumptions (hypotheses) that we could make as to the composition of the box. To each of these hypotheses there will correspond a definite probability of getting a white ball. In this example, we have the following hypotheses and the corresponding probabilities of getting a white ball.

| | | | $P$(white) |
|---|---|---|---|
| 1) | 4 white | 1 black | 0.8 |
| 2) | 3 white | 2 black | 0.6 |
| 3) | 2 white | 3 black | 0.4 |
| 4) | 1 white | 4 black | 0.2 |

If we take a ball and it turns out to be white, the question then arises as to which of the above hypotheses is the most likely one. Solution of problems of this kind can be of value in judging the probability of random causes of an event that occurs in an experiment when there are several such causes. The possibility of solving such a problem (when properly stated) is clear from the following simple considerations.

In the present example, if it were not stated that there were black and white balls in each of the boxes, we would have to add two other hypotheses:

5) Five white and 0 black,
6) 0 white and five black.

The drawing of a white ball would then show us that the probability of the sixth hypothesis is zero.

Probabilities of hypotheses in the conditions of a problem before an experiment is made are called a priori probabilities, and probabilities that are calculated after an experiment resulting in some event are called a posteriori probabilities.

Let us now consider the following problem. Let us suppose that an event $C$ can be explained by $n$ mutually exclusive exhaustive hypotheses:

$$H_1, H_2, \ldots, H_n.$$

Let us suppose that the probability of each hypothesis is known from experiment. We denote these a priori probabilities by $P_1$, $P_2$, . . . , $P_n$. As we know,

$$\sum_{k=1}^{n} P_k = 1.$$

Finally, let us suppose, that, for each of these hypotheses, we know the probability of $C$ under the condition that the occurrence of $C$ is explained by that hypothesis. We denote these probabilities by $p_1, p_2, \ldots, p_n$. It follows that $p_k$ is the conditional probability of the event $C$, under the assumption that the cause corresponding to the hypothesis $H_k$ (for $k = 1, 2, \ldots, n$) was in fact the one which resulted in the occurrence of the event. What we wish to determine now is the probability of each of these hypotheses, if it is known that the event occurred.

Let us solve this problem. The conditional probability of the hypothesis $H_k$ (for $k = 1, 2, \ldots, n$) under the assumption that the event $C$ has taken place can be calculated from the division theorem (7.13):

$$P(H_k|C) = \frac{P(C \times H_k)}{P(C)},$$

where $P(C \times H_k)$ is the probability of the combination of the two events, namely, $C$ and $H_k$, that is, of the occurrence of $C$ as a consequence of the cause corresponding to the hypothesis $H_k$. To calculate $P(H_k|C)$, we must calculate $P(C \times H_k)$ and $P(C)$.

The first of these can be determined from the multiplication theorem for dependent events if we consider as the first event the occurrence of the hypothesis $H_k$:

$$P(C \times H_k) = P(H_k) P(C|H_k) = P_k p_k.$$

The probability of the event $C$ is, from formula (7.16), equal to the total probability of the event $C$:

$$P(C) = \sum_{s=1}^{n} P_s p_s;$$

therefore,

$$P(H_k|C) = \frac{P_k p_k}{\sum_{s=1}^{n} P_s p_s}; \qquad k = 1, 2, \ldots, n. \tag{7.17}$$

From this formula we can calculate the a posteriori probabilities of the hypotheses, that is, the probabilities given that the event $C$ has occurred.

The set of formulas (7.17) is usually known as Bayes' theorem.

COROLLARY. If the a priori (pre-experiment) probabilities of the hypotheses are unknown, the hypotheses should be considered as equally likely (in the absence of information). Consequently,

$$P_1 = P_2 = \ldots = P_n = \frac{1}{n}.$$

Then, from Bayes' formula,

$$P(H_k|C)=\frac{p_k}{\sum_{s=1}^{n} p_s}. \tag{7.18}$$

Thus, *if the hypotheses are equally likely before an experiment, the (a posteriori) probabilities of the hypotheses after the experiment are, if the event has occurred, proportional to the conditional probabilities of the event* (these conditional probabilities being calculated under the assumption that satisfaction of the corresponding hypotheses resulted in the occurrence of the event).

Example 1. Suppose that a box contains four balls. We know nothing of the content of the box except that there is at least one white and at least one black ball in it. We take a ball out, and it turns out to be white. Then we replace it. Find the probable composition of the box on the basis of this result.

From the condition of the problem, the following assumptions are possible for the composition of the box.

I. Three white and one black,
II. Two white and two black,
III. One white and three black.

Since there are no other conditions, these three assumptions can be considered as equally likely. Denoting the probabilities of these hypotheses by $P_1, P_2$, and $P_3$, we have

$$P_1=P_2=P_3=\frac{1}{3}.$$

The probability of getting a white ball under hypothesis I is 3/4; under II, it is 1/2; and under III, it is 1/4. From Bayes' formulas, we obtain the probabilities of the hypotheses after the experiment

$$P(\text{I, black}|\text{white})=\frac{\frac{1}{3}\cdot\frac{3}{4}}{\frac{1}{3}\cdot\frac{3}{4}+\frac{1}{3}\cdot\frac{1}{2}+\frac{1}{3}\cdot\frac{1}{4}}=\frac{\frac{1}{4}}{\frac{1}{2}}=\frac{1}{2},$$

$$P(\text{II, black}|\text{white})=\frac{\frac{1}{3}\cdot\frac{1}{2}}{\frac{1}{2}}=\frac{1}{3},$$

$$P(\text{III, black}|\text{white})=\frac{\frac{1}{3}\cdot\frac{1}{4}}{\frac{1}{2}}=\frac{1}{6}.$$

$$\text{check}\quad \frac{1}{2}+\frac{1}{3}+\frac{1}{6}=1.$$

We see that the result of the experiment compels us to change our judgment as to the probabilities of the hypotheses. Before the experiment, they were assumed to be equally likely, but after the experiment, they have different probabilities and the most probable one turns out to be the first.

Example 2. Let us consider a variation of example 1. Suppose that before the experiment we know only that the box can contain white balls and balls of different colors. Then, our table of hypotheses is as follows:

I. Four white balls and no ball of another color, $p_1 = 1$,
II. Three white balls and 1 ball of another color, $p_2 = 3/4$,
III. Two white balls and 2 balls of another color, $p_3 = 1/2$,

IV. One white ball and 3 balls of another color, $p_4 = 1/4$,
V. 0 white balls and 4 balls of another color, $p_5 = 0$.

We take the a priori probability of each of these hypotheses to be 1/5.

Suppose that we then take a ball and that it turns out to be white. Then, the a posteriori probabilities of these hypotheses, calculated by means of Bayes' formulas, are

$$P(\text{I}\mid\text{white}) = \frac{1}{1+\frac{3}{4}+\frac{1}{2}+\frac{1}{4}+0} = \frac{1}{2\frac{1}{2}} = 0.4$$

$$P(\text{II}\mid\text{white}) = \frac{\frac{3}{4}}{2\frac{1}{2}} = 0.3; \quad P(\text{III}\mid\text{white}) = \frac{\frac{1}{2}}{2\frac{1}{2}} = 0.2$$

$$P(\text{IV}\mid\text{white}) = \frac{\frac{1}{4}}{2\frac{1}{2}} = 0.1; \quad P(\text{V}\mid\text{white}) = \frac{0}{2\frac{1}{2}} = 0.$$

As we would expect, the fifth hypothesis is, on the basis of the result of the experiment, impossible.

Chapter 8

# THE PROBLEM OF REPEATED TRIALS

## 36. STATEMENT OF THE PROBLEM AND DERIVATION OF THE BASIC FORMULA

Definition 1. If, in the case of a random experiment, a random event $C$ may or may not occur, we shall call the establishment of conditions under which we can determine whether the given event has occurred or not a *trial.*

Every observation that is actually carried out is a trial.

Definition 2. Repeated trials in each of which the random event $C$ may or may not occur are said to be *independent with respect to the event* $C$ if the probability of the event's occurring is, in the case of each trial, independent of the results of other trials (that is, if this probability is independent of how many times the event has occurred in other trials).

Example 1. A coin is tossed one hundred times. The probability of getting heads on the 91st trial is 1/2 independent of whether the coin has landed heads 0 times, 10 times, or even 90 times in the previous 90 trials.

We note that this example contradicts the general impression. If a coin has landed heads 90 times, a player, getting ready to toss the coin the 91st time, is likely to expect the coin to fall tails this time rather than heads, in other words, to assign a greater probability to tails than to heads. The lack of foundation of this view can be easily seen. As one author commented: "A coin has no memory." Therefore, when the coin is tossed the 91st time, the probability of its landing heads depends only on the properties of the coin, just as in the case of any other toss. As we shall see later, the situation here is somewhat more complicated. The probability of the coin's landing heads 90 times in a row is very small, and the probability of its landing 91 times in a row is also very small, but this has to do with the probability of the set of results and not with the probability of the result of any individual experiment, which is always 1/2, independent of the results of the preceding experiments.

We note that the very small probability of the coin's landing heads 90 times in a row (which we obtain under the assumption that the probability of its landing heads is equal to 1/2 in each single experiment) may compel us to doubt the validity of this assumption if the coin does actually fall heads 90 times in a row. For example, it is possible that for some reason or other, the coin is so lacking in symmetry that the probability of its landing heads in any particular toss is close to unity. However, we may not assume this assertion as valid, since an event of very low probability can nonetheless happen. It is only when a series of experiments (for example, with 100 tosses of the coin in each) invariably lead to analogous results (a marked preponderance of heads) that there is a basis for reconsideration of the assumption of equal probability of the coin's landing heads or tails in a single toss.

The problem of repeated trials is formulated as follows: suppose that $n$ trials are performed, all of them independent with respect to the event $C$. Suppose that the probability of the event is equal to a constant $p$ in each trial. Calculate the probability of the event's occurring $k$ times (where $0 \leqslant k \leqslant n$); the order of occurrence and non-occurrence is immaterial.

We shall derive the basic formula for solving this problem. Let us denote by $C$ the occurrence of the event in any trial and let us denote by $\bar{C}$ non-occurrence of the event. The probability of $\bar{C}$ we denote by $q$. Then,

$$p + q = 1.$$

Consider one of the possible sequences of occurrences and non-occurrences of the event in $n$ trials in which the event $C$ occurs $k$ times:

$$C,\ C,\ \bar{C},\ \bar{C},\ \bar{C},\ C,\ \bar{C},\ \ldots,\ \bar{C},\ \bar{C}.$$

In this listing, the symbol $C$ should appear $k$ times and the symbol $\bar{C}$ should appear $n-k$ times. If we denote this sequence by the letter $A_1$, by the theorem on multiplication of probabilities of independent events we have

$$P(A_1) = p \cdot p \cdot q \cdot q \cdot q \cdot p \cdot q\ \ldots\ q \cdot q = p^k q^{n-k}.$$

Clearly, the probability of any other sequence of results such that the event occurs $k$ times is also $p^k q^{n-k}$ since the corresponding product of the probabilities differs only by the order of the factors. The probability of the event occurring $k$ times (in any order), which we denote by $P_{k,n}$, is calculated from the theorem on addition of probabilities:

$$P_{k,n} = \sum_{s=1}^{m} P(A_s) = m p^k q^{n-k},$$

where $m$ is the number of possible sequences. This number is the number of ways in which we can write the letter "$C$" $k$ times in $n$ places. Therefore, $m$ is equal to the number of combinations of $k$ elements that can be taken from a set of $n$ elements: $C_n^k$.

We thus obtain the basic formula

$$P_{k,n} = C_n^k p^k q^{n-k} = \frac{n!}{k!(n-k)!} p^k q^{n-k}. \tag{8.1}$$

If $n$ and $k$ are not small, we may use tables of binomial coefficients and factorials to calculate $P_{n,k}$.

Example 2. Suppose that a die is thrown five times. Determine the probability of a 1 being thrown three times.

In this case,

$$p = \frac{1}{6},\quad q = 1 - \frac{1}{6} = \frac{5}{6},\quad n = 5,\quad k = 3;$$

hence

$$P_{3,5}=C_5^3\cdot\left(\frac{1}{6}\right)^3\left(\frac{5}{6}\right)^2=\frac{5\cdot4}{1\cdot2}\cdot\frac{1}{216}\cdot\frac{25}{36}=\frac{125}{3888}.$$

## 37. THE PROBABILITY DISTRIBUTION FOR THE NUMBER OF TIMES THAT AN EVENT MAY OCCUR

If an experiment is performed $n$ times, before the experiment we can only say that an event will occur 0 times, 1 time, 2 times, . . . , or $n$ times. If we set $k=0, 1, 2, \ldots, n$ in formula (3.12), we obtain

$$\left.\begin{array}{c} P_{0,n}=q^n;\quad P_{1,n}=npq^{n-1};\\ P_{2,n}=\frac{n(n-1)}{1\cdot2}p^2q^{n-2},\ \ldots,\ P_{n-1,n}=np^{n-1}q,\ P_{n,n}=p^n. \end{array}\right\} \tag{8.2}$$

It is easy to see that these probabilities represent the consecutive terms of Newton's binomial expansion:

$$(q+p)^n=q^n+npq^{n-1}+\ \ldots\ +p^n. \tag{8.3}$$

The probability that the event will occur $k$ times is equal to the term of the expansion containing $p^k$. Therefore, the table of values for $P_{k,n}$ for all values of $k$ is called the *probability distribution*.

Since $p+q=1$, it follows from the last equation that

$$P_{0,n}+P_{1,n}+\cdots+P_{n,n}=1. \tag{8.4}$$

The same equation follows from formula (3.4) since the outcomes represented by no occurrence, one occurrence, two occurrences, . . . , $n$ occurrences of the event exhaust all the possible cases and one of them must come about.

Example 1. Suppose that $p=0.4$, that $q=0.6$, and that $n=5$. Consequently, $k$ may assume the values 0, 1, 2, 3, 4, and 5. We compute $P_{k,n}$, and present the probability of distribution in the form of a table:

| $k$ | 0 | 1 | 2 | 3 | 4 | 5 |
|---|---|---|---|---|---|---|
| $P_{k,n}$ | 0.07776 | 0.25920 | 0.34560 | 0.23040 | 0.07680 | 0.01024 |

For a check, we add up all the numbers $P_{k,n}$. The result is unity, as we would expect.

The probability distribution can be represented on a graph. On the abscissa, we lay off numbers from 0 to $n$ representing the possible numbers of times that the event may occur and we lay off the probabilities on the ordinate. It should be noted that the graph consists of individual points since the number of occurrences is not a continuous variable but takes only integral values from 0 to $n$. In such problems, we say that $k$ assumes discrete values (in the present problem, positive integers). Figure 1 shows the graph of the example considered above. The same graph may be constructed in a slightly different manner by letting the abscissa represent not the number of occurrences but its ratio to the number of trials, $k/n$, and letting the ordinate represent the products of the probabilities multiplied by the number of trials (Fig. 2).

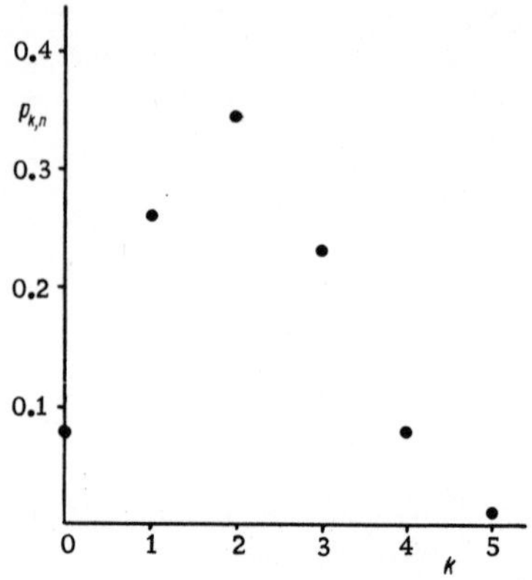


Fig. 1. The probability distribution in the problem on repeated trials. In this figure, the number of trials $n = 5$ and the probability of the event $p = 0.4$.

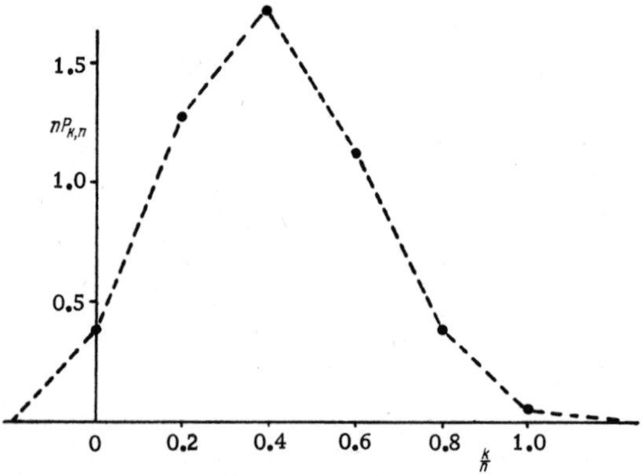


Fig. 2. The probability distribution in the problem on repeated trials. The number of trials $n = 5$ and the probability $p = 0.4$.

The points on the graph correspond to various numbers of times (from 0 to $n$) that the event occurs. The points are joined by dashed rather than solid lines to emphasize that the graph consists of individual points.

This method of construction is convenient in that the base of the graph is always equal to a unit of length on the abscissa and the ordinates will not be too small. Having constructed a graph by the second method (Fig. 2), let us lay off on both sides of the base (which is a segment of unit length extending to the right from the coordinate origin) a segment of length $1/n$ and let us construct a continuous broken line as shown in Figure 2. It is easy to show that the area bounded by this broken line and the part of the abscissa that it intersects is equal to unity. Since this area is equal to the sum of the areas of two triangles and $n$ trapezoids, we have

$$S=\frac{1}{n}\left[\frac{1}{2}nP_{0,n}+\frac{1}{2}n(P_{0,n}+P_{1,n})+\frac{1}{2}n(P_{1,n}+P_{2,n})+\dots\right.$$
$$\left.\dots+\frac{1}{2}n(P_{n-1,n}+P_{n,n})+\frac{1}{2}nP_{n,n}\right]=$$
$$=P_{0,n}+P_{1,n}+\dots+P_{n,n}=1.$$

Example 1. Show the probability distribution when there are five trials if $p=1/2$.

| $k$ | 0 | 1 | 2 | 3 | 4 | 5 |
|---|---|---|---|---|---|---|
| $P_{k,5}$ | $\frac{1}{32}$ | $\frac{5}{32}$ | $\frac{10}{32}$ | $\frac{10}{32}$ | $\frac{5}{32}$ | $\frac{1}{32}$ |

Example 2. Show the probability distribution when there are four trials if $p=2/3$. Taking the fourth power of 1/3 + 2/3 according to the binomial theorem, we obtain

| $k$ | 0 | 1 | 2 | 3 | 4 |
|---|---|---|---|---|---|
| $P_{k,4}$ | $\frac{1}{81}$ | $\frac{8}{81}$ | $\frac{24}{81}$ | $\frac{32}{81}$ | $\frac{16}{81}$ |

We shall now demonstrate certain general properties of the binomial probability distribution just obtained. Since this distribution is discrete, the usual analytical techniques are not applicable for studying $P_{k,n}$ as a function of $k$. In order to carry out our investigation, we find the ratios of the probabilities of adjacent values of $k$:

$$\frac{P_{1,n}}{P_{0,n}},\quad\frac{P_{2,n}}{P_{1,n}},\quad\frac{P_{3,n}}{P_{2,n}},\quad\dots,\quad\frac{P_{k,n}}{P_{k-1,n}},\quad\frac{P_{k+1,n}}{P_{k,n}},\quad\dots,\quad\frac{P_{n-1,n}}{P_{n-2,n}},\quad\frac{P_{n,n}}{P_{n-1,n}}.$$

If we use the basic formula to calculate the general term of this sequence, we obtain

$$\frac{P_{k+1,n}}{P_{k,n}}=\frac{n-k}{k+1}\,\frac{p}{q}.$$

It follows from this expression that the terms in the sequence of ratios decrease monotonically with increasing $k$. Therefore, we note the following basic cases:

## 1. *The First Ratio Does Not Exceed Unity.*

n this case, all the remaining ratios are less than unity:

$$\frac{P_{1,n}}{P_{0,n}}\leqslant 1,\quad\frac{P_{2,n}}{P_{1,n}}<1,\quad\dots,\quad\frac{P_{k+1,n}}{P_{k,n}}<1,\quad\dots,\quad\frac{P_{n,n}}{P_{n-1,n}}<1.$$

Therefore,

$$P_{0,n} \geqslant P_{1,n} > P_{2,n} > \cdots > P_{n-1,n} > P_{n,n}.$$

(1a) If $P_{1,n}/P_{0,n} < 1$, the binomial distribution probabilities decrease monotonically and the largest probability will be for $k = 0$; that is, the most likely number of times that the event will occur is 0. The graph of the distribution for this case is shown in Figure 3 (1a).

(1b) If the first ratio is equal to unity, the first two probabilities in the binomial distribution are equal to each other and the succeeding probabilities decrease monotonically. Here, the two most likely numbers of times that the event will occur are 0 and 1, and these have equal probabilities. The graph of this distribution is shown in Figure 3 (1b).

## 2. *The First Ratio Is Greater Than Unity And The Last Is Less Than Unity.*

In this case, because of the monotonic decrease of the ratios, somewhere in the sequence there must be one jump from a ratio exceeding unity to a ratio less than unity. Since the probabilities are discrete numbers, their ratios are also discrete. Therefore, there may be two subcases:

(2a) Some ratio is greater than unity and the following one is less than unity.

(2b) One of the ratios is exactly equal to unity (in which case the preceding one is greater and the following one is less than unity).

Let us consider these subcases separately.

(2a) We have

$$\cdots \frac{P_{x-1,n}}{P_{x-2,n}} > \frac{P_{x,n}}{P_{x-1,n}} > 1; \quad \frac{P_{x+1,n}}{P_{x,n}} < 1, \quad \frac{P_{x+2,n}}{P_{x+1,n}} < 1, \ \ldots;$$

hence,

$$\ldots P_{x-2,n} < P_{x-1,n} < P_{x,n} > P_{x+1,n} > P_{x+2,n}.$$

From these inequalities, it is clear that the probability distribution has a maximum at $n = x$. To decide what this most likely number of times of occurrence, $x$, is, we replace the probabilities in the two inequalities

$$\frac{P_{x,n}}{P_{x-1,n}} > 1, \quad \frac{P_{x+1,n}}{P_{x,n}} < 1$$

by the expressions given for them in the basic formula. Then, we obtain

$$\frac{n-x+1}{x}\frac{p}{q} > 1, \quad \frac{n-x}{x+1}\frac{p}{q} < 1$$

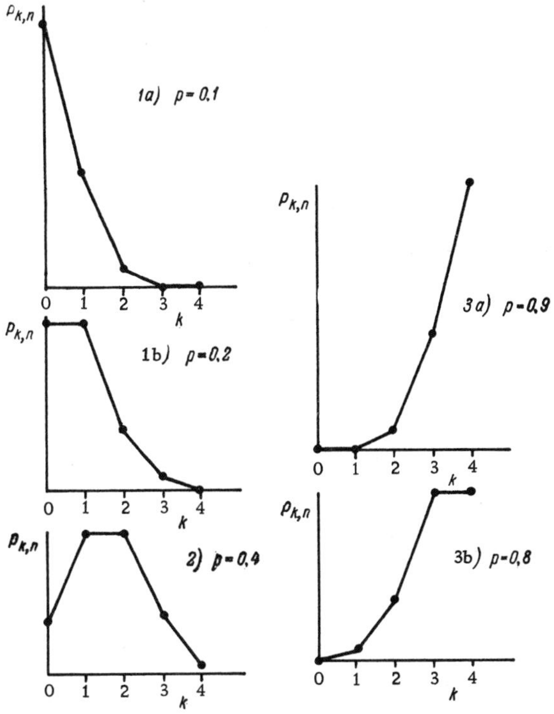


Fig. 3. Forms of the probability distribution in the problem of repeated trials for $n = 4$ and various values of $p$.

| k | 0 | 1 | 2 | 3 | 4 |
|---|---|---|---|---|---|
| 1a | 0.66 | 0.29 | 0.05 | 0.0036 | 0.0001 |
| 1b | 0.41 | 0.41 | 0.15 | 0.03 | 0.0016 |
| 2 | 0.13 | 0.35 | 0.35 | 0.15 | 0.02 |
| 3a | 0.0016 | 0.03 | 0.15 | 0.41 | 0.41 |
| 3b | 0.0001 | 0.0036 | 0.05 | 0.29 | 0.66 |

or

$$xp + xq < np + p, \quad xp + xq > np - q.$$

Since $p + q = 1$, we have

$$np - q < x < np + p.$$

The difference between these bounds for $x$ is equal to

$$np + p - (np - q) = p + q = 1,$$

Therefore, if $np+p$ (and hence $np-q$) is a fraction, there will be only one integer between them. It will be equal to the integral part of $np+p$, and this is the most likely number of occurrences. The graph of such a distribution is shown in Figure 3 (2).

Under the hypotheses of subcase (2a), that is, under the assumption of a unique maximum in the distribution, the numbers $np+p$ and $np-q$ are fractions. If $np+p$ is an integer, $np-q$ will also be an integer (1 less than $np+p$) and the problem would seem to have no solution, but, as we shall soon see, this is not the case.

Note that subcase (1a), in which the probabilities decrease monotonically, would satisfy the inequalities obtained above. For if

$$1 > np+p > 0, \quad np-q < 0,$$

then, $x = 0$.

Thus, we obtain a simple condition for a maximum at the beginning of the distribution:

$$p < \frac{1}{n+1} \quad \text{or} \quad n < \frac{q}{p}.$$

Let us examine subcase (2b). Here, we assume that

$$\cdots \frac{P_{x,n}}{P_{x-1,n}} > \frac{P_{x+1,n}}{P_{x,n}} = 1 > \frac{P_{x+2,n}}{P_{x+1,n}} > \cdots$$

Hence,

$$\cdots < P_{x-1,n} < P_{x,n} = P_{x+1,n} > P_{x+2,n} > \cdots$$

Thus, there are two adjacent numbers, $x$ and $x+1$, of times that the event may occur which have probabilities greater than both the numbers that are less than $x$ and the numbers that are greater than $x+1$. The distribution has a dense maximum; that is, two adjacent ordinates appear as maxima on the graph (see Fig. 3). Since the entire pattern of distribution that we have described follows from the fact that one of the ratios is equal to unity, this is the basic equation for finding the most likely numbers of times of occurrence in this subcase. We have

$$\frac{P_{x+1,n}}{P_{x,n}} = \frac{n-x}{x+1} \cdot \frac{p}{q} = 1,$$

so that

$$x = np - q, \quad x+1 = np+p.$$

Since the number of times of occurrence must be an integer, it follows from these equations that we obtain subcase (2b) if $np+p$ and $np-q$ are integers.

Case (1b) is included in these equations. For if $np - q = 0$ and $np + p = 1$, it follows that $x = 0$ and $x + 1 = 1$.

### 3. *The Last Ratio is Equal to or Greater Than Unity.*

In this case,

$$\frac{P_{n,n}}{P_{n-1,n}} \geqslant 1.$$

Since the ratios decrease, all the other ratios are greater than unity. Therefore,

$$P_{0,n} < P_{1,n} < P_{2,n} < \cdots < P_{n-1,n} \leqslant P_{n,n}.$$

(3a) If $P_{n-1,n} < P_{n,n}$ , we have a monotone increasing probability distribution and the most likely number of times that the event will occur is $n$ (which is the number of trials) (See Fig. 3). This subcase is included in the equations for subcase (2a). For if $np + p$ is a fraction greater than $n$ and if $np - q < n$, we have $x = n$. and, consequently,

$$p > \frac{n}{n+1} \quad \text{or} \quad n < \frac{p}{q}.$$

(3b) If $P_{n-1,n} = P_{n,n}$, the distribution at the end has two adjacent identical maxima, which will occur if

$$p = \frac{n}{n+1} \quad \text{or} \quad n = \frac{p}{q}$$

(see curve 3b, Fig. 3).

Subcase (2b) is included in case (3b). For if $np + p = n$, then $np - q = n - 1$. Thus, the conditions for case (2) can be considered the most general cases since they automatically include cases (1) and (3). From what has been said, we have the following rule for determining the most likely number or numbers of times that the event will occur.

Compute the value of

$$np + p.$$

If this number is a fraction, the integral part of it is equal to the most likely number of times of occurrence. If $np + p$ is an integer, the numbers $np + p$ and $np + p - 1$ (or $np + p$ and $np - q$) represent the common probability of the two most likely numbers of times that the event will occur.

The most likely (most probable) number of times of occurrence is the number of times whose probability is greater than the probability of each other single possible number of times of occurrence. Note that it does not at all follow from this that it is likely that the event will take place exactly the most probable number of times. On the contrary, in almost all problems, it is less likely that the event will occur exactly that many times than that it will not occur exactly that number of times.

Example 1. Determine the most likely number of occurrences when $n = 15$ and $p = 2/3$. We calculate the bounds between which the most likely number of occurrences lies:

$$np - q = 9\frac{2}{3}, \quad np + p = 10\frac{2}{3}.$$

Since the bounds are mixed numbers, we have only one most likely number of occurrences:

$$10\frac{2}{3} > x > 9\frac{2}{3}.$$

Consequently, $x = 10$.

Example 2. Determine the most likely number of occurrences when $n = 9$ and $p = 0.6$.

We calculate the bounds

$$np + p = 6, \quad np - q = 5.$$

Since these bounds are integers, we have two most likely numbers of times of occurrence, namely, 5 and 6.

In this example, let us calculate the probability of one of these most likely numbers:

$$P_{5,9} = \frac{9 \cdot 8 \cdot 7 \cdot 6}{1 \cdot 2 \cdot 3 \cdot 4} (0{,}6)^5 \cdot (0{,}4)^4 \approx 0{,}25.$$

It is clear from the last example that the most likely number of times of occurrence has a small probability even when the number of trials is relatively small.

It is thus more probable that the number of occurrences will be some number other than 5 than that it will be 5 (probability of 0.75 to 0.25). This illustrates the remark made just before example 1.

It can be shown that for the number of times of occurrence to be one of several numbers close to the most likely one is much more probable than for it to be certain other numbers. To show this, it will be useful to solve some problems of the following type:

Suppose that the number of trials is 8 and that the probability of the event is equal to 1/4. Compare the probabilities of the two events:

(a) The number of occurrences will be 1, 2, or 3 (all numbers close to the most likely number of occurrences);

(b) the number of occurrences will be 5, 6, or 7.

It will also be instructive to compare the probability of the event (a) with the probability of the event occurring some number of times other than 1, 2, or 3.

## 38. LAPLACE'S APPROXIMATION FORMULA FOR CALCULATING THE PROBABILITIES OF THE POSSIBLE NUMBER OF TIMES OF OCCURRENCE OF AN EVENT

In Section 36, we derived formula (8.1)

$$P_{k,n} = \frac{n!}{k!\,(n-k)!} p^k q^{n-k}$$

for calculating the probability of an event $C$ occurring exactly $k$ times in $n$ trials if the trials are independent and the probability $C$ is equal to $p$ in each trial.

If $n$ is large, it is not convenient to make calculations on the basis of this formula. Therefore, we shall give an approximation formula for calculating $P_{k,n}$ that can be used if $n$ exceeds 10 or 20.

Stirling's formula for approximating the values of factorials is familiar from analysis:

$$m! \approx \sqrt{2\pi}\, m^m e^{-m} \sqrt{m}. \tag{8.5}$$

Calculations made on the basis of this formula yield a small relative error even at small values of $m$. As the value of $m$ increases, the accuracy also increases. To illustrate this, we give a comparison of the exact values of certain factorials with the approximate values calculated from Stirling's formula:

| | $m$ | 4 | 7 | 10 | 20 |
|---|---|---|---|---|---|
| Exact | $m!$ | 24 | 5 040 | 3 628 800 | $2\,432{,}9 \cdot 10^{14}$ |
| Approximate | $(m!)$ | 23,51 | 4 980,6 | 3 598 700 | $2\,422{,}7 \cdot 10^{14}$ |
| | $\frac{m! - (m!)}{m!}$ | 0,020 | 0,012 | 0,008 | 0,004 |

If we substitute the value of the factorials $n!$, $k!$, and $(n-k)!$ obtained from Stirling's formula into formula (1.8), we obtain, after some elementary manipulations,

$$P_{k,n} = \frac{1}{\sqrt{2\pi}} \sqrt{\frac{n}{k\,(n-k)}} \cdot \left(\frac{np}{k}\right)^k \left(\frac{nq}{n-k}\right)^{n-k}.$$

Let us replace the number $k$ of occurrences in this formula with the deviation $u$ of the number of occurrences from a number $np$ that is close to the most likely number of occurrences:

$$u = k - np.$$

Then,

$$P_{k,n} = \frac{1}{\sqrt{2\pi}} \frac{1}{\sqrt{npq\left(1+\frac{u}{np}\right)\left(1-\frac{u}{nq}\right)}} \cdot \left(\frac{np}{np+n}\right)^{np+u} \left(\frac{nq}{nq-u}\right)^{nq-u}.$$

If we divide the numerator and denominator of the third and fourth factors by $np$ and $nq$ respectively, we may write

$$P_{k,n} = \frac{1}{\sqrt{2\pi}} \frac{1}{\sqrt{npq}} \cdot \frac{1}{\sqrt{\left(1+\frac{u}{np}\right)\left(1-\frac{u}{nq}\right)}} \cdot \left(1+\frac{u}{np}\right)^{-np-u} \cdot \left(1-\frac{u}{nq}\right)^{-nq+u}.$$

Up to now, we have made only identical transformations when using Stirling's formula. Let us now suppose that the number of trials $n$ is large and that the number of occurrences $k$ differs only slightly from $np$. Furthermore, let us assume that $p$ is not close either to zero or to unity. It follows from these assumptions that the number $u$ is small in comparison with $np$ and $nq$. On the basis of these assumptions, we find the expression for $P_{k,n}$. Since $u/(np)$ and $u/(nq)$ are, by hypothesis, small fractions, the third factor can be replaced with unity. Note that we are neglecting the number

$$\frac{p-q}{2}\cdot\frac{u}{\sqrt{npq}}$$

and the second and higher powers of the fractions $u/(np)$ and $u/(nq)$. This is easy to show if we write the binomial expansions of

$$\left(1+\frac{u}{np}\right)^{-\frac{1}{2}} \text{ and } \left(1-\frac{u}{nq}\right)^{-\frac{1}{2}}.$$

To simplify the fourth factor, we use the identity

$$\ln\left(1+\frac{u}{np}\right)^{-np-u}=-(np+u)\ln\left(1+\frac{u}{np}\right).$$

Expanding the logarithm on the right in powers of $u/(nq)$, we obtain

$$\ln\left(1+\frac{u}{np}\right)^{-(np+u)}=-np\left(1+\frac{u}{np}\right)\left(\frac{u}{np}-\frac{u^2}{2n^2p^2}+\ldots\right)=$$
$$=-np\left(\frac{u}{np}+\frac{u^2}{n^2p^2}-\frac{u^2}{2n^2p^2}+\ldots\right)=-u-\frac{u^2}{2np};$$

hence,

$$\left(1+\frac{u}{np}\right)^{-(np+u)}=e^{-u-\frac{u^2}{2np}+\ldots}.$$

In the same way, we transform the last factor:

$$\ln\left(1-\frac{u}{nq}\right)^{-(nq-u)}=nq\left(1-\frac{u}{nq}\right)\left(\frac{u}{nq}+\frac{u^2}{2n^2q^2}+\ldots\right)=$$
$$=nq\left(\frac{u}{nq}-\frac{u^2}{2n^2q^2}+\ldots\right)=u-\frac{u^2}{2nq}+\ldots$$

Thus,

$$\left(1-\frac{u}{nq}\right)^{-(nq-n)}=e^{u-\frac{u^2}{2nq}+\ldots}.$$

If, in the fourth and fifth factors, we keep only the second powers of $u$, we obtain the approximating formula for $P_{k,n}$:

$$P_{k,n}=\frac{1}{\sqrt{npq}}\frac{1}{\sqrt{2\pi}}e^{-\frac{u^2}{2npq}}. \tag{8.6}$$

If we now replace $u$ with its value $u=k-np$, we have Laplace's formula in closed form:

$$P_{k,n}=\frac{1}{\sqrt{npq}}\frac{1}{\sqrt{2\pi}}e^{-\frac{(k-np)^2}{2npq}}. \tag{8.7}$$

To simplify the writing of Laplace's formula, we introduce, in place of the number of trials $k$, the random variable $z$, defined by

$$z=\frac{k-np}{\sqrt{npq}}.$$

To two values of $k$ that are different from unity there correspond, according to this formula, the following values of $z$:

$$z=\frac{k-np}{\sqrt{npq}} \text{ and } z+\Delta z=\frac{k+1-np}{\sqrt{npq}}; \qquad \text{hence} \qquad \Delta z=\frac{1}{\sqrt{npq}}.$$

If we now substitute $z$ and $\Delta z$ into formula (8.7), we reduce it to the following simple form:

$$P_{k,n}=\frac{1}{\sqrt{2\pi}}e^{-\frac{z^2}{2}}\Delta z, \tag{8.8}$$

where

$$z=\frac{k-np}{\sqrt{npq}}, \qquad \Delta z=\frac{1}{\sqrt{npq}}. \tag{8.9}$$

The function

$$\frac{1}{\sqrt{2\pi}}e^{-\frac{z^2}{2}}$$

is encountered in many probability-theory problems. It is called the Laplace-Gauss function. A table of values of this function from $z = 0.00$ to $z = 3.00$ with a step of 0.01 is given in the back of the present book.

This table can easily be used in conjunction with formulas (8.8) and (8.9) to calculate approximate values for the probability that an event will occur a certain number of times.

Formula (8.7) gives rather exact values of $P_{k,n}$ even for small values of $n$ if $p$ is close to 0.5. As an example, we use the table of values of $P_{k,n}$ for $n=20$, $p=0.4$, and $q=0.6$. We confine ourselves to three decimal places:*

| $k$ | 2 | 4 | 6 | 8 | 10 | 12 | 14 | 16 |
|---|---|---|---|---|---|---|---|---|
| Exact values of $P_{k,n}$ . . | 0.003 | 0.035 | 0.124 | 0.180 | 0.117 | 0.036 | 0.005 | 0.000 |
| Approximate values . . . . . | 0.004 | 0.035 | 0.120 | 0.182 | 0.118 | 0.035 | 0.004 | 0.000 |

It is clear from this table that the error does not exceed 0.004. The relative error is less for values of $k$ that are close to $np=8$, that is, that are close to the most likely number of occurrences. For values of $k$ that are appreciably different from the most likely number, the approximating formula gives less satisfactory values for the probability. The same is true of all simplifications that were made in deriving the formula.

Formula (8.7) makes it easy to investigate the probability distribution. According to this formula, $P_{k,n}$ has a maximum at $k=np$. This approximate value $k_m$ of the most likely number of occurrences can differ from the actual value by an amount not exceeding the correct fraction ($p$ or $q$), since the most likely number of occurrences lies between the numbers $np-q$ and $np+p$ or is equal to each of these numbers in the case of two most likely numbers of times of occurrence.

Substituting $k=np$ in (8.7) we get the following formula for the approximate value of the probability of the most likely number of occurrences:

$$P_{m,n}=\frac{1}{\sqrt{2\pi}}\,\frac{1}{\sqrt{npq}}.$$

If $n=9$, $p=0.6$, and $q=0.4$, we obtain from this formula $k_m=5.4$ (instead of exactly 5 or 6) and $P_{m,n}=0.253$ (instead of 0.25 in example 2 on page 122).

## 39. AN APPROXIMATING CURVE FOR THE PROBABILITY DISTRIBUTION

From formula (8.7), it is also easy to draw an approximate graph of the probability distribution for the various numbers of times that an event can occur. Let us lay off the values of $y=nP_{k,n}$ along the ordinate and the numbers $x=k/n-p$ along the abscissa; that is, we place the coordinate origin in a position corresponding to the approximation of the most likely number of times of occurrence. Then, the equation of the curve approximately representing the probability distribution function can be written in the form

$$y=\frac{1}{\sqrt{\frac{pq}{n}}}\cdot\frac{1}{\sqrt{2\pi}}\,e^{\frac{-x^2}{2\frac{pq}{n}}}. \tag{8.10}$$

*The use of the term "exact" means that the figures are correct to three decimal places not that these are the absolutely exact values of $P_{k,n}$.

This curve is symmetric about the ordinate and has a maximum on it. It has two inflection points at $x=\pm\sqrt{\frac{pq}{n}}$. The $x$-axis is an asymptote of this curve. The ordinates of the curve are easily calculated if we use Table I for the function $\frac{1}{\sqrt{2\pi}}e^{-\frac{z^2}{2}}$. In the present case,

$$z=\frac{x}{\sqrt{\frac{pq}{n}}}.$$

The curve representing the case in which $n=5$, $p=0.5$, and $q=0.5$ is shown in Figure 4. The figure shows that even when $n=5$, the approximating curve represents the exact graph of the distribution satisfactorily.

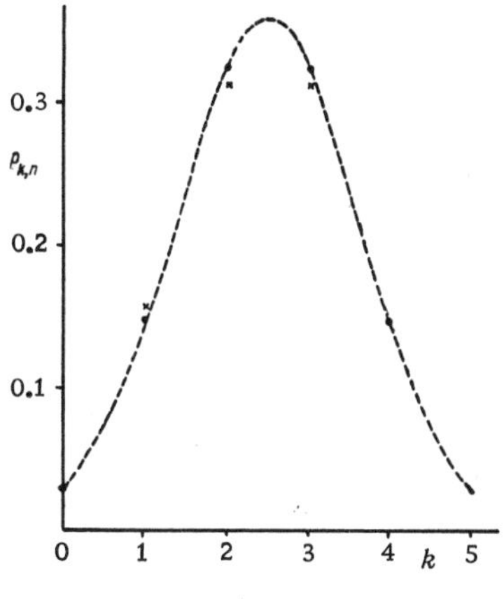


Fig. 4. Comparison of the values of the probabilities of $P_{k,n}$ calculated from the exact formula (indicated by the crosses) for $n=5$ and $p=q=0.5$ and from Laplace's approximating formula (dots). The dashed curve was constructed from formula (8.7).

## 40. POISSON'S DISTRIBUTION (THE LAW OF RARE EVENTS)

The derivation of the approximating formula for $P_{k,n}$ that was given in Section 38 is not satisfactory if $p$ is very small (or very close to unity). To obtain an approximate expression for $P_{k,n}$ in the case of small values of $p$, we rewrite the basic formula in the form

$$P_{n,k}=\frac{n(n+1)(n-2)\ldots n-k+1}{k!}\left(\frac{a}{n}\right)^k\left(1-\frac{a}{n}\right)^{n-k},$$

where $a=np$. The denominators of the first two factors are switched and the denominator $n^k$ is written as $n \cdot n \cdot n \ldots n$. The first factor is then further factored so that we have

$$P_{k,n}=\frac{n}{n}\cdot\frac{n-1}{n}\cdots\frac{n-k+1}{n}\cdot\frac{a^k}{k!}\left(1-\frac{a}{n}\right)^n\left(1-\frac{a}{n}\right)^{-k}.$$

If $k$ and $a$ are fixed, $p$ will approach 0 as $n$ approaches $\infty$. Therefore,

$$\lim_{n\to\infty}\frac{n-m}{n}=1, \quad \lim_{n\to\infty}\left(1-\frac{a}{n}\right)^n=e^{-a}, \quad \lim_{n\to\infty}\left(1-\frac{a}{n}\right)^{-k}=1$$
$$(0\leqslant m\leqslant k-1).$$

If $k$ and $a$ are small in comparison with $n$ and if $p$ is small in comparison with unity, all the factors in the last equation for $P_{k,n}$ except $a^k/k!$ can be replaced with their limiting values. Then,

$$P_{k,n}\approx\frac{a^k e^{-a}}{k!}. \tag{8.11}$$

Obviously, an analogous distribution can be constructed for the case in which $p$ is close to unity.

Poisson's distribution (8.11) is used in problems dealing with rare events (the emission of beta rays, weak solutions, etc.). A table of the Poisson distribution function is given in the back of the book for values of the arguments $a$ and $k$.

Chapter 9

# DISCRETE RANDOM VARIABLES

## 41. RANDOM VARIABLES

In the study of natural occurrences, we often encounter quantities whose numerical values we cannot state in advance (that is, before observation), even though we may know certain conditions under which these occurrences will take place.

For example, we know that every measurement is accompanied by some errors, including random errors. Or, for example, we do not know the characteristics (color index, parallax, etc.) of a star taken at random from a catalog until they are measured.*

Consider the set of small planets, the elements of the orbits having been determined for each of them. When we study the general properties of such a set, we consider these elements as random for an arbitrarily chosen asteroid. This assertion should be understood as follows: In every set of asteroids, each of the elements, for example, the mean distance, has quite different values. If we choose an arbitrary (undefined) planet, we cannot say in advance what its mean distance is. Quantities of this sort are said to be *random*. Quantities whose values can be stated are customarily called defined quantities.

We also speak of random variables even in those cases when the phenomenon is thoroughly studied and the law of its behavior is known. From Ohm's law, we can predict the current if we know the voltage and resistance, but measurements may show a slight deviation from the predicted value. Such a deviation is an error in measurement (some part of which is brought about by random causes and cannot be predicted in advance). The question of random errors in measurements is therefore studied in probability theory.

Random variables can be of various types. Let us consider two types. We shall call a random variable *discrete* if it can take only a finite or countable set of values.

*To understand the last example properly, we should take into account the fact that the physical characteristics of the star itself are not random but are determined by its origin and evolution. They can be treated as random if we choose the star in a random manner.

In the problem of repeated trials, we met a classical example of a discrete random variable, one having only integral values. For example, if a hundred trials are made, the number of occurrences of the event is a random variable assuming values from 0 to 100. The probabilities of these values can be calculated from an exact or approximate formula.

Suppose that lottery tickets are issued at five dollars each and that some of the winning tickets pay one hundred dollars, some pay fifty dollars, and some pay ten dollars. The other tickets pay nothing. The profit made by the owner of such a lottery ticket is a random variable whose values are 95, 45, 5, or -5 dollars. These numbers are obtained by subtracting the original cost of the ticket from what the ticket pays. The fourth value represents a ticket that does not pay off. It must be included in the set of values for this set to be complete.

Another example of a discrete random variable (again with integral values) is the number of stars in multiple systems of stars. If we consider the set of all multiple systems, the number of stars in a system can be 2, 3, 4, . . . and will be random with respect to the choice of an arbitrary member of the set.

A *continuous* random variable can assume *any* value in some definite interval of values. The only random variables of this type that we shall examine are those for which it is possible to determine the probability of taking a particular value in some given interval. This interval, containing all possible values of a continuous random variable, is called its *range*. Some simple examples of the continuous type of random variable are the absolute magnitudes of stars of a particular spectral class, elements of the orbits of small planets, errors in measurements, etc. In the first two examples, the element of chance appears in the study of the entire set of objects when an arbitrarily and randomly chosen object is examined.

In this chapter, we shall consider only discrete random variables with a finite number of possible values. We shall also assume that these values of the random variable are the only ones possible and that they are mutually exclusive, that is, that the entire set of values is known and that the occurrence of one of them excludes the occurrence of all other values.

From the point of view of probability theory, the question of the values of a discrete variable is defined if the probability of the individual numerical values of the random variable $X$ are given.

Let us denote the probabilities of the consecutive values $x_1, x_2, \dots, x_n$ by $p_1, p_2, \dots, p_n$ and let us write the data in the form of a so-called distribution table:*

| | |
|---|---|
| numerical values of $X$ | $x_1, x_2, \dots, x_n$ |
| probabilities | $p_1, p_2, \dots, p_n$ |

With these notations, $X$ (without subscript) essentially denotes a function, whereas $x$ denotes its arbitrary value. Since we are assuming that all possible values $x_k$ are listed, from the theorem on addition of probabilities, we obtain

$$p_1 + p_2 + \dots + p_n = 1.$$

*We have already encountered examples of such tables in the preceding chapter.

A defined quantity, of course, has one value and the probability of that value is equal to unity.

Definition. Two random variables that come up in a single problem are said to be mutually independent if the probability of each value of one of them is independent of the value assumed by the other.

It is only in the simplest problems that this definition can be applied with sufficient justification. For example, if two players throw a pair of dice each, the number of points that will appear on the dice will be random and independent. It is much more difficult to establish independence in physical problems. If we examine such characteristics as the absolute magnitudes and radial velocities of the stars belonging to a particular set of stars, there is no physical reason for believing that there is a (probability) connection between these values. However, we cannot be completely sure that no such connection exists. If quantities like these are considered together, we must use caution with regard to the assumption of their independence. We may also note that in a number of problems the assumption of independence is a hypothesis that must be checked by observation.

If we denote the values of a random variable $X$ by $x_r$ (for $r = 1, 2, \ldots, m$) and the values of $Y$ by $y_s$ (for $s = 1, 2, \ldots, n$), the condition of independence of $X$ and $Y$ can be written as follows:

$$P(x_r \mid y_s) = P(x_r), \quad P(y_s \mid x_r) = P(y_s) \tag{9.1}$$

for all possible values of $r$ and $s$.

## 42. THE EXPECTATION OF A DISCRETE RANDOM VARIABLE

Definition. The expectation of a discrete random variable $X$ is the sum of the product of its numerical values and their respective probabilities. We denote the expectation by $E(X)$ or $\bar{x}$. (Other notations are $M_X$ and $M(X)$.) By definition,

$$E(X) = \sum_{k=1}^{n} p_k x_k. \tag{9.2}$$

To clarify this concept of expectation, let us consider the following problem:

Suppose that one hundred lottery tickets are issued and that they are sold for five dollars each. Suppose that eighteen of them are winning tickets, two paying fifty dollars, six paying twenty-five dollars, and ten paying five dollars. The price of the ticket is not refunded. Determine the expectation of the profit for an owner of a single ticket.

By assumption, this profit is a random variable. Therefore, we need to compile a table of all the possible values of the profit and the probabilities of these values:

| | | | | |
|---|---|---|---|---|
| $X$ | 45 | 20 | 0 | —5 |
| $p$ | 0.02 | 0.06 | 0.10 | 0.82 |

(The last column represents the case in which the ticket does not pay off.) By definition, the expectation (in dollars) will be

$$E(X) = 45 \cdot 0.02 + 20 \cdot 0.06 + 0 \cdot 0.10 - 5 \cdot 0.82 = -2.$$

If we calculate the overall profit for all the tickets, we obtain \$300 - \$500 = -\$200 since the total amount of winning payments is three hundred dollars and the cost of all the tickets is five hundred dollars. If we divide the total profit by the number of tickets, we obtain the average profit for a single ticket. This average profit is exactly equal to the expectation. Both numbers are obtained by the same operations though performed in a somewhat different order.

Thus, the expectation corresponds to the arithmetic mean. These numbers are equal when we know precisely all the values of $X$ and their probabilities. Therefore, the expectation is sometimes called the theoretical average value of a random variable.

## *Properties of the Expectation.*

I. If the values of a random variable have dimensions, its expectation will have the same dimensions. This follows immediately from the definition, since the values of $x$ are multiplied by pure numbers (the values of the probabilities).

II. The expectation is a positive number if all the values of $X$ are positive; it can be either positive or negative if the values of $X$ include negative numbers.

III. The expectation of a defined quantity is equal to its numerical value.

Since, by hypotheses, $X$ can assume only one defined value $c$, the probability of this value is equal to 1:

$$E(X) = c \cdot 1 = c.$$

IV. The expectation of the product of a random variable $X$ and a fixed number $c$ is equal to the product of this fixed number and the expectation of the random variable.

Since a random variable is not an ordinary defined number, we must first come to an agreement as to what the product of a random variable and a fixed number means. The usual definition of such a product is as follows: the product of a random variable and a fixed number is the new random variable whose range consists of the products formed by multiplying the values in the range of the original random variable by the fixed number; the probabilities of these new range values are equal to the probabilities of the corresponding values of the original random variable. From this definition, if

$$X \left\| \begin{matrix} x_1, & x_2, & \ldots, & x_n, \\ p_1, & p_2, & \ldots, & p_n, \end{matrix} \right.$$

the distribution table for the random variable $cX$ will be

$$cX \left\| \begin{matrix} cx_1, & cx_2, & \ldots, & cx_n, \\ p_1, & p_2, & \ldots, & p_n. \end{matrix} \right.$$

Therefore,

$$E(X) = \sum_{k=1}^{n} cx_k p_k = c \sum_{k=1}^{n} x_k p_k = cE(X).$$

V. If $m$ and $M$ are the smallest and largest of the values of $x$,

$$m \leqslant E(X) \leqslant M.$$

To show this, write

$$E(X) = x_1p_1 + x_2p_2 + \dots + x_np_n.$$

Let us replace all the numbers $x_k$ on the right side of this equation with $m$. Since the numbers $p_1, p_2, \dots, p_n$, being probabilities, are all positive, the right side of the equation cannot increase. Therefore,

$$E(X) \geqslant mp_1 + mp_2 + \dots + mp_n =$$
$$= m(p_1 + p_2 + \dots + p_n) = m \cdot 1 = m.$$

In the same way, we can show that

$$E(X) \leqslant M.$$

We note that this conditional inequality becomes an equality only if $X$ is a constant.

## 43. THEOREMS ON THE ADDITION AND MULTIPLICATION OF EXPECTATIONS

### 1. The Addition Theorem.

*The expectation of the sum of two or more random variables is equal to the sum of their expectations.*

Suppose that we have two random variables:

$$X \left\| \begin{matrix} x_1, & x_2, & \dots, & x_n, \\ p_1, & p_2, & \dots, & p_n; \end{matrix} \right. \qquad Y \left\| \begin{matrix} y_1, & y_2, & \dots, & y_m, \\ P_1, & P_2, & \dots, & P_m. \end{matrix} \right.$$

In the general case in which $X$ takes on one of its $n$ values, $Y$ can take any of its $m$ values. Therefore, the sum $X+Y$ takes on the $mn$ values that can be obtained by adding a value of $X$ to a value of $Y$. The distribution table for $X+Y$ is of the form

$$X+Y \left\| \begin{matrix} x_1+y_1, & \dots, & x_1+y_m; & x_2+y_1, & \dots, & x_k+y_l, & \dots, & x_n+y_m, \\ p_{11}, & \dots, & p_{1m}; & p_{21}, & \dots, & p_{kl}, & \dots, & p_{nm}, \end{matrix} \right.$$

where the $p_{kl}$ (for $k = 1, \dots, n$ and $l = 1, \dots, m$) are the known values of $x_k + y_l$, that is, the probabilities of the combination of $x_k$ with $y_l$. The sum $X+Y$ takes the value $x_k + y_l$ if both the following two events occur: $X$ takes the value $x_k$ and $Y$ takes the value $y_l$. Therefore, $p_{kl}$ is the probability of the composite event composed of two events, namely, the occurrence of $x_k$ and the occurrence of $y_l$. Since the conditions of the theorem do not stipulate that the probability of $x_k$ must be independent of the occurrence or non-occurrence of $y_l$ (that is, since $X$ and $Y$ may be dependent), we must use the theorem for the multiplication of probabilities in its general form. Therefore,

$$p_{kl}=p_k P(y_l|x_k)=P_l P(x_k|y_l). \tag{9.3}$$

where, as before, $P(x_k|y_l)$ is the probability that $X$ will take the value $x_k$ if it is given that $Y$ takes the value $y_l$. The number of equations of the form (9.3) is $mn$. Here, $k$ assumes all integral values from 1 to $n$ and $l$ assumes all integral values from 1 to $m$. From the definition of expectation,

$$E(X+Y)=\sum_{l=1}^{m}\sum_{k=1}^{n}(x_k+y_l)p_{kl}.$$

Let us perform the multiplication indicated in the term to be summed. Then, let us replace $p_{kl}$ with the middle expression in equation (9.3) when it is a coefficient of $x_k$ and let us replace it with the expression on the right of equation (9.3) when it is a coefficient of $y_l$. If we now break the summation into two parts by separating the $x$-terms and the $y$-terms and reverse the order of summation in the first part, we obtain

$$E(X+Y)=\sum_{k=1}^{n}p_k x_k\left\{\sum_{l=1}^{m}P(y_l|x_k)\right\}+\sum_{l=1}^{m}P_l y_l\left\{\sum_{k=1}^{n}P(x_k|y_l)\right\}.$$

It is easy to show that each of the sums in the braces is equal to unity. Specifically, from the theorem on the addition, expressed for conditional probabilities,

$$\sum_{l=1}^{m}P(y_l|x_k)=P(y_1+y_2+\dots+y_m|x_k).$$

(The addition on the right side is symbolic, meaning the occurrence of $y_1$, or $y_2$, . . . , or $y_m$.) Since the list of values is complete, it is certain that one of them will occur no matter what the value of $x_k$ is. Therefore,

$$\sum_{l=1}^{m}P(y_l|x_k)=1$$

for all values of $x_k$. In an analogous manner, we obtain

$$\sum_{k=1}^{n}P(x_k|y_l)=1$$

for all $y_l$. Therefore,

$$E(X+Y)=\sum_{k=1}^{n}p_k x_k+\sum_{l=1}^{m}P_l y_l=E(X)+E(y). \tag{9.4}$$

It should be noted that no restrictions have been imposed on the random variables $X$ and $Y$ in the proof of this theorem.

## 2. The Multiplication Theorem

*The expectation of a product of independent random variables is equal to the product of their expectations.*

Suppose that we have the random variables

$$X \left\| \begin{matrix} x_1, & x_2, & \ldots, & x_n, \\ p_1, & p_2, & \ldots, & p_n; \end{matrix} \right. \qquad Y \left\| \begin{matrix} y_1, & y_2, & \ldots, & y_m, \\ P_1, & P_2, & \ldots, & P_m. \end{matrix} \right.$$

The product of the two random variables is the random variable whose values are obtained by multiplying each value of one of the random variables by every value of the other. The distribution table for the product variable is as follows:

$$XY \left\| \begin{matrix} x_1y_1, & x_2y_1, & \ldots, & x_ny_1; & x_1y_2, & \ldots, & x_ny_2, & \ldots, & x_ky_l, & \ldots, & x_ny_m, \\ p_{11}, & p_{21}, & \ldots, & p_{n1}, & p_{12}, & \ldots, & p_{n2}, & \ldots, & p_{kl}, & \ldots, & p_{nm}. \end{matrix} \right.$$

Since the original random variables are independent, the probability of the combination of values $x_k$ and $y_l$ (for $k = 1, 2, \ldots, n$ and $l = 1, 2, \ldots, m$) is equal to the product of their probabilities:

$$p_{kl} = p_k P_l.$$

Therefore,

$$E(XY) = \sum_{k=1}^{n} \sum_{l=1}^{m} p_k P_l x_k y_l.$$

If we take $p_k x_k$ from under the inner summation sign, we obtain

$$E(XY) = \sum_{k=1}^{n} p_k x_k \left( \sum_{l=1}^{m} P_l y_l \right).$$

The sum in the parentheses is the expectation of $Y$. That is, it is a definite number that can be taken from under the first summation sign. Then, the first sum is the expectation of $X$. Thus,

$$E(XY) = E(X)\,E(Y). \tag{9.5}$$

This theorem is easily generalized to the case of an arbitrary number of mutually independent random variables:

$$E(XYZ\ldots) = E(X)\,E(Y)\,E(Z)\ldots \tag{9.6}$$

It should be especially noted that the multiplication theorem is valid only for *independent* random variables. If the random variables are dependent, the content of the theorem is considerably changed since we must then know the probability of $x_k$ given $y_l$ for every combination of values of $k$ and $l$.

## 44. THE VARIANCE OF A RANDOM VARIABLE AND ITS PROPERTIES

Consider a random variable $X$, whose expectation we shall denote by $\bar{x}$.

Definition. The *variance* of a random variable is the expectation of the square of the deviation of its values from its expectation.

Suppose that our random variable $X$ has the values $x_1, x_2, \ldots, x_n$, and that the probabilities of these values are $p_1, p_2, \ldots, p_n$, respectively. Let us form the new random variable $X-\bar{x}$, whose values will then be $x_1-\bar{x}, x_2-\bar{x}, \ldots, x_n-\bar{x}$. The probabilities of these values are the same as the probabilities of the values $x_1, x_2, \ldots, x_n$ since $\bar{x}$ is a fixed number. The values $x_1-\bar{x}, \ldots, x_n-\bar{x}$ are called the *deviations* of the values of the random variable from its expectation. The new random variable $X-\bar{x}$ is the deviation of the random variable from its expectation. Let us square the values $x_1-\bar{x}, \ldots, x_n-\bar{x}$. The results will be the values of another random variable, namely, the square of the deviation of the random variable from its expectation. The probabilities of these values of this variable are the same as the probabilities of the values of $X$. Let us make a table of the values of the square of the deviation as we have done for other random variables:

| $(X-\bar{x})^2$ | $(x_1-\bar{x})^2$, | $(x_2-\bar{x})^2$, | $\ldots$, | $(x_n-\bar{x})^2$, |
|---|---|---|---|---|
| | $p_1$, | $p_2$, | $\ldots$, | $p_n$. |

The variance of a random variable $X$ is denoted by var $X$ or $\sigma_x^2$. By definition,

$$\operatorname{var} X \equiv \sigma_x^2 = E\{(X-\bar{x})^2\} \tag{9.7}$$

or

$$\operatorname{var} X = \sum_{k=1}^{n} p_k (x_k-\bar{x})^2.$$

In some texts the variation is called the dispersion and is denoted by $D$.

### Properties of the Variance

I. *The variance of a random variable is a nonnegative number*; it vanishes only if the random variable has only one value. This is true because of the numbers

$$(x_k-\bar{x})^2, \qquad k=1, 2, \ldots, n$$

are nonnegative and hence, var $X$ is a nonnegative number because of property II of the expectation. The sum

$$\sum_{k=1}^{n} p_k (x_k - \bar{x})^2$$

can vanish only if each of the terms is 0, that is, only if

$$x_1 = x_2 = \ldots = x_n = \bar{x},$$

and in this case $x$ is a constant whose value is $\bar{x}$.

II. *The variance of a constant is equal to* 0. This is true because the expectation in this case is equal to that constant and its deviation is equal to 0 with probability 1. This means that the variance is equal to 0.

III. *The variance of a random variable is equal to the difference between the expectation of the square of that random variable and the square of its expectations.* To see this, we apply properties IV and III to the expectation of $(X - \bar{x})^2$ to obtain

$$\operatorname{var} X = E\{X - \bar{x}\}^2 = E\{X^2 - 2\bar{x}X + \bar{x}^2\} = E(X^2) - 2\bar{x}E(X) + \bar{x}^2.$$

Since $E(X) = \bar{x}$,

$$\operatorname{var} X = E(X^2) - 2\bar{x}^2 + \bar{x}^2 = E(X^2) - \bar{x}^2$$

or

$$\operatorname{var} X = E(X^2) - [E(X)]^2. \tag{9.8}$$

IV. *The variance of the product of a random variable X and a constant c is equal to the product of the square of the constant and the variance of the random variable.*

Proof: Suppose that

$$E(X) = \bar{x}, \quad \sigma_X^2 = E[(X - \bar{x})^2].$$

From property IV of the expectation,

$$E(cX) = cE(X) = c\bar{x}.$$

Therefore,

$$\operatorname{var} cX = E\{(cX - c\bar{x})^2\} = E\{c^2(X - \bar{x})^2\} = c^2E\{(X - \bar{x})^2\}$$

or

$$\sigma_{cX}^2 = c^2\sigma_X^2. \tag{9.9}$$

V. *The variance of a sum of mutually independent random variables is equal to the sum of their variances.*

We shall prove this only for two terms. The proof is the same for a larger number.

Let us denote by $\bar{x}$ and $\bar{y}$ the expectations of the random variables $X$ and $Y$. Since

$$E(X+Y)=\bar{x}+\bar{y}$$

according to the theorem on the addition of expectations, it follows from (9.8) that

$$\text{var}\,(X+Y)=E\,\{(X+Y)^2\}-(\bar{x}+\bar{y})^2.$$

If we expand the terms $(X+Y)^2$ and $(\bar{x}+\bar{y})^2$ and use the theorem on the addition of expectations and properties IV and III of expectations, we obtain

$$\text{var}\,(X+Y)=E\,(X^2)+2E\,(XY)+E\,(Y^2)-\bar{x}^2-2\bar{x}\bar{y}-\bar{y}^2.$$

Since $X$ and $Y$ are assumed independent,

$$E\,(XY)=E\,(X)\,E\,(Y)=\bar{x}\bar{y}.$$

The second and fifth terms of the right side of the preceding equation cancel each other out. If we use equation (9.4) of the preceding section, we obtain our formula for the addition of variances:

$$\text{var}\,(X+Y)=\text{var}\ X+\text{var}\ Y$$

or

$$\sigma^2_{(X+Y)}=\sigma^2_x+\sigma^2_y. \tag{9.10}$$

It is easy to show in the same way that

$$\text{var}\,(X-Y)=\text{var}\ X+\text{var}\ Y=\sigma^2_{(X-Y)}=\sigma^2_x+\sigma^2_y. \tag{9.11}$$

VI. If

$$U=aX+bY+cZ+\ \dots\ +r,$$

*where $X$, $Y$, and $Z$ are mutually independent random variables and $a$, $b$, $c$, ..., $r$ are constants, the variance $U$ is determined by the formula*

$$\sigma^2_U=a^2\sigma^2_x+b^2\sigma^2_y+c^2\sigma^2_z+\ \dots\ +0.$$

From the theorem on addition of variances (generalized for the algebraic sum of several terms),

$$\sigma^2_U=\sigma^2_{aX}+\sigma^2_{bY}+\sigma^2_{cZ}+\ \dots\ +\sigma^2_r;$$

$$\sigma^2_{aX}=a^2\sigma_x,\ \ \sigma^2_{bY}=b^2\sigma^2_y;\ \ \sigma^2_{cZ}=c^2\sigma^2_z;$$

so that, according to property II,

$$\sigma_r^2 = 0.$$

Comparing the last two equations, we obtain

$$\operatorname{var} U = a^2 \operatorname{var} X + b^2 \operatorname{var} Y + c^2 \operatorname{var} Z + \ldots + 0. \tag{9.12}$$

## 45. EXPECTATION AND VARIANCE OF THE NUMBER OF OCCURRENCES

Suppose that we perform $n$ independent trials with respect to an event $C$ and that in each of these trials the probability of $C$ is equal to $p$. The number of occurrences $k$ of the event $C$ is a discrete random variable, which can assume the values 0, 1, 2, 3, . . . , $n$. As was shown in Sections 36-37, the distribution table of this random variable is of the form

| $k$ | 0 | 1 | 2 | ... | $m$ | ... | $n-1$ | $n$, |
|---|---|---|---|---|---|---|---|---|
| $P_{k,n}$ | $q^n$ | $npq^{n-1}$ | $\frac{n(n-1)}{2} p^2 q^{n-2}$ | ... | $\frac{n(n-1)\ldots(n-m+1)}{m!} p^m q^{n-m}$ | ... | $np^{n-1}q$ | $p^n$. |

Let us derive formulas for the expectation and the variance of the number of occurrences of the event. From the distribution table, we get

$$\begin{aligned} E(k) &= 0 \cdot q^n + 1 \cdot npq^{n-1} + \\ &+ 2\,\frac{n(n-1)}{2}\,p^2 q^{n-2} + \ldots + \frac{n(n-1)\ldots(n-m+1)}{(m-1)!}\,p^m q^{n-m} + \ldots + \\ &\qquad + n(n-1)\,p^{n-1}q + np^n, \end{aligned}$$

or

$$\begin{aligned} E(k) = np\Big[ & q^{n-1} + (n-1)\,pq^{n-2} + \ldots \\ & \ldots + \frac{(n-1)\ldots(n-m+1)}{(m-1)!}\,p^{m-1}q^{n-m} + \ldots \\ & \ldots + (n-1)\,p^{n-2}q + p^{n-1}\Big]. \end{aligned}$$

The expression in the square brackets is the binomial expansion of $(q+p)^{n-1}$. But $q+p=1$. Therefore,

$$E(k) = np.$$

Note that $E(k)$ is equal to the most likely number of occurrences or differs from it by an amount less than unity.

Let us turn now to the matter of determining the variance of the number of occurrences. By definition, the variance is the expectation of the square of the deviation of a random variable from its expectation. From the results of the preceding problem, $E(k) = np$.

Therefore, if we denote the variance of the number of occurrences by $\sigma_k^2$ and apply property III of variances and equation (9.8), we obtain

$$\sigma_k^2 = E(k^2) - n^2p^2.$$

To calculate $E(k^2)$, we use a device appearing in the book by V. I. Romanovskii.

It follows from the identity

$$k^2 = k(k-1) + k$$

that

$$E(k^2) = E\{k(k-1)\} + E(k).$$

Since $k$ is a random variable assuming the value 0, 1, 2, . . . , $n$, the quantity $k(k-1)$ is also a random variable, whose values are

$$0,\ 0,\ 2,\ 3\cdot 2,\ 4\cdot 3,\ \ldots$$

The probabilities of these values are the same as the probabilities of the corresponding values of $k$. Therefore,

$$\begin{aligned} E\{k(k-1)\} &= 0\cdot q^n + 0\cdot npq^{n-1} + 2\frac{n(n-1)}{1\cdot 2}p^2q^{n-2} + \\ &+ 3\cdot 2\frac{n(n-1)(n-2)}{1\cdot 2\cdot 3}p^3q^{n-3} + 4\cdot 3\frac{n(n-1)(n-2)(n-3)}{1\cdot 2\cdot 3\cdot 4}p^4q^{n-4} + \ldots \\ &\ldots + \frac{m(m-1)n(n-1)\ldots(n-m+1)}{1\cdot 2\cdot 3\ldots(m-2)(m-1)m}p^mq^{n-m} + \ldots \\ &\ldots + n(n-1)(n-2)p^{n-1}q + n(n-1)p^n = \\ &= n(n-1)p^2\Big[q^{n-2} + (n-2)\cdot pq^{n-3} + \frac{(n-2)(n-3)}{1\cdot 2}p^2q^{n-4} + \ldots \\ &\ldots + \frac{(n-2)(n-3)\ldots(n-m+1)}{1\cdot 2\ldots(n-2)}p^{m-2}q^{n-m} + \ldots \\ &\ldots + (n-2)p^{n-3}q + p^{n-2}\Big]. \end{aligned}$$

It is easy to see that the expression in the square brackets is the binomial expansion of $(q+p)^{n-2}$, which is equal to unity. Thus,

$$E\{k(k-1)\} = n(n-1)p^2,$$

so that

$$E(k^2) = n(n-1)p^2 + np.$$

Therefore,

$$\sigma_k^2 = n^2p^2 - np^2 + np - n^2p^2 = np(1-p)$$

or, finally,

$$\sigma_k^2 = npq.$$

Note that both the expectation and the variance of the number of occurrences appear essentially in the approximate formula of Laplace (8.7) for the problem of repeated trials. If we replace $\sqrt{npq}$ with $\sigma_k$ and $np$ with $\bar{k}$, this formula becomes

$$P_{k,n} \approx \frac{1}{\sigma_k} \frac{1}{\sqrt{2\pi}} e^{-\frac{(k-\bar{k})^2}{2\sigma_k^2}}. \qquad (9.13)$$

Chapter 10

# THE LAW OF LARGE NUMBERS

The law of large numbers is the name applied to the set of theorems on the probabilities of events in the case of a large number of trials or on the probabilities of the values of sums of random variables when the number of variables added is great.

## 46. THE CHEBYSHEV-MARKOV LEMMA

LEMMA. *If a random variable* $X$ *assumes only nonnegative values and its expectation is equal to* $\bar{x}$, *the probability that* $X$ *will assume a value less than* $t^2\bar{x}$ *(where* $t^2$ *is an arbitrary positive number) is greater than* $1 - 1/t^2$; *that is,*

$$P(X < t^2\bar{x}) > 1 - \frac{1}{t^2}.$$

Let us denote by $M$ the largest value of the random variable $X$. If $t^2$ is so great that $t^2\bar{x} \geqslant M$, the conclusion of the lemma is obviously valid because in that case

$$P(X < t^2\bar{x}) = 1.$$

The case in which $0 < t^2 < 1$ is also of no interest because then

$$1 - \frac{1}{t^2} < 0$$

and we obtain the obvious result that the probability is greater than a negative number.

Thus, we may assume that

$$\bar{x} \leqslant t^2\bar{x} < M.$$

It follows from this inequality and from property V of the expectation (see Section 42) that among the values of $X$ there is at least one greater and one less than $t^2\bar{x}$. Let us consider those values of $X$ that are at least as great as $t^2\bar{x}$ and let us denote them by $x_1, x_2, \ldots, x_k$. Then, we can write the distribution table in the form

| $X$ | $x_1, x_2, \ldots, x_k$ | $x_{k+1}, \ldots, x_n,$ |
|---|---|---|
| | $p_1, p_2, \ldots, p_k$ | $p_{k+1}, \ldots, p_n.$ |

By definition,

$$E(X) = \bar{x} = x_1p_1 + x_2p_2 + \ldots + x_kp_k + x_{k+1}p_{k+1} + \ldots + x_np_n.$$

Let us discard all the terms on the right whose subscripts are equal to or greater than $k+1$. Since all the $x_s$ are assumed to be nonnegative and the $p_s$ are positive (for $s = 1, 2, \ldots, n$), the right side can only decrease as a result of this discarding of terms. Therefore,

$$\bar{x} \geqslant x_1p_1 + x_2p_2 + \ldots + x_kp_k.$$

Let us replace all the $x_r$ (for $r = 1, 2, \ldots, k$) on the right side of this inequality by $t^2\bar{x}$, which is either less than all the numbers for which it is substituted or equal to one of them. Since all the $p_r$ are positive, the right side decreases.

Therefore,

$$\bar{x} > t^2\bar{x}(p_1 + p_2 + \ldots + p_k)$$

or, since $t^2 > 1$,

$$p_1 + p_2 + \ldots + p_k < \frac{1}{t^2}.$$

From the theorem on addition of probabilities, the left side of this inequality is the probability that $X$ will take one of the values $x_1, x_2, \ldots, x_k$, that is, that the value of $X$ will be at least equal to $t^2\bar{x}$.

If we denote by $P(X \geqslant t^2\bar{x})$, the probability that $X \geqslant t^2\bar{x}$, we have

$$P(X \geqslant t^2\bar{x}) < \frac{1}{t^2}.$$

The quantity $X$ has a value either greater than $t^2\bar{x}$ or equal to it or less than it. Therefore,

$$P(X < t^2\bar{x}) + P(X \geqslant t^2\bar{x}) = 1.$$

If we compare this last equation with the preceding inequality, we obtain

$$P(X < t^2\bar{x}) > 1 - \frac{1}{t^2}, \tag{10.1}$$

which completes the proof.

Thus we see that if $t^2$ is a very large number in the inequality

$$P(X \geqslant t^2\bar{x}) < \frac{1}{t^2}$$

values of $X$ much greater than its expectation are extremely unlikely.

## 47. THEOREM OF J. BERNOULLI

Definition. The ratio of the number of occurrences $k$ to the number of trials $n$ in the problem of repeated trials is called the *relative frequency*. If we perform experiments, this quantity is the ratio of the number of times that the event has occurred to the total number of trials.

Bernoulli showed that when a large number of trials are made, the relative frequency must, in the majority of cases, be close to the probability. This is the gist of Bernoulli's theorem. We give two formulations of the theorem.

Formulation I. *Suppose that an infinite number of trials are made that are independent with respect to an event C and suppose that the probability of the event p is constant for all of them. Then, we may expect with probability arbitrarily close to unity that when a sufficiently large number n of trials are made, the differences between the relative frequency k/n and the probability p will be arbitrarily small in absolute value.*

Formulation II. *With the same assumptions as in the first formulation, for any two positive numbers* $\varepsilon$ *and* $\delta$, *no matter how small, there exists a number N such that when the number of trials exceeds N, the probability that* $k/n - p < \varepsilon$ *will be greater than* $1 - \delta$; *that is,*

$$P\left[\left|\frac{k}{n} - p\right| < \varepsilon\right] > 1 - \delta \quad \text{for} \quad n > N(\varepsilon, \delta) = \frac{pq}{\delta\varepsilon^2}. \tag{10.2}$$

The second formulation differs from the first in the following ways: the deviation of the relative frequency from the probability is bounded by the number $\varepsilon$, the number $\delta$ gives an indication of the closeness of the probability to 1, and the number $N$, defined in terms of $\varepsilon$ and $\delta$, represents a number of trials that is large enough for the stated inequality to be true.

Proof: The random variable $(k - np)^2$ can have only nonnegative values.

The expectation of this variable is known. It is the variance of the number of occurrences, which is equal to $npq$ (see Section 45). If we apply Chebyshev's lemma to the random variable $(k - np)^2$, we obtain

$$P[(k - np)^2 < t^2 npq] > 1 - \frac{1}{t^2}.$$

The probability that this inequality will be satisfied is unchanged if we replace it with an equivalent inequality. The inequality in the square brackets is equivalent to the inequality

$$\left|\frac{k}{n}-p\right|<t\sqrt{\frac{pq}{n}},$$

in which $t$ is assumed to be positive. Therefore,

$$P\left\{\left|\frac{k}{n}-p\right|<t\sqrt{\frac{pq}{n}}\right\}>1-\frac{1}{t^2}.$$

Let us determine $t$ in such a way that

$$t\sqrt{\frac{pq}{n}}=\varepsilon;$$

From this condition, we obtain

$$t^2=\frac{n\varepsilon}{pq}.$$

Then,

$$P\left\{\left|\frac{k}{n}-p\right|<\varepsilon\right\}>1-\frac{pq}{n\varepsilon}. \qquad (10.3)$$

The derivation of this inequality essentially proves the theorem in its first formulation since for given values of $p$ and $q$ and for an arbitrarily small positive number $\varepsilon$, there always exists a sufficiently large number $N$ such that the number on the right side of the inequality can be made arbitrarily close to 1 if $n>N$. To prove the theorem in its second formulation, let us assume $\varepsilon$ and $\delta$ given and let us define $N$ by

$$N=\frac{pq}{\delta\varepsilon^2}, \qquad \delta=\frac{pq}{N\varepsilon^2}. \qquad (10.4)$$

If $n>N$

$$\frac{pq}{n\varepsilon^2}<\frac{pq}{N\varepsilon^2}=\delta,$$

and, consequently,

$$\frac{pq}{n\varepsilon^2}<\delta, \qquad 1-\frac{pq}{n\varepsilon^2}>1-\delta.$$

We shall not violate the inequality (10.3) if we replace its first term with $1-\delta$. This proves the theorem in its second formulation.

It should be noted that in the definition of $N$ and in the proof of Bernoulli's theorem, we used the lemma just proven (after the double transformation of an exact equality into an inequality). Therefore, the value of $N$ that we obtain in this manner is *sufficient* but it should not be considered *necessary*. A more exact evaluation shows that the inequalities of Bernoulli's theorem are valid even with the number of trials $N$.

It is possible to find a *sufficiently* large number of trials to ensure the validity of the inequality in Bernoulli's theorem even if we do not know the value of the probability. Consider the quantity $pq = v$, which is the product of two numbers whose sum is unity. Let us find the maximum value of the function

$$v = p(1 - p).$$

If we set the first derivative equal to 0, we see that $v$ has an extremum at $p = 1/2$ (and $q = 1/2$) ($v$ takes the value $1/4$); the sign of the second derivative shows that it is a maximum. Therefore, no matter what the values of $p$ and $q$, we always have

$$v = pq \leqslant \frac{1}{4}.$$

Therefore, on the basis of equation (10.4), a sufficiently large number of trials for all values of $p$ is

$$N' = \frac{1}{4\delta\varepsilon^2}. \qquad (10.5)$$

This remark is significant for the converse of Bernoulli's theorem, according to which we may take the observed frequency of occurrences as the approximate value of the unknown probability. This is not the exact content of the converse of Bernoulli's theorem, which is formulated analogously to the direct theorem given above.

Let us consider some examples of the application of Bernoulli's theorem.

Example 1. A coin is tossed. Find a sufficient number of trials for us to be able to expect with a probability greater than 0.9 that the relative frequency will differ from the probability of 1/2 by an amount less than 1/5 in absolute value.

In the present case, $p = q = 1/2$, $\varepsilon = 0.2$, $\delta = 1 - 0.9 = 0.1$. From formula (10.4), we obtain

$$N = \frac{\frac{1}{2} \cdot \frac{1}{2}}{0.2^2 \cdot 0.1} \approx 63.$$

Thus, we can assert that if $n \geqslant 63$, the probability that $k \mid n - 1 \mid 2 < 0.2$ will be greater than 0.9:

$$P\left(\left|\frac{k}{n} - \frac{1}{2}\right| < 0.2\right) > 0.9.$$

We note that this inequality allows rather wide bounds for the number of occurrences, for the inequality $k \mid n - 1 \mid 2 < 0.2$ is equivalent to the two inequalities

$$-0.2 < \frac{k}{n} - 0.5 < 0.2$$

or

$$0.3n < k < 0.7n.$$

The same number of trials is obtained if we use the "cruder" formula

$$N' = \frac{1}{4\delta\varepsilon^2}.$$

This is explained by the fact that in the present case $v = pq = 1/4$. We set $n = 100$. Then,

$$30 < k < 70.$$

To find narrower bounds for $k$, we would need to decrease $\varepsilon$, which would considerably increase $N$ as can be seen from formula (10.4) since we have $\varepsilon^2$ in the denominator.

Example 2. A coin is tossed two hundred times. Estimate the probability that

$$\left| \frac{k}{100} - 0.5 \right| < 0.1.$$

Here $p = q = 0.5$ and $\varepsilon = 0.1$. We take two hundred for the value of $N$.

A lower bound on the probability of the inequality given will be known if we determine $\delta$. From formula (10.4),

$$\delta = \frac{\frac{1}{2} \cdot \frac{1}{2}}{200 \cdot 0.1^2} = \frac{1}{8}.$$

Thus, when we have tossed the coin two hundred times, we may expect, with a probability exceeding $1 - 1/8 = 0.875$, that

$$\left| \frac{k}{200} - 0.5 \right| < 0.1$$

or

$$80 < k < 120.$$

Example 3. A coin is tossed nine hundred times. What are bounds within which the number of heads will be expected to lie with a probability exceeding 0.99?

Here, $p = 1/2$, $q = 1/2$, $1 - \delta = 0.99$, and $\delta = 0.01$. For $N$ we take 900. We determine $\varepsilon$ from formula (10.4):

$$\varepsilon^2 = \frac{pq}{N\delta} = \frac{1}{36} \qquad \varepsilon = \frac{1}{6}$$

Consequently,

$$\left| \frac{k}{900} - 0.5 \right| < \frac{1}{6}$$

or

$$300 < k < 600.$$

Thus, we may expect with probability exceeding 0.99 that the number of times that the coin falls heads will lie between 300 and 600 if the coin is tossed 900 times.

Example 4. A die is thrown 1,200 times. Estimate the probability that the number of sixes will lie between 150 and 250.

In this example, as in the preceding examples, the bounds on the number of occurrences of the event are symmetric about the expectation of the number of occurrences, which in the present case is equal to $1{,}200 \cdot (1/6) = 200$. This value of the bounds is explained by the form in which Bernoulli's theorem is proven:

$$P\left( \left| \frac{k}{n} - p \right| < \varepsilon \right) > 1 - \delta.$$

From these bounds, we determine $\varepsilon$ first:

$$-\varepsilon < \frac{k}{1200} - \frac{1}{6} < +\varepsilon,$$

$$200 - 1200\varepsilon < k < 200 + 1200\,\varepsilon,$$

$$200 - 1200\varepsilon = 150; \qquad \varepsilon = \frac{1}{24}.$$

Let us check the right side:

$$200 + 1200\varepsilon = 200 + 1200 \cdot \frac{1}{24} = 250.$$

We set $N = 1{,}200$. In order to obtain a figure for the probability, we need to compute $\delta$. From formula (10.4), we obtain

$$\delta = \frac{\frac{1}{6} \cdot \frac{5}{6}}{1200 \cdot \frac{1}{24^2}} = \frac{1}{15}.$$

Thus, we may expect with a probability exceeding 14/15 that if the die is thrown 1,200 times sixes will fall between 150 and 250 times.

We note that if we use the cruder formula (10.5) to determine $\delta$,

$$N' = \frac{1}{4\delta\varepsilon^2},$$

we get a much less satisfactory result: $\delta = 3/25$.

## 48. LAPLACE'S LIMIT THEOREM

THEOREM. *Suppose that trials are made that are independent with respect to a certain event and that in each of them the probability of the event is a constant $p$. If the number of trials $n$ increases without bound, the limit, as $n \to \infty$, of the probability that the number of occurrences $k$ of the event will lie between the numbers $k_1$ and $k_2$ (for $k_1 < k_2$) is*

$$\frac{1}{\sqrt{2\pi}} \int_{z_1}^{z_2} e^{-\frac{t^2}{2}}\, dt,$$

*where*

$$z_1 = \frac{k_1 - np}{\sqrt{npq}}; \qquad z_2 = \frac{k_2 - np}{\sqrt{npq}}$$

*or, more briefly,*

$$\lim_{n \to \infty} P(k_1 \leqslant k \leqslant k_2) = \frac{1}{\sqrt{2\pi}} \int_{z_1}^{z_2} e^{-\frac{t^2}{2}}\, dt. \tag{10.6}$$

Proof: Formula (8.8)

$$P_{k,n} = \frac{1}{\sqrt{2\pi}} e^{-\frac{t^2}{2}} \Delta t,$$

where

$$t = \frac{k - np}{\sqrt{npq}}, \qquad \Delta t = \frac{1}{\sqrt{npq}}$$

was derived in Section 38 for calculating the approximate value of the probability $k$. Here, $\Delta t$ is the increase in $t$ corresponding to two values of $k$ differing by unity. From the theorem on addition of probabilities,

$$P(k_1 \leqslant k \leqslant k_2) = \sum_{k=k_1}^{k} P_{k,\,n} \tag{10.7}$$

(for example, $P(6 \leqslant k \leqslant 10) = P_{6,\,n} + P_{7,\,n} + P_{8,\,n} + P_{9,\,n} + P_{10,\,n}$). We denote by $z_1$ and $z_2$ the values of $z$ corresponding to the numbers $k_1$ and $k_2$:

$$z_1 = \frac{k_1 - np}{\sqrt{npq}}, \qquad z_2 = \frac{k_2 - np}{\sqrt{npq}}.$$

If we replace all the numbers $P_{k,\,n}$ in (10.7) with their approximate values according to the transformed formula (8.8), we obtain the approximate equation

$$P(k_1 \leqslant k \leqslant k_2) = \sum_{t=z_1}^{z_2} \frac{1}{\sqrt{2\pi}} e^{-\frac{t^2}{2}} \Delta t, \tag{10.8}$$

where the summation is carried out for all values of $t$ corresponding to the integral values of $k$ from $k_1$ to $k_2$. It follows from the expression for $\Delta t$ that $\Delta t \to 0$ as $n \to \infty$. The function $e^{-\frac{t^2}{2}}$, which takes discrete values for finite $n$, is continuous. Therefore, if we replace the sum in (10.8) with an integral, we obtain the exact equation:

$$\lim_{n \to \infty} P(k_1 \leqslant k \leqslant k_2) = \frac{1}{\sqrt{2\pi}} \int_{z_1}^{z_2} e^{-\frac{t^2}{2}} dt.$$

Let us now break the integral in the basic formula just obtained into two integrals and then reverse the limits of integration in one of them, as follows:

$$\int_{z_1}^{z_2} e^{-\frac{t^2}{2}} dt = \int_{z_1}^{0} e^{-\frac{t^2}{2}} dt + \int_{0}^{z_2} e^{-\frac{t^2}{2}} dt = \int_{0}^{z_2} e^{-\frac{t^2}{2}} dt - \int_{0}^{z_1} e^{-\frac{t^2}{2}} dt.$$

Let us define

$$\Phi(z) = \int_{0}^{z} \frac{1}{\sqrt{2\pi}} e^{-\frac{t^2}{2}} dt. \tag{10.9}$$

The basic formula can now be written in the form

$$\lim_{n\to\infty} P(k_1 \leqslant k \leqslant k_2) = \Phi(z_2) - \Phi(z_1). \quad (10.10)$$

The values of the function $\Phi(z)$ can, for small values of $z$ be calculated by expanding the function in (10.9) in a Maclaurin series, integrating the series obtained termwise, and then finding the first few partial sums of the integrated series.

It will be sufficient to calculate the function $\Phi(z)$ for positive values of $z$ since this is an odd function. That is, by replacing $z$ with $-z$ and $t$ with $-\tau$ in the integral (10.9), we obtain

$$\Phi(-z) = \int_0^{-z} \frac{1}{\sqrt{2\pi}} e^{-\frac{t^2}{2}}\, dt = -\int_0^{z} \frac{1}{\sqrt{2\pi}} e^{-\frac{\tau^2}{2}}\, d\tau,$$

or

$$\Phi(-z) = -\Phi(z). \quad (10.11)$$

Values of the function $\Phi(z)$ for $0.00 \leqslant z \leqslant 5.00$ are given in Table III at the end of the book.

In practice, Laplace's theorem is used for finding the approximate value of this probability for large values of $n$. In this case,

$$P(k_1 \leqslant k \leqslant k_2) \approx \Phi(z_2) - \Phi(z_1),$$

where

$$z_1 = \frac{k_1 - np}{\sqrt{npq}},$$

$$z_2 = \frac{k_2 - np}{\sqrt{npq}}.$$

Laplace's theorem can be put in yet another form. The inequalities $k_1 \leqslant k \leqslant k_2$ are equivalent to the inequalities

$$\alpha_1 \leqslant \frac{k}{n} - p \leqslant \alpha_2,$$

where

$$\alpha_1 = \frac{k_1}{n} - p, \quad \alpha_2 = \frac{k_2}{n} - p.$$

Then,

$$z_1 = \frac{k_1 - np}{\sqrt{npq}} = \frac{\alpha_1}{\sqrt{\frac{pq}{n}}}; \quad z_2 = \frac{k_2 - np}{\sqrt{npq}} = \frac{\alpha_2}{\sqrt{\frac{pq}{n}}}.$$

The numbers $\alpha_1$ and $\alpha_2$ can be given instead of the numbers $k_1$ and $k_2$. They represent the bounds between which the deviation of the relative frequency $k/n$ from the probability $p$ lies; they can be either negative or positive.

The probability is not changed if we replace this inequality with an equivalent one. Therefore, we may write

$$\lim_{n\to\infty} P\left(\alpha_1 < \frac{k}{n} - p < \alpha_2\right) = \frac{1}{\sqrt{2\pi}} \int_{z_1}^{z_2} e^{-\frac{t^2}{2}}\,dt = \Phi(z_2) - \Phi(z_1),$$

where

$$z_1 = \frac{\alpha_1}{\sqrt{\frac{pq}{n}}}, \qquad z_2 = \frac{\alpha_2}{\sqrt{\frac{pq}{n}}}.$$

In particular, if $\alpha_1 < 0$ and $\alpha_2 = -\alpha_1 = \alpha$, then, because $\Phi(z)$ is an odd function,

$$\lim_{n\to\infty} P\left(\left|\frac{k}{n} - p\right| < \alpha\right) = 2\Phi\left(\frac{\alpha}{\sqrt{\frac{pq}{n}}}\right).$$

If $n$ is a large number, we may write the approximate equation

$$P\left(\left|\frac{k}{n} - p\right| < \alpha\right) \approx 2\Phi\left(\frac{\alpha}{\sqrt{\frac{pq}{n}}}\right). \tag{10.12}$$

The function $\Phi(z)$ assumes values only slightly different from 0.5 when $z$ is greater than 3. Therefore, the limit of $P$ is close to unity if $\alpha$ exceeds $3\sqrt{\frac{pq}{n}}$. ($\Phi(z) = 0.49865$ if $z = 3$). Suppose, for example, that $n = 100$ and $p = q = 0.5$. Then, $3\sqrt{\frac{pq}{n}} = 0.15$ and, on the basis of Laplace's theorem, we may assert that the absolute value of the deviation of $k/n$ from $p$ will almost certainly be less than 0.15 (that is, with probability close to unity). (This assertion is true only approximately.) Although Laplace's theorem is valid only in the limit, it is frequently used for calculating probabilities even when $n$ is finite. Quite satisfactory results are obtained if $npq$ is of the order of 100 or greater.

Example 1. A coin is thrown one hundred times. Calculate the probability of its landing tails between forty and sixty times. Here, $n = 100$, $p = q = 0.5$, $\sqrt{npq} = 5$, $k_1 = 40$, and $k_2 = 60$. Therefore, $z_1 = -2$ and $z_2 = 2$. We obtain as an approximation

$$P(40 < k < 60) = \Phi(2) - \Phi(-2) = 2\Phi(2).$$

From the table, we find $\Phi(2) = 0.4772$. Therefore,

$$P(40 < k < 60) = 0.95.$$

Example 2. A die is thrown 2,400 times. Determine the probability that the absolute value of the difference between the relative frequency and the probability of the die falling on six will not exceed 1/24.

Here, $p = 1/6$, $q = 5/6$, $npq = 333$, and

$$-\alpha_1 = \alpha_2 = \alpha = \frac{1}{24}, \quad -z_1 = z_2 = 2.74:$$

consequently,

$$P\left(\left|\frac{k}{2400} - \frac{1}{6}\right|\right) < \frac{1}{24} \approx 2\Phi(2.74) = 0.994.$$

## 49. INEQUALITIES AND CHEBYSHEV'S THEOREM

Let us consider $n$ pairwise independent random variables $X^{(1)}$, $\bar{x}_2$, . . . ,$X^{(n)}$. Here, the superscripts are indices; that is, they are used as a way of numbering these random variables. They do not indicate the values that the random variables may take. Each of them may take several values, the number of which can be different from variable to variable.

Let us denote the expectations of these random variables by $\bar{x}_1$, $\bar{x}_2$, . . . $\bar{x}_n$ and their variances by $\sigma_1^2$, $\sigma_2^2$, . . . , $\sigma_n^2$. Consider the sum of these random variables

$$X = X^{(1)} + X^{(2)} + \ldots + X^{(n)};$$

We denote the expectation and the variance of this sum by

$$\bar{x} = E(X),$$
$$\sigma^2 = E\{(X - \bar{x})^2\}.$$

From the theorems on the addition of expectations and variances, we have

$$\bar{x} = \bar{x}_1 + \bar{x}_2 + \ldots + \bar{x}_n,$$
$$\sigma^2 = \sigma_1^2 + \sigma_2^2 + \ldots + \sigma_n^2.$$

The random variable $(X - \bar{x})^2$ can assume only nonnegative values, and its expectation is known. Therefore, we may apply the Chebyshev-Markov lemma to it:

$$P[(X - \bar{x})^2 < \sigma^2 t^2] > 1 - \frac{1}{t^2} \quad .^*$$

Let us replace the inequality in the square brackets with the equivalent inequality

$$|X - \bar{x}| < \sigma t$$

*We recall that $t^2$ is an arbitrary positive number.

(The probability of obtaining the inequality is not changed by this.) Then, we obtain

$$P\{|X-\bar{x}|<t\sigma\}>1-\frac{1}{t^2}. \quad (10.13)$$

If $X$ is understood to refer to one random variable only, we shall call this inequality *Chebyshev's first inequality.* It enables us to set a bound for the probability of a given deviation from $\bar{x}$ for an arbitrary distribution law.

If we replace $X$, $\bar{x}$, $\sigma^2$ in inequality (10.13) with the expressions that we listed above for these quantities, we obtain

$$P\{|X^{(1)}+X^{(2)}+\ldots+X^{(n)}-(\bar{x}_1+\bar{x}_2+\ldots+\bar{x}_n)|< \\ <t\sqrt{\sigma_1^2+\ldots+\sigma_n^2}\}>1-\frac{1}{t^2}. \quad (10.14)$$

We shall call this inequality *Chebyshev's second inequality.* If we divide both sides of the inequality appearing inside the braces, by $n$, we obtain Chebyshev's second inequality in a different form:

$$P\left\{\left|\frac{X^{(1)}+X^{(2)}+\ldots+X^{(n)}}{n}-\frac{\bar{x}_1+\bar{x}_2+\ldots+\bar{x}_n}{n}\right|< \\ <\frac{t\sqrt{\sigma_1^2+\ldots+\sigma_n^2}}{n}\right\}>1-\frac{1}{t^2}. \quad (10.15)$$

Here, $(X^{(1)}+X^{(2)}+\ldots+X^{(n)})/n$ is the arithmetic mean of the random values of the given variables and $(\bar{x}_1+\bar{x}_2+\ldots+\bar{x}_n)/n$ is the arithmetic mean of their expectations. Chebyshev's inequality, when written in the second form, gives an estimate of the probability that the absolute value of the deviation of the first mean from the second mean will be less than a quantity depending on the sum of the variances of the given random variables.

Let us now prove Chebyshev's theorem.

THEOREM. *Suppose that the random variables $X^{(1)}$, $X^{(2)}$, . . . , $X^{(n)}$ are pairwise independent and that they have given expectations $\bar{x}_1$, $\bar{x}_2$, . . . , $\bar{x}_n$ and given uniformly bounded variances. Then, we may expect with a proability arbitrarily close to unity that the absolute value of the difference between the arithmetic mean of the given variables and the arithmetic mean of their expectations will be arbitrarily small in absolute value if n is sufficiently large.*

Let us denote by $\varepsilon$ an upper bound on the absolute value of the difference between the arithmetic means referred to in the theorem. Then, Chebyshev's theorem can be written as follows:

*For any two positive numbers $\varepsilon$ and $\delta$, the inequality*

$$P\left\{\left|\frac{X^{(1)}+X^{(2)}+\ldots+X^{(n)}}{a}-\frac{\bar{x}_1+\bar{x}_2+\ldots+\bar{x}_n}{n}\right|<\varepsilon\right\}>1-\delta$$

*will be valid for every value of $n>N(\varepsilon, \delta)$, where N is a fixed positive number whose value can be determined from the values of $\varepsilon$ and $\delta$.*

Proof: Let us write Chebyshev's inequality in the second form:

$$P\left\{\left|\frac{X^{(1)}+X^{(2)}+\dots+X^{(n)}}{n}-\frac{\bar{x}_1+\bar{x}_2+\dots+\bar{x}_n}{n}\right|< \right.$$
$$\left. <\frac{t\sqrt{\sigma_1^2+\sigma_2^2+\dots+\sigma_n^2}}{n}\right\}>1-\frac{1}{t^2}.$$

To convert this inequality into the inequality that we wish to prove, let us choose $t$ such that

$$\frac{t\sqrt{\sigma_1^2+\sigma_2^2+\dots+\sigma_n^2}}{n}=\varepsilon; \quad t=\frac{n\varepsilon}{\sqrt{\sigma_1^2+\sigma_2^2+\dots+\sigma_n^2}}.$$

We then have

$$P\left\{\left|\frac{X^{(1)}+X_2^{(2)}+\dots+X_n^{(n)}}{n}-\frac{\bar{x}_1+\bar{x}_2+\dots+\bar{x}_n}{n}\right|<\varepsilon\right\}>$$
$$>1-\frac{\sigma_1^2+\sigma_2^2+\dots+\sigma_n^2}{n^2\varepsilon^2}.$$

By hypothesis, the variances are uniformly bounded by some number $B$; that is,

$$\sigma_1^2<B, \quad \sigma_2^2<B, \dots, \sigma_n^2<B,$$

so that

$$\sigma_1^2+\sigma_2^2+\dots+\sigma_n^2<nB.$$

On the right side of the inequality for $P$, let us replace $\sigma_1^2+\sigma_2^2+\dots+\sigma_n^2$ with $nB$. Obviously, this does not violate the inequality. Consequently,

$$P\left\{\left|\frac{X^{(1)}+X^{(2)}+\dots+X^{(n)}}{n}-\frac{\bar{x}_1+\bar{x}_2+\dots+\bar{x}_n}{n}\right|<\varepsilon\right\}>1-\frac{B}{n\varepsilon^2}.$$

We now choose the number $N$ such that $B/(N\varepsilon^2)=\delta$; that is, we choose $N=B/(\varepsilon^2\delta)$. Then, $B/(n\varepsilon^2)$ will be less than $\delta$ if $n>N$. If we replace $B/(n\varepsilon^2)$ with $\delta$ on the right side of the inequality, we shall not violate the inequality. Thus,

$$P\left\{\left|\frac{X^{(1)}+X^{(2)}+\dots+X^{(n)}}{n}-\frac{\bar{x}_1+\bar{x}_2+\dots+\bar{x}_n}{n}\right|<\varepsilon\right\}>1-\delta, \quad (10.16)$$

provided

$$n>N=\frac{B}{\varepsilon^2\delta}, \quad (10.17)$$

which completes the proof of the theorem.

COROLLARY. *Suppose that a random variable X has a given expectation a and a definite variance $\sigma^2$. Suppose that a number of independent observations are made to determine the values of X. Then, we may expect, with a probability differing from unity by an arbitrarily small amount that when a sufficiently large number of observations are made, the arithmetic mean of the observed values will differ in absolute value by an arbitrarily small amount from the expectation of X.*

Proof: Note that these random values of $X$, obtained from independent observations, can be considered independent random variables $\xi^{(1)}, \xi^{(2)}, \ldots, \xi^{(n)}$. Since each of them can have only those values that $X$ has (and with the same probabilities), the expectation and the variance of each of them is the same as for $X$. Using the notations that we used for Chebyshev's theorem, we may write

$$\bar{\xi}_1 = \bar{\xi}_2 = \ldots = \bar{\xi}_n = a,$$
$$\sigma_1^2 = \sigma_2^2 = \ldots = \sigma_n^2 = \sigma^2.$$

Therefore, the important condition for boundedness of the variances in Chebyshev's theorem is satisfied. Here, we take $\sigma^2$ for the bound $B$. Applying Chebyshev's theorem to the random variables $\xi^{(1)}, \xi^{(2)}, \ldots, \xi^{(n)}$, we obtain

$$P\left\{\left|\frac{\xi^{(1)} + \xi^{(2)} + \ldots + \xi^{(n)}}{n} - a\right| < \varepsilon\right\} > 1 - \delta, \quad n > N_1 = \frac{\sigma^2}{\varepsilon^2\delta}, \qquad (10.18)$$

which proves the corollary: $N_1$ is a sufficiently large number of observations.

The corollary to Chebyshev's theorem is of great significance in applications. It states that when a sufficiently large number of observations are made, we may expect, with a probability close to unity—in short, we may be virtually certain—that the average observed value will differ from the expectation, i.e., from the theoretical arithmetic mean, by an arbitrarily small amount.

Let us consider an example of the application of this corollary to Chebyshev's theorem.*

Let us suppose that a quantity $a$ (for example, a length) has a definite though unknown value. Suppose that this quantity is measured $n$ times. Because of the random errors that occur in the measurements, we obtain different numbers $a_1, a_2, \ldots, a_n$. The question then is how many measurements would be enough to ensure with a probability greater than 0.99 that the average value of these measurements differs from the exact value by an amount less than 0.1?

Since $a$ is assumed to have a fixed value, its expectation is equal to $a$. To solve the problem, we must know an upper bound on the variance of the random measurements. In specific problems of this type, an upper bound cannot be determined, since we do not

---

*It should be noted that examples of this kind serve primarily to clarify the content of the theorem. The estimates for a sufficiently large number of observations given in this theorem are exaggerated and, furthermore, the conditions of independence of observations cannot always be assumed to be fulfilled.

know the probabilities of the different values. However, if analogous measurements have been made before, we can exhibit a sort of upper bound on the variance on the basis of the results of the earlier measurements. (This question will be taken up in Chapter 4.) We simply assume that the upper bound on the variance in this problem is equal to 0.02.

Since in the present case, $\varepsilon = 0.1$, $\delta = 1 - 0.99$, and $\sigma^2 = 0.02$, we have

$$N_1 = \frac{0.02}{0.01 \cdot 0.01} = 200.$$

Thus, if the number of observations exceeds 200, we may expect with a probability exceeding 0.99 that the arithmetic mean of the measured values $a_1, a_2, \ldots, a_n$ differs from $a$ in absolute value by an amount not exceeding 0.1.

## 50. COMMENTS ON THE LAW OF LARGE NUMBERS. STATISTICAL PROBABILITIES

Putting Bernoulli's theorem in a few words, we may say that the relative frequency in the case of a large number of observations would differ only slightly from the probability. The significant feature of this assertion lies in the fact that it is only probable, although the probability can be made arbitrarily close to unity.

Therefore, if we were to perform the experiments described in the examples considered above, we should not expect that these experiments would definitely give agreement with the results of the calculations. To illustrate this, let us consider example 2 of Section 47. The results of the calculations showed that we may expect, with a probability exceeding 0.875 that the number of times the coin would fall heads would be between 80 and 120. In a particular experiment (in which the coin is tossed two hundred times), the number of times the coin falls heads may lie outside these limits, all the more so since the obtained lower bound on the probability is not very close to unity. To clarify the practical meaning of this result, we should imagine that a large number of such experiments (each consisting of tossing the coin 200 times) are performed. If we apply Bernoulli's theorem repeatedly, we may expect with a probability close to unity that in the majority of these experiments the number of times the coin will fall heads will lie between the limits indicated. (Speaking crudely, our prediction on the limits will be satisfied in seven trials out of eight on the average.)

If the experiments performed deviate considerably from the calculated results, we may conclude that, in the case of the phenomenon being examined, the conditions of Bernoulli's theorem are not fulfilled. The most stringent of these conditions is the requirement that the trials be independent.

In Bernoulli's theorem, the probability of the event was assumed known and the question was one of predicting (with some probability) limits between which the number of occurrences of the event would lie. Even in this form, the theorem points to the possibility of finding out the unknown probability of a random event from a large number of observations on the occurrence and nonoccurrence of the events in question.

Such a possibility follows from the converse of Bernoulli's theorem: if we may assume that in an infinite number of independent experiments an event has a constant probability (the value of which we do not know), then, with a probability arbitrarily close to unity, we may expect that the ratio of the number of actual occurrences of the events to the number of observations will differ by an arbitrarily small amount from the probability if the number of observations is sufficiently great. Therefore,

$$P\left\{\left|p - \frac{k}{n}\right| < \varepsilon\right\} > 1 - \delta \tag{10.19}$$

if $n > N(\varepsilon, \delta)$, where $N$ can be determined from the values of $\varepsilon$ and $\delta$. For large values of n, we obtain

$$p \approx \frac{k}{n}. \tag{10.20}$$

Probabilities calculated on the basis of the results of observations are said to be statistical or empirical.

Chebyshev's theorem can be worded as follows: if the number of random variables is sufficiently large, the arithmetic mean of the random values of these variables will differ only slightly from the arithmetic mean of their expectations. The corollary to Chebyshev's theorem can be worded analogously. These statements of the theorem and its corollary show that when a sufficiently large number of independent observations are made, it is possible, with a probability close to unity, to obtain from observations an approximate value of the arithmetic mean of the expectations or the expectation of a single quantity.

It should be noted that the estimates on the necessary number of observations (obtained by application of the Bernoulli and Chebyshev theorems and resulting from the methods by which these theorems are proved) are much too large. Certain methods of making these approximations more exact are to be found in the works of S. N. Bernstein, A. Ya. Khinchin, and other authors.

In practice, the application of these theorems of the law of large numbers is restricted by the condition that the trials or the random variables be independent. It has been shown in a number of works on probability theory that this restriction can be removed if the relationship between the random variables that we are studying is very weak. Also, certain conditions under which the law of large numbers is applicable to dependent random variables have been established, but this question has not been studied sufficiently.

Laplace's theorem is ordinarily called the Laplace limit theorem, since it establishes a limit to which the probability that the number of occurrences lies between the given bounds converges. In order to avoid the excessively high estimates for a sufficiently large number of observations that are given by Bernoulli's theorem, we often use Laplace's theorem. However, we should note that this gives less definite results than does the application of Bernoulli's theorem, since we do not then have an estimate of the error made in replacing a formula that is valid in the limit as $n \to \infty$ with the same formula for a finite value of $n$.

As a check on the law of large numbers, many different experiments (such as, for example, the tossing of coins) have been performed. The results of these experiments show that the predictions that one would make on the basis of the theorem turn out to be true in almost all experiments. (Of course, the experiments were such that the conditions of the theorems were satisfied.)

The question of the applicability of the law of large numbers to natural phenomena is rather complicated. Assertions similiar to those that we made in certain examples must be made with suitable restrictions and must be checked by systematic observations.

Chapter 11

# CONTINUOUS RANDOM VARIABLES

## 51. THE DISTRIBUTION FUNCTION OF A CONTINUOUS RANDOM VARIABLE

In this chapter, we shall consider random variables that may assume arbitrary values in some region. Let us denote by $X$ a continuous random variable that can take any real value in an interval $(a, b)$. In such a case, it is impossible to state the probability of each individual value and we should not pose the problem of the probabilities of specific values since there are infinitely many of them. In the case of continuous random variables it is meaningful only to speak of the probability of the value falling in a certain interval. This interval may contain the range of the variable or may intersect that range. Usually, the problem is one of calculating the probability that a random variable $X$, defined in an interval $(a, b)$, will assume a value in a subinterval $(\alpha, \beta)$ of $(a,b)$. We shall consider this the basic problem. In particular, the region $(a,b)$ may extend from 0 to $\infty$ or from $-\infty$ to $+\infty$.

In the case of a discrete variable, to solve the problem of the probability that a random variable will take a value in the interval specified, we needed to give a table of values of the variable and the probabilities of these values. If the variable is continuous, instead of a table (distribution of probabilities) we must be given certain functions (the distribution functions).

In what follows, let us represent the basic problem graphically. Suppose that a segment $AB$ on the real axis represents the set of possible values of the random variable. Let us put the event—the random variable $X$ will take the value $x$—in correspondence with the choosing of the point $x$ in a random selection of a point on the real line. If $(\alpha, \beta)$ represents the given interval, the graphical interpretation of the basic problem is the problem of calculating the probability that this point will fall on the segment $\alpha\beta$ (see Fig. 5). Such a probability is a function of the coordinates of the end points $\alpha$ and $\beta$, but giving such a function as a function of two arguments would unnecessarily complicate the theory. Instead, the distribution function is given. This distribution function is defined as follows:

a one-argument function $F(x)$ whose value is equal to the probability that the random variable will take a value less than the argument $x$ of this function is known as a distribution function of a continuous random variable.* By definition, we then have the equation

$$P(X < x) = F(x), \tag{11.1}$$

in which the left side should be read "the probability that the random variable $X$ will assume a value less than $x$." It follows from the definition of a distribution function $F(x)$ that

$$\left.\begin{array}{lll} F(x)=0, & \text{if} & x \leqslant a, \\ F(x)=1, & \text{if} & x \geqslant b. \end{array}\right\} \tag{11.2}$$

If $x$ increases monotonically from $a$ to $b$, the function $F(x)$ will also increase monotonically from 0 to 1 since the increase in $x$ widens the region of possible values of the variable and hence increases the probability that the variable will assume a value in that region.

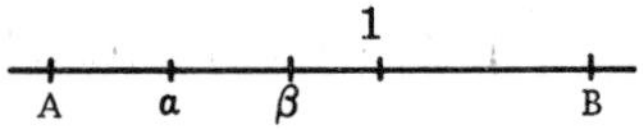


Fig. 5. A representation of the basic problem for continuous random variables.

On the basis of these properties, we may assert that a graph of a distribution function will have the shape shown in Figure 6. To the left of the domain of definition, the graph is a straight line coinciding with the $x$-axis. Between $a$ and $b$, it is a monotonically ascending curve with ordinates varying from 0 to 1. To the right of the point $B$, it is a straight line parallel to the abscissa but at unit distance above it.**

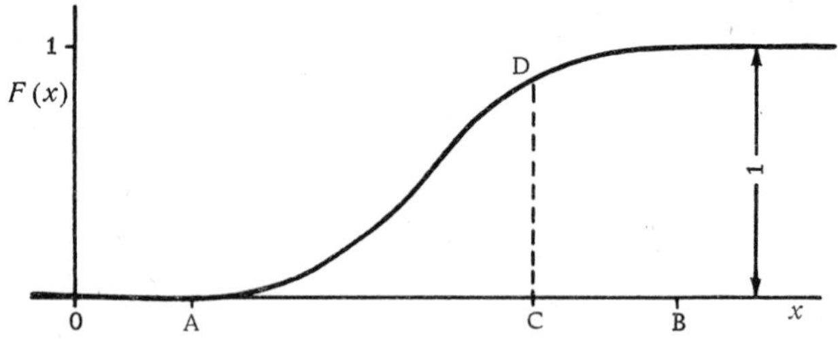


Fig. 6. The graph of a distribution function of a continuous random variable. $OA = a$, $OC = x$, $OB = b$, $CD = P(X < x)$.

---

*Note that the concept of a distribution function can be extended without change to the case of discrete variables.

**It is not difficult to show that the graph of a distribution function in the case of a discrete random variable is that of a step function (like the profile of a stairway).

To show the expediency of having a distribution function given, let us show that if we know it we can easily solve the basic problem stated above.

Suppose that we wish to determine the probability of a random variable assuming a value in an interval $(a, b)$. Then,

$$F(\beta) = P(X < \beta), \quad F(\alpha) = P(X < \alpha).$$

Since the interval from $a$ to $\beta$ consists of two non-intersecting parts (namely, the part from $a$ to $\alpha$ and the part from $\alpha$ to $\beta$), the random event (i.e. falling to the left of the point $\beta$) has two mutually exclusive parts, namely, falling to the left of $\alpha$ and falling between $\alpha$ and $\beta$. From the theorem on the addition of probabilities, we may write

$$P(X < \alpha) + P(\alpha < X < \beta) = P(X < \beta).$$

Therefore,

$$P(\alpha < X < \beta) = P(X < \beta) - P(X < \alpha)$$

or (11.3)

$$P(\alpha < X < \beta) = F(\beta) - F(\alpha).$$

The last equation shows that if we know the distribution function of a continuous random variable, it is quite simple to solve the basic problem: the probability that a random variable will assume a value in a certain interval is equal to the difference between the values of the distribution function at the upper and lower end points of the interval.

One of the problems in the study of random variables consists in choosing certain numerical characteristics of a random variable and in finding a method of calculating them. One of these characteristics—the median—is closely connected with the distribution function. The *median* of a random variable is that value determined by the condition that the values of the variable greater and less than the median be equally likely; that is,

$$P(X < m) = P(X > m) = \frac{1}{2}. \tag{11.4}$$

If the distribution function $F(x)$ is given, the median is determined by the equation $F(x) = 0.5$, which, because of the monotonicity of $F(x)$, will have a unique solution. On the graph of $F(x)$, the median is represented in an obvious manner: we draw a straight line parallel to the $x$-axis at a distance 0.5 above it; the abscissa of the point of intersection of this line with the curve represents the median.

## 52. PROBABILITY DENSITY

Suppose that we know the distribution function $F(x)$ of a random variable $X$ defined in the interval $(a, b)$. When we calculate the probability of the random variable taking a value in the part of this interval from $x$ to $x+\Delta x$ (where $\Delta x > 0$) we obtain

$$P(x < X < x+\Delta x) = F(x+\Delta x) - F(x).$$

If we divide both sides of this equation by $\Delta x$, we have

$$\frac{P(x < X < x+\Delta x)}{\Delta x} = \frac{F(x+\Delta x) - F(x)}{\Delta x}. \qquad (11.5)$$

The quotient on the left is the ratio of the probability of the variable falling on the segment of length $\Delta x$ to the length $\Delta x$. This quantity can be called the average probability density on the segment $\Delta x$ with origin at the point $x$. The quotient on the right is the ratio of the corresponding increase in the distribution function to the increase of the argument. In this equation, let us pass to the limit as $\Delta x \to 0$, assuming that $F(x)$ is a differentiable function. The limit of the left side is the probability density at the point $x$ in analogy with the concept of linear density at a point. The limit of the right side is equal to the derivative of the distribution function. If we denote the probability density by $p(x)$, we have a simple relationship between the probability density and the distribution function: the probability density is equal to the derivative of the distribution function with respect to the argument of the distribution:*

$$p(x) = \frac{dF(x)}{dx}. \qquad (11.6)$$

Let us note certain properties of the probability density:

I. *The probability density is a nonnegative quantity at all values of the argument.*

This follows from the fact that $p(x)$ is the derivative of a nondecreasing function $F(x)$.

II. *If a random variable is defined in a finite interval from a to b, the probability density p (x) is 0 when x < a or x > b.*

This is true because values of $x$ outside the region $(a, b)$ are impossible and hence, the possibility of the variable assuming a value in any interval outside that region is equal to 0. Therefore, the probability density is also equal to 0.

Because of this property, we may always formally assume that a random variable is given for the entire real line from $-\infty$ to $+\infty$, but with $p(x)$ having different types of values for three subintervals of the real line; that is, $p(x)$ is equal to 0 to the left of $a$, positive from $a$ to $b$, and equal to 0 to the right of $b$.

III. *The value of p (x) within the interval or at its end points can be any nonnegative number of + ∞.*

---

*Because of this equality, the probability density is sometimes called the "differential distribution function" and the distribution function that we defined above is called the "integral distribution function."

This follows from the fact that the derivative of the monotonic increasing function $F(x)$ defined in this interval is in no way bounded. In connection with this, we should note that we must not confuse the probability density with the probability (whose values never exceed unity).

IV. *From the definition of probability density, we have the approximate equation*

$$P(x < X < x + \Delta x) \approx p(x)\,\Delta x, \tag{11.7}$$

*where $\Delta x$ is a sufficiently small positive number.*

In computation, this equation is often written as if it were exact. This introduces no error if the logic of the problem indicates a passage to the limit as $\Delta x \to 0$.

V. *The solution of the basic problem is given by the formula.*

$$P(\alpha < X < \beta) = \int_{\alpha}^{\beta} p(x)\,dx. \tag{11.8}$$

This formula is obvious if we remember the solution of the basic problem by means of the distribution function $F(x)$ and consider the relationship between $p(x)$ and $F(x)$. (Specifically, $F(x)$ is a primitive of $p(x)$.)

VI. *If a random variable is given in a finite region from a to b, then*

$$\int_{a}^{b} p(x)\,dx = 1, \tag{11.9}$$

*that is, the area between the x-axis and the graph of the probability density is equal to 1.*

This is true because the left side is, by formula (11.8), the probability that the variable will fall in the interval from $a$ to $b$ and, by hypothesis, the variable can take values only in this interval. This means that the probability of its falling in the interval $(a, b)$ is equal to unity. The equation written above is sometimes called the condition of normalization of the probability density. This means that condition (11.9) must be imposed on the probability density if this function is to some degree arbitrarily chosen.

The graph of the probability density is usually called the *distribution curve*. It can have one or several maxima in the interval in question. The value of the random variable corresponding to the maximum ordinate of this curve is called the *mode*.

## 53. EXPECTATION, VARIANCE, AND MOMENTS

In Chapter 9, the expectation of a random variable was defined only for those random variables that could assume only a finite number of discrete values (though the definition could easily be extended to variables having an infinite number of discrete values).

The concept of distribution functions of continuous random variables makes it possible to introduce the concept of the expectation of a continuous random variable.

Definition 1. If $X$ is a continuous random variable that assumes values $x$ in the interval from $a$ to $b$ (where $a < b$) and if $p(x)$ is the probability density of this variable, its *expectation* is defined to be

$$E(X) = \bar{x} = \int_a^b xp(x)\,dx. \tag{11.10}$$

Formula (11.10) may be considered as defining the theoretical average value of a continuous random variable.

Definition 2. The expectation of a random variable is called the *center of its distribution.*

In the probability density graph, the point on the $x$-axis whose abscissa is the expectation of the random variable is also called the center of distribution. (This name is explained by the fact that the center of gravity of a nonhomogeneous line segment the abscissas of whose ends are equal to $a$ and $b$ is determined by the same formula as the expectation if the density at the point is equal to $p(x)$.)

Definition 3. The expectation of an arbitrary single-valued continuous function $\varphi(X)$ of a continuous random variable $X$ whose probability density is $p(x)$ is defined by the formula

$$E\{\varphi(X)\} = \int_a^b \varphi(x)\,p(x)\,dx. \tag{11.11}$$

This definition is justified by the fact that the probability of $\varphi(X)$ assuming values between $\varphi(x_1)$ and $\varphi(x_2)$ is equal to the probability that $X$ will assume a value between $x_1$ and $x_2$ no matter what $x_1$ and $x_2$ are.

Formula (11.11) defines the theoretical average value of the function $\varphi(X)$.

All the properties of the expectation that were given for discrete variables remain valid for continuous ones.

Let us turn now to the concept of the moments of a random variable.

Definition 4. The *initial moment of order* $s$ of a random variable $X$ defined in an interval $(a, b)$ with probability density $p(x)$ is the number

$$\nu_s = \int_a^b x^s p(x)\,dx, \tag{11.12}$$

that is, the expectation of the $s$th power of the random variable (where $s$ is a positive number).

From the normalization condition and the definition of expectation,

$$\nu_0 = 1,$$

$$\nu_1 = E(X) = \bar{x}.$$

Definition 5. The *central moment of order* $s$ of a random variable $X$ with probability density $p(x)$ is the number

$$\mu_s = \int_a^b (x - \bar{x})^s p(x)\, dx, \tag{11.13}$$

that is, the expectation of the $s$th power of the deviation of the random variable from its expectation.

It follows from the definition that

$$\mu_0 = 1, \tag{11.14}$$

$$\mu_1 = 0, \tag{11.15}$$

since

$$\mu_0 = \int_a^b p(x)\, dx = \nu_0 = 1,$$

$$\mu_1 = \int_a^b xp(x)\, dx - \bar{x} \int_a^b p(x)\, dx = \bar{x} - \bar{x} \cdot 1 = 0.$$

Furthermore,

$$\mu_2 = \int_a^b (x - \bar{x})^2 p(x)\, dx = \sigma_x^2, \tag{11.16}$$

that is, the central moment of second order is the expectation of the square of the deviation of the random variable from its expectation. From the definition given in the chapter on discrete random variables, such an expectation is called the *variance*. If we extend this definition to continuous random variables, we may say that the central moment of second order is the variance of a continuous random variable. The properties given in Section 44 for the variance of a random variable remain valid for continuous ones, because in the proof of these properties we did not use the discreteness of the variables. Let us derive formulas expressing the central moments in terms of the initial moments. First, we expand the factor $(x - \bar{x})^s$ according to the binomial formula. We obtain

$$\mu_s = \int_a^b x^s p(x)\, dx - s\bar{x} \int_a^b x^{s-1} p(x)\, dx +$$

$$+ \frac{s(s-1)}{1 \cdot 2} \bar{x}^2 \int_a^b x^{s-2} p(x)\, dx + \ldots + (-1)^k C_s^k \bar{x}^k \int_a^b x^{s-k} p(x)\, dx + \ldots$$

$$\ldots + \frac{s(s-1)}{1 \cdot 2} \bar{x}^{s-2} (-1)^{s-2} \int_a^b x^2 p(x)\, dx +$$

$$+ (-1)^{s-1} s\bar{x}^{s-1} \int_a^b xp(x)\, dx + (-1)^s \bar{x}^s \int_a^b p(x)\, dx.$$

All the integrals are equal to the initial moments:

$$\nu_s,\ \nu_{s-1},\ \ldots,\ \nu_2,\ \nu_1,\ \nu_0.$$

As was shown above, $\nu_0 = 1$ and $\nu_1 = \bar{x}$. Therefore, the last two terms can be simplified and, consequently,

$$\mu_s = \sum_{k=0}^{s-2} (-1)^k C_s^k \bar{x}^k \nu_{s-k} + (-1)^{s-1} (s-1) \bar{x}^s. \tag{11.17}$$

In particular,

$$\left.\begin{aligned} \mu_2 &= \nu_2 - \bar{x}^2, \\ \mu_3 &= \nu_3 - 3\nu_2\bar{x} + 2\bar{x}^{-3}, \\ \mu_4 &= \nu_4 - 4\nu_3\bar{x} + 6\nu_2\bar{x}^2 - 3\bar{x}^4. \end{aligned}\right\} \tag{11.18}$$

It would have been possible to treat the moments as (free) numerical characteristics of the random variable, but the dimensions of the moment of order $s$ are equal to the dimensions of $X$ taken to the power $s$, which is inconvenient. It is more natural to treat the numbers $\sqrt[s]{\mu_s}$, in particular $\sigma = \sqrt{\mu_2}$ as the numerical characteristics. Use of the central moment excludes the influence of the origin from which the variable $X$ is measured, but it does not exclude the influence of the scale used in the measurement of this quantity. For that reason we should take the numbers

$$m_s = \frac{\sqrt[s]{\mu_s}}{\sigma} \quad \text{for} \quad s > 2$$

for the moment numerical characteristics. The numbers $m_s$ do not depend on the way in which the quantity $x$ is measured; that is, they do not depend either on the choice of origin or on the choice of units. These are pure numbers and they can be used for comparing different random variables with each other.

The moment characteristics supplement the basic characteristics, which depend both on the point chosen as origin and on the scale: that is, they supplement the average value $\bar{x}$, the median $m$, and the mean square deviation $\sigma_x$. For odd values of $s$, the smallness of the number $m_s$ can serve as an indication that the distribution (the probability density) is nearly symmetrical about the center of distribution.

## 54. UNIFORM PROBABILITY DISTRIBUTION

To illustrate the general situation, let us take the simplest case, the one in which the probability density is constant in the interval from $a$ to $b$. In this case, the graph of the probability density is a line segment parallel to the $x$-axis (Fig. 7a). In order that the area bounded above by the distribution curve be equal to unity (the normalization condition), we must require that the constant value of the probability density be equal to $1/_{b-a}$.

The distribution function $F(x)$ can be found by integrating the probability density with the initial condition $F(a) = 0$:

$$F(x) = \int_a^x \frac{dt}{b-a},$$

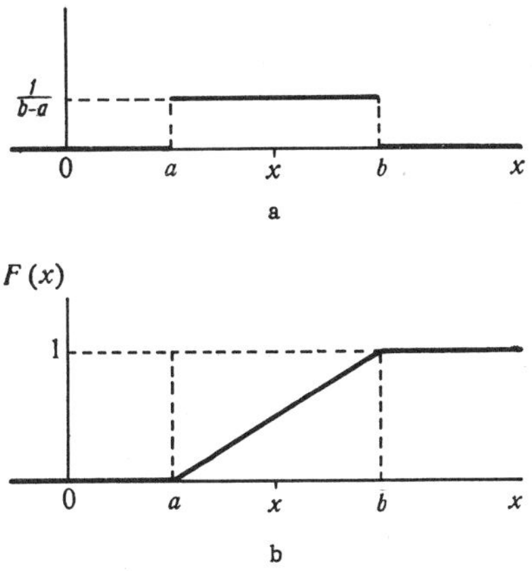


Fig. 7. The case of uniform distribution. (a) The graph of the probability density; (b) the graph of the distribution function.

and hence,

$$F(x) = \frac{x-a}{b-a}.$$

The graph of the distribution function is a line segment intersecting the $x$-axis at the point $X=a$ and having ordinate equal to unity at $X=b$ (Fig. 7b). The probability that $X$ will have a value between $\alpha$ and $\beta$ is obtained from the formula

$$P(\alpha < X < \beta) = \frac{\beta - \alpha}{b-a}.$$

The expectation is

$$\bar{x} = \int_a^b \frac{x\,dx}{b-a}$$

or

$$\bar{x} = \frac{b+a}{2}.$$

This result is rather obvious. The distribution is symmetric and therefore the center of distribution must be at the geometric center of the interval. The median in the case of uniform distribution coincides with the expectation.

If we displace the origin of a uniformly distributed random variable to the center of distribution, we obtain the new variable

$$Y = X - \frac{b+a}{2} = X - \bar{x}.$$

Obviously,

$$\bar{y} = \bar{x} - \bar{x} = 0.$$

The probability density $Y$ can be written in the form

$$p(y) = \frac{1}{2c},$$

where $2c = b - a$ is the length of the interval.

The variance of the uniformly distributed variable $Y$ is equal to the variance of the variable $X$ since these two variables differ only by the displacement of the origin, which has no effect on the variance. This common variance is

$$\operatorname{var} X = \operatorname{var} Y = \int_{-c}^{c} \frac{y^2\,dy}{2c} = \frac{c^2}{3},$$

$$\sigma_x = \frac{c}{\sqrt{3}} = 0.58c.$$

In the case of uniform distribution, the quantity $c$ is the absolute value of the limiting deviation from the center. It is related to $\sigma_x$ by the equation $c = \sigma_x \sqrt{3}$.

## 55. FORMULATION OF LYAPUNOV'S THEOREM. THE NORMAL PROBABILITY DISTRIBUTION

In the study of natural phenomena, we need to deal with random variables that can be considered as sums of a large number of independent random variables. Lyapunov's limiting theorem characterizes (with certain restrictions) the distribution law for such sums. This theorem is formulated as follows:

Suppose that

$$Z = X^{(1)} + X^{(2)} + \ldots + X^{(n)},$$

where $X^{(1)}, X^{(2)}, \ldots, X^{(n)}$ are mutually independent random variables having given expectations, variances, and "absolute" central moments of order $2+\alpha$:

$$E(X^{(k)}) = \bar{x}_k, \quad \operatorname{var}(X^{(k)}) = \sigma_k^2, \quad E(|X^{(k)} - \bar{x}_k|^{2+\alpha}) = \gamma_k,$$

where $\alpha$ is some positive number. Suppose that

$$\lim_{n \to \infty} \frac{\sum_{k=1}^{n} \gamma_k}{\sigma^{2+\alpha}} = 0.$$

Then, the probability that

$$t_1\sigma < Z - \bar{z} < t_2\sigma, \tag{11.19}$$

where $\bar{z} = \sum_{k=1}^{n} \bar{x}_k$ and $\sigma^2 = \sum_{k=1}^{n} \sigma_k^2$, will, as $n \to \infty$, approach the limiting value

$$\frac{1}{\sqrt{2\pi}} \int_{t_1}^{t_2} e^{-\frac{\tau^2}{2}} d\tau. \tag{11.20}$$

The assertion of this theorem can be formulated approximately in a somewhat different manner: for a sufficiently large number $n$ of random variables added together, the probability of the inequality $\alpha < Z < \beta$ will be arbitrarily close to the quantity

$$\frac{1}{\sigma\sqrt{2\pi}} \int_{\alpha}^{\beta} e^{-\frac{(\tau - \bar{z})}{2\sigma^2}} d\tau. \tag{11.20a}$$

It is clear from this formulation of Lyapunov's limit theorem that when the number of random variables is increased without bound, the probability density of the sum approaches the function

$$p(x) = \frac{1}{\sigma\sqrt{2\pi}} e^{-\frac{(x-a)^2}{2\sigma^2}} \tag{11.21}$$

provided that the random variables being summed satisfy the conditions of the theorem. The distribution law with probability density given by formula (11.21) is called a *normal distribution,* and we say that the random variable having such a distribution is normal. The numbers $a$ and $\sigma$ should be thought of as parameters.

An analogous distribution law is given by Laplace's approximate formula for the problem of repeated trials. In the theory and application of random variables, the normal distribution is often used by extending the law derived for a random variable of the defined type (number of occurrences) to arbitrary random variables. Lyapunov's theorem states the conditions of applicability of a normal distribution. It is suitable in those cases in which the random variable being studied can be treated as the sum of a large number of random variables. The essential point is that the random variables being summed may obey any law of distribution.

S. N. Bernstein has given a supplementary condition for the numbers $\gamma_k$ to exist and for the ratio of the sum of these numbers to the given power of $\sigma$ to approach 0, namely that none of the individual random variables should differ too much from the others in magnitude or variance. Attempts have been made to formulate a distribution law for the sum of uniformly distributed random variables. These attempts have shown that even when the number of variables is as small as twenty, a good approximation to the exact normal law is obtained.

## 56. AN APPROXIMATE DERIVATION OF THE NORMAL LAW

The proof of Lyapunov's theorem is too long to include in the present volume. Therefore, we shall consider a simplified derivation of the normal law proposed by Pearson. We introduce the following conditions: (1) The values of the random variable $X$ are deviations from some constant value $a$; (2) Each of the individual deviations is the result of a random action of a large number of causes, each of which effects a small random deviation; (3) These causes act independently of each other.

These conditions were first introduced in the theory of measurement errors, where the measured quantity has a definite numerical value and the different numbers that we obtain on taking measurements are the result of various random causes (a chance gust of wind, the jolt resulting from the slamming of a door far from the laboratory, etc.). The difference between the observed and the (unknown) actual value is a random error of observation.

When we speak of the distribution of a quantity such as the inclination of a set of asteroids, we may speak of the deviation from some constant value, but these deviations should not be called errors. In this case, the second of the conditions listed is less justified since the deviation of an individual value from some constant level is the result of the action not only of random causes but also of systematic ones (for example, disturbances from large planets in the case of the asteroids). Therefore, the second condition should, in this case, be considered only as a simplification in setting up a theoretical scheme.

We can give a clearer formulation of these conditions as follows:

(1) The deviation $U$ of the variable $X$ from the value $a$ is caused by the action of $n$ causes, each of which brings about a deviation $+\varepsilon$ or $-\varepsilon$ that is small in absolute value.

(2) Elementary deviations that have equal absolute values are equally likely:

$$P(\varepsilon) = P(-\varepsilon) = \frac{1}{2};$$

(3) The causes of the elementary deviations are mutually independent; that is, the probability that one of these causes will effect a deviation of $+\varepsilon$ (or $-\varepsilon$) does not depend on the deviations resulting from the remaining causes.

We note that assumptions (2) and (3) impose quite stringent restrictions on the set-up. Furthermore, they may be considered as sufficiently close to the actual conditions in the theory of errors. On the other hand, the restriction that the absolute value of the deviation be the same for all the variables is not essential, but is introduced only to simplify subsequent calculations.

Starting with these three assumptions, let us now find the probability density of the variable $U$. Suppose that $k$ causes have brought about positive deviations $\varepsilon$ and that the remaining $n-k$ causes have brought about negative deviations. Then, the value of the net deviation $U$, which we shall denote by $u_k$, will be

$$u_k = k\varepsilon + (n-k)(-\varepsilon) = (2k-n)\varepsilon.$$

The probability of such a value is calculated from formula (8.1) for the problem of repeated trials, since the effect of each of the causes can be compared to a trial in which the event (deviation $+\varepsilon$) may or may not occur. By the second assumption, $p = q = 1/2$. Therefore,

$$P_{k,n} = \frac{n!}{k!\,(n-k)!} \cdot \left(\frac{1}{2}\right)^n.$$

Since our problem consists in establishing the relationship between the variable $U$ and the probability density, we shall assume now that not $k$ but $k+1$ causes yielded values of $+\varepsilon$. Then,

$$u_{k+1}=(2k+2-n)\,\varepsilon,\quad P_{k+1,\,n}=\frac{n!}{(k+1)!\,(n-k-1)!}\left(\frac{1}{2}\right)^n.$$

Let us denote by $\Delta u$ the length of the interval $(u_k, u_{k+1})$ and let us denote its center by $u$. From the preceding formulas,

$$\Delta u = u_{k+1}-u_k=2\varepsilon,$$

$$u=\frac{u_{k+1}+u_k}{2}=(2k-n+1)\,\varepsilon.$$

Let us assume that the probability that the random variable $U$ will take values in the interval $(u_k, u_{k+1})$ is approximately equal to the average of $P_{k,\,n}$ and $P_{k+1,\,n}$. Then, if we denote by $y$ the probability density of the variable $U$ relative to the center $u$ of the interval in question, we obtain

$$y=\frac{P}{\Delta u},$$

where

$$P=\frac{P_{k,\,n}+P_{k+1,\,n}}{2},\qquad \Delta u=u_{k+1}-u_k.$$

Therefore,

$$\Delta y=\frac{\Delta P}{\Delta u},$$

where

$$\Delta P=P_{k+1,\,n}-P_{k,\,n},$$

and, consequently,

$$\frac{\Delta y}{y}=\frac{\Delta P}{P}.$$

If we calculate $\Delta P$ and $P$, we obtain

$$\Delta P=\left(\frac{1}{2}\right)^n\frac{(n-2k-1)!\,n!}{(k+1)!\,(n-1)!},$$

$$P=\left(\frac{1}{2}\right)^n\frac{(n+1)!\,n!}{(k+1)!\,(n-k)!}.$$

Therefore,

$$\frac{\Delta y}{y}=\frac{2\,(n-2k-1)}{n+1}=\frac{(n-2k-1)\,\varepsilon\cdot 2\varepsilon}{(n+1)^2\,\varepsilon^2}.$$

To obtain the probability density of $y$, we must find the relationship between $y$ and $u$. Since $(n-2k-1)\,\varepsilon=-u$, and $2\varepsilon=\Delta u$,

$$\frac{\Delta y}{y}=-\frac{u\,\Delta u}{(n+1)\,\varepsilon^2}.$$

For finite $n$, this equation gives an approximate relationship between the variable $U$, its probability density $y$, and their increments. Let us now let $n$ approach $\infty$. Then, it is natural to assume that $\varepsilon$ approaches 0, since otherwise infinitely large deviations would be possible without their probabilities being infinitesimally small.

Let us assume also that $(n+1)\varepsilon^2$ approaches a finite positive limit $\sigma^2$. When we take the limit, we obtain the differential equation of the probability density curve

$$\frac{dy}{y}=\frac{-u\,du}{\sigma^2}.$$

Integration of this equation yields

$$y=Ce^{-\frac{u^2}{2\sigma^2}},$$

where $C$ is an arbitrary constant and $\sigma$ is a parameter. The probability density must satisfy the normalization condition. It follows from the equation that we have just obtained that $u$ is unbounded. Therefore, we have

$$\int_{-\infty}^{\infty} Ce^{-\frac{u^2}{2\sigma^2}}du=1.$$

This equation makes possible the expression of $C$ in terms of $\sigma$. If we make the substitution $u/\sigma=t$, we obtain

$$C\sigma\int_{-\infty}^{\infty} e^{-\frac{t^2}{2}}dt=1.$$

It can be shown that

$$\int_{-\infty}^{\infty} e^{-\frac{t^2}{2}}dt=\sqrt{2\pi},$$

so that

$$C=\frac{1}{\sigma\sqrt{2\pi}}.$$

Finally, the probability density of a normal distribution is written as

$$y=\frac{1}{\sigma\sqrt{2\pi}}e^{-\frac{u^2}{2\sigma^2}} \tag{11.22}$$

In this equation, $u$ is the deviation of the value of the random variable from some constant number $a$. If, instead of the deviation, we introduce the value of the variable $x$ (note that $(x=u+a)$, ) in this equation, we obtain the probability density of a normal distribution in the general form:

$$y=\frac{1}{\sigma\sqrt{2\pi}}e^{-\frac{(x-a)^2}{2\sigma^2}} \tag{11.23}$$

## 57. PARAMETERS OF THE NORMAL LAW. GAUSS' CURVE

To clarify the meaning of the parameters $a$ and $\sigma$ in the normal law, let us find the expectation and the variance of a random variable obeying that law.

From formula (11.10), we obtain

$$E(X)=\int_{-\infty}^{+\infty}\frac{x}{\sigma\sqrt{2\pi}}e^{-\frac{(x-a)^2}{2\sigma^2}}dx.$$

Let us make the change of variable

$$\frac{x-a}{\sigma}=t, \quad dx=\sigma\,dt.$$

We then obtain

$$E(X)=\int_{-\infty}^{+\infty}\frac{\sigma t}{\sqrt{2\pi}}e^{-\frac{t^2}{2}}dt+a\int_{-\infty}^{\infty}\frac{1}{\sqrt{2\pi}}e^{-\frac{t^2}{2}}dt.$$

In the first term, the integrand is an odd function of the argument $t$. The integral of such a function over the interval $(-\infty, +\infty)$ is equal to 0. The integral in the second term expresses the normalization condition for a normal law of the particular form ($a=0$, $\sigma=1$). Therefore, this integral is equal to unity. Consequently,

$$E(X)=\bar{x}=a.$$

Thus, the parameter $a$ is the average value of the random variable $X$..

Let us now find the variance of a normally distributed variable. From formula (11.16), we have

$$\operatorname{var} X=\int_{-\infty}^{\infty}\frac{(x-a)^2}{\sigma\sqrt{2\pi}}e^{-\frac{(x-a)^2}{2\sigma^2}}dx.$$

If we again replace $x$ with $x-a/\sigma=t$, we obtain

$$\operatorname{var} X=\sigma^2\int_{-\infty}^{\infty}\frac{t^2}{\sqrt{2\pi}}e^{-\frac{t^2}{2}}dt.$$

If we use the familiar formula for integration by parts

$$\int_a^b u\,dv=uv\big|_a^b-\int_a^b v\,du$$

setting

$$u=\frac{t}{\sqrt{2\pi}}, \quad dv=te^{-\frac{t^2}{2}}dt,$$

so that

$$v = -e^{-\frac{t^2}{2}}.$$

we obtain

$$\operatorname{var} X = -\sigma^2 \frac{te^{-\frac{t^2}{2}}}{\sqrt{2\pi}}\Bigg|_{-\infty}^{\infty} + \sigma^2 \int_{-\infty}^{\infty} \frac{1}{\sqrt{2\pi}} e^{-\frac{t^2}{2}} dt.$$

The first term is equal to 0 because the exponential function $e^{-\frac{t^2}{2}}$ decreases with increase in $t$ more rapidly than any power of $t$ increases; in particular, it decreases more rapidly than $t$ itself increases. Therefore,

$$\operatorname{var} X = \sigma^2, \tag{11.24}$$

that is, the parameter $\sigma$ in a normal law of distribution is the mean square deviation. If we set $a = \bar{x}$ in the formula for the normal law, we can write it in the form

$$y = \frac{1}{\sigma\sqrt{2\pi}} e^{-\frac{(x-\bar{x})^2}{2\sigma^2}}. \tag{11.25}$$

If the average value $\bar{x}$ is equal to 0 and the mean square deviation $\sigma$ is unity, we have the so-called *standard normal law* of distribution:

$$w = \frac{1}{\sqrt{2\pi}} e^{-\frac{z^2}{2}} \tag{11.26}$$

Tables (cf. Table I at the end of the book) have been compiled for the probability density $w$ of such a standard law. We note that equation (11.25) can be reduced to the standard form (11.26) by means of the substitution

$$\left.\begin{aligned} w &= \sigma y, \\ z &= \frac{x-\bar{x}}{\sigma}. \end{aligned}\right\} \tag{11.27}$$

Let us investigate the shape of the curve of a normal distribution (11.25), frequently known as *Gauss' curve.*

The following are the more elementary results of an analysis of this curve.

The entire curve is located on one side of the $x$-axis (which is its asymptote) and is symmetric about the center of distribution $x = \bar{x}$. The curve has a maximum equal to $\frac{1}{\sigma\sqrt{2\pi}}$ at the center of the distribution $x = \bar{x}$ and it has two inflection points at $x = \bar{x} \pm \sigma$.

From formulas (11.27) Gauss' curve (11.25) with arbitrary $\sigma$ can be obtained from the standard curve (11.26) corresponding to

$\sigma = 1$ and $x = 0$ by dividing the ordinates by $\sigma$, decreasing the abscissas by an amount $\bar{x}$, and then multiplying them by $\sigma$. Thus, for $\sigma > 1$, we obtain a curve that is more extended along the horizontal axis with a lower maximum ordinate than is the case with a standard curve. For $\sigma < 1$, the maximum ordinate is greater than for $\sigma = 1$. Figure 8 shows Gauss' curves for $\sigma = 1/2$, $\sigma = 1$, and $\sigma = 2$ (the scale being the same for all three curves).

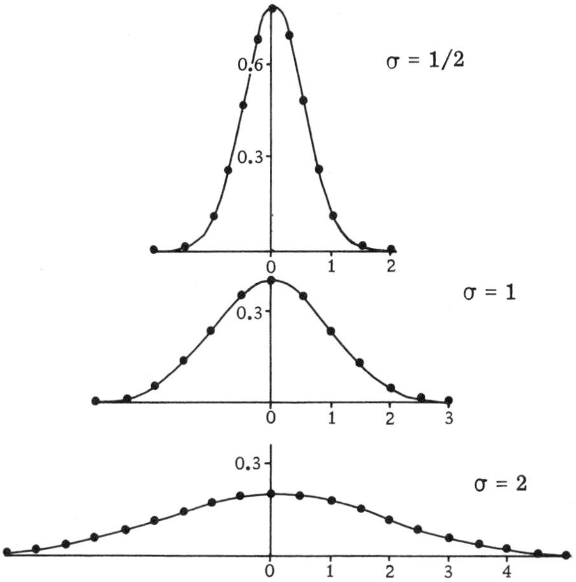


Fig. 8. Curves of a normal distribution for various values of the variance $\sigma^2$.

## 58. A FUNCTION OF A NORMAL DISTRIBUTION. CALCULATION OF PROBABILITIES

As was noted at the beginning of the preceding chapter, the basic problem in the study of a continuous random variable is the calculation of the probability

$$P(\alpha < X < \beta).$$

This problem is usually solved by means of formula (11.3) in connection with the distribution function $F(x)$.

Let us find this function for a normal law. Since $F(x)$ is a primitive with respect to the probability density $p(x)$ and $F(-\infty) = 0$,

$$F(x) = \int_{-\infty}^{x} p(t)\,dt = \frac{1}{\sigma\sqrt{2\pi}} \int_{-\infty}^{x} e^{-\frac{(t-\bar{x})^2}{2\sigma^2}}\,dt. \tag{11.28}$$

Because of the symmetry of the normal law about the center of distribution, $F(\bar{x}) = 1/2$. Therefore,

$$F(x) = \frac{1}{2} + \frac{1}{\sigma\sqrt{2\pi}} \int_{\bar{x}}^{x} e^{-\frac{(t-\bar{x})^2}{2\sigma^2}}\, dt.$$

If, for a standard normal law, we set $\bar{x} = 0$, $\sigma = 1$, and $x = z$, we have

$$F(z) = \frac{1}{2} + \frac{1}{\sqrt{2\pi}} \int_{0}^{z} e^{-\frac{t^2}{2}}\, dt. \tag{11.29}$$

The second term on the right is usually denoted by $\Phi(z)$ and is called the *probability integral.* In this notation,

$$F(z) = \frac{1}{2} + \Phi(z).$$

If in the expression for $F(x)$, we make the change of variable $t - \bar{x} / \sigma = z$, we get

$$F(x) = \frac{1}{2} + \Phi\left(\frac{x - \bar{x}}{\sigma}\right). \tag{11.30}$$

Thus, by means of the probability integral $\Phi(z)$, it is easy to find the distribution function for a normal law with given values of $\bar{x}$ and $\sigma$. As was mentioned in Section 48, detailed tables (cf. Table III at the end of the book) have been compiled for the function $\Phi(z)$.*

According to formulas (11.3) and (11.30), the probability that the random variable will take some value in the interval $(\alpha, \beta)$ is expressed by the formula

$$P(\alpha < X < \beta) = \Phi\left(\frac{\beta - \bar{x}}{\sigma}\right) - \Phi\left(\frac{\alpha - \bar{x}}{\sigma}\right). \tag{11.31}$$

If, instead of the random variable $X$, we consider its deviation from its mean value $U = X - \bar{x}$, this formula takes the form

$$P(A < U < B) = \Phi\left(\frac{B}{\sigma}\right) - \Phi\left(\frac{A}{\sigma}\right), \tag{11.32}$$

*Sometimes, we are given tables either of $2\Phi(z)$ or

$$\int_{0}^{z} \frac{1}{\sqrt{\pi}} e^{-t^2}\, dt$$

instead of the function $\Phi(z)$. By a proper substitution, one of these functions can easily be converted into the other.

where $A=\alpha-\bar{x}$ and $B=\beta-\bar{x}$ are the end points of the interval containing those values of the variable $U$ for which the probability is being sought.

We can put formula (11.32) in a simpler form if the interval $(A, B)$ is symmetric about the center of distribution. As was shown in Section 44, the function $\Phi(z)$ is an odd function. Therefore, it follows from (11.32) that when $B>0$ and $A=-B$,

$$P(|U|<B)=2\Phi\left(\frac{B}{\sigma}\right). \quad (11.33)$$

Let us now see what the probabilities are for various deviations from the theoretical mean value in the case of a random variable that obeys a normal law.

By use of formula (11.33) we calculate the probability that $U$ will not exceed $\sigma$ in absolute value:

$$P(|U|<\sigma)=2\Phi(1).$$

According to the tables, $\Phi(1)=$ 0.3413. This means that

$$P(|U|<\sigma)=0.6826\approx\frac{2}{3}. \quad (11.34)$$

If we assume (in the case of a large number of observations) that the probability will differ only slightly from the relative frequency, we may say that if the distribution is close to the normal distribution the absolute value of the deviation will in two thirds of all cases be no greater than $\sigma$. This assertion is often called the *sigma rule*. In the theory of errors, $\sigma$ is called the *mean error*, and in statistics it is called the *mean square deviation* or simply the *mean deviation*. The name *standard deviation* is also used for $\sigma$.

Let us now derive the "three-sigma" rule. We calculate the probability of $U$ not exceeding $3\sigma$ in absolute value:

$$P(|U|<3\sigma)=2\Phi(3)=0.9973. \quad (11.35)$$

From this, we have the *3-sigma rule*: if the distribution is close to a normal distribution, it is very unlikely that the deviation will exceed $3\sigma$ in absolute value.

In a similiar manner, we may show that

$$P(|U|<4\sigma)=0.9994; \qquad P(|U|<2\sigma)\approx 0.95.$$

The probable deviation is defined as that number $r$ such that the probability of $U$ not exceeding r in absolute value is equal to 1/2. By definition,

$$P(|U|<r)=0.5,$$

N

but,

$$P(|U|<r)=2\Phi\left(\frac{r}{\sigma}\right),$$

and therefore, $\Phi(r/\sigma) = 0.25$.

From the tables, we obtain

$$\frac{r}{\sigma}=0.6745 \quad \text{or} \quad r\approx\frac{2}{3}\sigma.$$

If we replace the probability with the relative frequency, we may say that in approximately half of all cases $|U|$ will be less than the probable deviation if the number of observations is great. It should be emphasized again that conclusions of this nature are derived for *theoretical* distributions. They can be carried over to observed distributions only when the observed distribution differs only slightly from the normal distribution.

## 59. THE MOMENTS OF A NORMAL DISTRIBUTION

If we write the equation of the normal distribution in the form (11.22), we obtain the initial first-order moment

$$\nu_1=\int_{-\infty}^{+\infty}\frac{x}{\sigma\sqrt{2\pi}}e^{-\frac{(x-a)^2}{2\sigma^2}}dx.$$

It was shown in Section 57 that

$$\nu_1=a=\bar{x}. \tag{11.36}$$

We may say that the normal distribution written in the form (11.25) is the distribution of the deviations of the random variable from its theoretical mean value. Therefore, the central moments of the normal distribution can be obtained by using the following form of the probability density:

$$p(u)=\frac{1}{\sigma\sqrt{2\pi}}e^{-\frac{u^2}{2\sigma^2}}.$$

From this, we find

$$\mu_2=\frac{1}{\sigma\sqrt{2\pi}}\int_{-\infty}^{\infty}u^2e^{-\frac{u^2}{2\sigma^2}}du,$$

but $\mu_2$ is the variance and it was shown in Section 51 that the variance is equal to $\sigma^2$. Consequently,

$$\mu_2=\sigma^2. \tag{11.37}$$

Furthermore, we have

$$\mu_3=\frac{1}{\sigma\sqrt{2\pi}}\int_{-\infty}^{\infty}u^3e^{-\frac{u^2}{2\sigma^2}}du=0, \tag{11.38}$$

because the integrand is an odd function of $u$. If we integrate by parts, we can easily show that

$$\mu_4 = 3\sigma^4 = 3\mu_2^2. \tag{11.39}$$

The expressions for $\mu_3$ and $\mu_4$ can be used as a preliminary criterion in determining whether the observed distribution may be considered as an approximately normal distribution. The answer is negative if $\mu_3$ differs greatly from 0 and/or $\mu_4$ differs greatly from $3\sigma^4$.*

We can easily obtain a general expression for an arbitrary-order central moment of a normal distribution. A moment of arbitrary odd order is equal to 0 since the integrand in the expression

$$\mu_{2k+1} = \frac{1}{\sigma\sqrt{2\pi}} \int_{-\infty}^{\infty} u^{2k+1} e^{-\frac{u^2}{2}} du \tag{11.40}$$

is an odd function of $u$ and the integral is taken from $-\infty$ to $+\infty$. For an arbitrary even-order moment, we can derive a recursion formula. By definition,

$$\mu_{2k} = \frac{1}{\sqrt{2\pi}} \int_{-\infty}^{\infty} u^{2k} \frac{1}{\sigma} e^{-\frac{u^2}{2\sigma^2}} du = \frac{\sigma}{\sqrt{2\pi}} \int_{-\infty}^{\infty} u^{2k-1} \frac{u}{\sigma^2} e^{-\frac{u^2}{2\sigma^2}} du.$$

If we use the formula for integrating by parts

$$\int_a^b w\, dv = wv \Big|_a^b - \int_a^b v\, dw,$$

setting

$$w = u^{2k-1}, \qquad dv = \frac{u}{\sigma^2} e^{-\frac{u^2}{2\sigma^2}} du$$

so that

$$v = -e^{-\frac{u^2}{2\sigma^2}}, \qquad dw = (2k-1)\, u^{2k-2}\, du$$

we obtain

$$\mu_{2k} = -\frac{1}{\sqrt{2\pi}} u^{2k-1} e^{-\frac{u^2}{2\sigma^2}} \Big|_{-\infty}^{\infty} + \frac{\sigma}{\sqrt{2\pi}} \int_{-\infty}^{\infty} (2k-1)\, u^{2k-2} e^{-\frac{u^2}{2\sigma^2}} du.$$

The first term vanishes for $u = -\infty$ and $u = +\infty$, which is easy to show by applying l'Hospital's rule $k$ times. The second term can be transformed as follows:

$$\frac{\sigma}{\sqrt{2\pi}} \int_{-\infty}^{\infty} (2k-1)\, u^{2k-2} e^{-\frac{u^2}{2\sigma^2}} du =$$

$$= (2k-1)\,\sigma^2 \frac{1}{\sigma\sqrt{2\pi}} \int_{-\infty}^{\infty} u^{2k-2} e^{-\frac{u^2}{2\sigma^2}} du = (2k-1)\,\sigma^2 \mu_{2k-2}.$$

Thus,

$$\mu_{2k} = (2k-1)\,\sigma^2 \mu_{2k-2} = (2k-1)(2k-3)\,\sigma^4 \mu_{2k-4} = \ldots;$$

---

*A method of calculating the moments of an observed distribution will be taken up in Part V.

therefore,

$$\mu_{2k} = (2k-1)(2k-3)\ldots 3\cdot 1\cdot(\sigma^2)^k\mu_0, \tag{11.41}$$

or

$$\mu_{2k} = 1\cdot 3\cdot 5\ldots(2k-3)(2k-1)\,\sigma^{2k}, \tag{11.42}$$

since $\mu_0 = 1$. In particular for $k = 2, 3, 4$,

$$\left.\begin{aligned} \mu_4 &= 1\cdot 3\mu_2^2 = 3\sigma^4; \\ \mu_6 &= 1\cdot 3\cdot 5\mu_2^3 = 15\sigma^6, \\ \mu_8 &= 1\cdot 3\cdot 5\cdot 7\mu_2^4 = 105\sigma^8. \end{aligned}\right\} \tag{11.43}$$

## 60. DISTRIBUTIONS OTHER THAN THE NORMAL

If values of a random variable are obtained under conditions satisfying the Lyapunov theorem, the normal law must satisfactorily represent the results of observations of the random variable. The question of comparing the theoretical distribution with the empirical will be examined in detail in Part V of this book. Here, we mention one of the methods of comparison: (a) Numerical values of the parameters of the chosen theoretical law of distribution are selected; (b) the values of the theoretical distribution function are determined for a number of chosen values of the variable; (c) the corresponding empirical probabilities (that is, the ratios of the numbers of observed values not exceeding the values chosen in (b) to the number of all observations) are calculated. Comparison of the theoretical and empirical probabilities makes possible a determination of the degree of agreement of the theory with observations.

The study of a large number of empirical distributions of different variables has shown that the normal law does not always satisfactorily represent observations. In addition to variables that are not sufficiently close to the normal law, there are variables that, because of their physical properties, cannot obey a normal law.

For example, let us consider the distribution of stellar parallaxes. For two obvious reasons, this distribution cannot obey a normal law. In the first place, the normal law is defined for the entire real axis, that is, from $-\infty$ to $+\infty$, whereas parallax is a positive quantity, and, consequently, the curve of distribution must be bounded on the left. Since, in the case of stars, there can in practice be no large parallaxes, the distribution curve is also bounded on the right. In the second place, the number of stars increases with decrease in parallax, so that the maximum probability density will occur with a parallax value equal to 0. Since stars with large parallax are rare, the curve must approach the $x$-axis asymptotically with increase in parallax. The result is that the distribution curve must have a shape somewhat like the letter $J$; that is, it must differ quite sharply from a Gaussian curve.

A second example is the distribution of absolute values of velocities of the members of some set of moving bodies, for example, of asteroids. Again, this quantity assumes only nonnegative values, and therefore, the distribution curve is bounded on the left. Since infinite velocities cannot have physical meaning, the curve must also be bounded on the right, although it is considerably more difficult in this case to state where the bound lies.

From what has been said, it follows that both in solving the basic problem and in describing random variables, we may not confine ourselves just to a normal law. We must construct other theoretical distributions by using the observed probability patterns or other theoretical considerations. We shall briefly consider certain kinds of distribution curves that arise in practice.

## 1. Type-A Charlier Curve.

The form of a function representing a probability distribution in the case in which the normal law is not suitable can be chosen from the following considerations. If the normal law

$$p(x) = \frac{1}{\sigma\sqrt{2\pi}} e^{-\frac{(x-\bar{x})^2}{2\sigma^2}}$$

is not satisfactory, the probability density can be written in the form

$$\varphi(x) = p(x)\,\Pi(x),$$

where $\Pi(x)$ is a polynomial of degree no higher than four. Charlier called it the *perturbational polynomial*.* Let us replace the values of $x$ with their deviations $u$ from the mean value $\bar{x}$. Then,

$$\varphi(u) = p(u)\,\Pi(u).$$

To determine the five coefficients of a fourth-degree polynomial, we may obtain five equations by determining the moments from zeroth to fourth order inclusively.

In the general case, this system has one solution. The coefficients of the polynomial $\Pi(x)$ are expressed in terms of the central moments of order 2, 3, and 4. Instead of the third- and fourth-order moments, we introduce the *asymmetry* $A$ and the *excess* $E$, defined by

$$A = \frac{\mu_3}{\sigma^3}, \qquad (11.44)$$

*The terminology is borrowed from celestial mechanics. It means that the polynomial $\Pi(x)$ changes $p(x)$ in such a way that a probability density will be obtained that represents the observations more satisfactorily.

$$E = \frac{\mu_4}{\sigma^4} - 3. \tag{11.45}$$

It follows from Section 59 that, for a normal law, $A = E = 0$. Therefore, we may assume that $A$ and $E$ characterize the deviation of the distribution from the normal. The coefficients $a_0$, $a_1$, $a_2$, $a_3$, and $a_4$ of the polynomial $\Pi(u)$ can be expressed in terms of $A$, $E$, and $\sigma$:

$$a_0 = 1 + \frac{1}{8}E, \quad a_1 = \frac{1}{2}\frac{A}{\sigma}, \quad a_2 = -\frac{1}{4}\frac{E}{\sigma^2},$$

$$a_3 = \frac{1}{6}\frac{A}{\sigma^3}, \quad a_4 = \frac{1}{24}\frac{E}{\sigma^4}.$$

If we choose the terms in the polynomial $P(u)$ with asymmetry and excess separately, it turns out that the coefficient of $A$ is equal to the product obtained by multiplying the third derivative of the normal density $p(x)$ by $-\sigma^3/6$ and that the coefficient of $E$ is equal to the product of the fourth derivative of $\Pi(u)$ and $\sigma^4/24$.

The probability density of Charlier's law then takes the form

$$\varphi(u) = p(u) - \frac{1}{6}A\sigma^3 p^{III}(u) + \frac{1}{24}E\sigma^4 p^{IV}(u). \tag{11.46}$$

It is clear from this equation that, for small values of $A$ and $E$, the terms containing asymmetry and excess are also small and, therefore, the main term in the expression above is the probability density of the normal distribution.

Tables are compiled for the functions $p^{III}(u)$ and $p^{IV}(u)$ for $\sigma = 1$. By means of these tables, it is easy to calculate $\varphi(u)$.

The solution of the basic problem is obtained quite simply:

$$P(\alpha < U < \beta) = \int_\alpha^\beta p(u)\,du - \frac{1}{6}A\sigma^3 \int_\alpha^\beta p^{III}(u)\,du + \frac{1}{24}E\sigma^4 \int_\alpha^\beta p^{IV}(u)\,du.$$

If we set $\sigma = 1$, that is, if we evaluate $u$ taking $\sigma = 1$, the integration becomes quite simple:

$$P(\alpha < U < \beta) = \Phi(\beta) - \Phi(\alpha) - \frac{1}{6}A[p^{II}(\beta) - p^{II}(\alpha)] + \\ + \frac{1}{24}E[p^{III}(\beta) - p^{III}(\alpha)].$$

Instead of $p^{II}(u)$, we may write $\Phi^{III}(u)$ and analogously, we may write $\Phi^{IV}(u)$ instead of $p^{III}(u)$. Tables have been compiled for the functions $\Phi^{III}(u)$ and $\Phi^{IV}(u)$.

## 2. *Pearson's Curves.*

Pearson obtained these distribution curves, whose equations he derived, from an approximative study of a more general probability-theory problem than that of repeated trials for different values of

$p$ and $q$. The simplified derivation of the normal distribution can be reduced to a special case of the more general problem. A number of authors have pointed out that Pearson's curves can be obtained by formally generalizing the same differential equation as that obtained for a Gaussian curve.

In the derivation of the normal law (see Section 56), the equation

$$\frac{dy}{y} = -\frac{u\,du}{\sigma^2}$$

contains a constant term in the denominator of the fraction on the right. We shall obtain curves of a more general form if instead of this constant, we have a function of $u$. If we assume that this function can be expanded in a Maclaurin series and if we keep only the first three terms, we obtain the differential equations for Pearson's curves:

$$\frac{dy}{y} = \frac{(x-a)\,dx}{b_0 + b_1 x + b_2 x^2}. \tag{11.47}$$

This equation contains four parameters: $a$, $b_0$, $b_1$, and $b_2$. When the equation is integrated, there will be yet another arbitrary constant, but it will be expressed in terms of these four parameters. For, from the normalization condition, the area underneath the curve must be equal to unity. This condition gives an equation for determining the arbitrary constant just as in the case of a normal distribution.

Integration of equation (11.47) gives a whole series of distribution functions (including functions with $U$-shaped and $J$-shaped curves), which can be used for making interpolations with observational data. Tables have been compiled to make the use of Pearson's curves easier. One can familiarize himself with Pearson's curves from the book *Krivye raspredeleniya i postroenie dlya nikh interpolyatsionnykh formul po sposobam Pirsona i Brunsa* (Distribution Curves and the Construction of Interpolational Formulas for them by the Methods of Pearson and Bruns) by L. K. Lakhtin, Moscow, 1922. As an example, we give the equation for a type-three Pearson curve that finds application in certain problems:

$$y = y_0 e^{-\gamma x}\left(1 + \frac{x}{l}\right)^m, \tag{11.48}$$

where

$$\gamma = \frac{2\mu_2}{\mu_3},\quad l = \mu_2\gamma,\quad m = \frac{4}{\beta_1} - 1,\quad \beta_1 = \frac{\mu_3^2}{\mu_2^3},$$

$$y_0 = \frac{\gamma^{m+1} l^m \cdot e^{-l\gamma}}{\Gamma(m+1)}.$$

Here,

$$\Gamma(m+1)=\int_0^\infty x^m e^{-x}\,dx$$

is Euler's integral of the second kind, which cannot be solved in terms of elementary functions unless $m$ is a nonnegative integer. Tables have also been compiled of this integral.

In addition to Pearson's curves, certain other distribution curves of a particular form have been constructed. However, it should be mentioned that in practice investigators prefer not to choose functions with more than four parameters. If the number of parameters were in excess of four, one would need to use calculated moments of higher than fourth order in setting up the equations for determining the parameters. Moments of high orders, as can easily be seen from the definition and the method of computing them, depend to a great extent on the "boundaries" of the distribution, which may be very unindicative of the distribution. For the same reason, only the first three terms are taken in the denominator in the differential equation of Pearson's curves.

It should be especially noted that cases are frequently encountered in which an empirical distribution curve has two maxima. For such distributions, even the mean value of the variable should not be considered as characteristic. In a number of such cases, we may assume that the statistical material represents the sum of two distributions, each of which is close to a normal distribution. In the case of such distributions, the question of decomposing them into two normal distributions has been worked out.

## 3. Maxwellian Distribution.

A Maxwellian distribution is a distribution of absolute values of velocities of molecules, point masses, or other particles that is obtained under the assumption that the components of the velocities have the same variances along each of the (rectangular) coordinate axes. It may be shown that the probability density of a Maxwellian distribution is of the form

$$p(v)=\frac{2}{\sqrt{2\pi}}\frac{v^2}{\sigma_0^3}e^{-\frac{v^2}{2\sigma_0^2}}, \tag{11.49}$$

where $v$ is the absolute value of the velocity and $\sigma_0$ is the single distribution parameter representing the mean square deviation along each of the coordinate axes. We state without proof the basic numerical characteristics of this distribution:

The mean value

$$\bar{v}=\frac{4}{\sqrt{2\pi}}\sigma_0\approx 1.596\sigma_0;\quad p(\bar{v})=\frac{16}{\pi\sqrt{2\pi}}e^{-\frac{4}{\pi}}\cdot\frac{1}{\sigma_0}\approx 0.569\cdot\frac{1}{\sigma_0};$$

the mode

$$v_m = \sigma_0 \sqrt{2} \approx 1.414\sigma_0; \qquad p(v_m) = \frac{4}{e\sqrt{2\pi}} \cdot \frac{1}{\sigma_0} \approx 0.588 \cdot \frac{1}{\sigma_0};$$

the mean square deviation

$$\sigma = \sqrt{3 - \frac{8}{\pi}}\,\sigma_0 \approx 0.674\sigma_0 \approx \frac{2}{3}\,\sigma_0;$$

the distribution function

$$F(v) = P(V < v) = 2\Phi\left(\frac{v}{\sigma_0}\right) - 2\,\frac{v}{\sigma_0}\,\Phi'\left(\frac{v}{\sigma_0}\right).$$

Values of the distribution function are given in the table

| $v$ | $F(v)$ | $v$ | $F(v)$ |
|---|---|---|---|
| 0 | 0.0000 | 2.0 | 0.7384 |
| 0.5 | 0.0309 | 2.5 | 0.9001 |
| 1.0 | 0.1986 | 3.0 | 0.9709 |
| 1.5 | 0.4779 | 3.5 | 0.9932 |
| 2.0 | 0.7384 | 4.0 | 0.9991 |

We also give the results of the computation of several probabilities:

$$P(V < v_m) = 0.427,$$
$$P(V < \bar{v}) = 0.535,$$
$$P(\bar{v} - \sigma < V < \bar{v} + \sigma) = 0.677,$$
$$P(\bar{v} - 2\sigma < V < \bar{v} + 2\sigma) = 0.995.$$

The last two probabilities differ only slightly from the analogous probabilities for a normal law. If we construct a normal distribution with center $\bar{v}$ and with mean square deviation $\sigma$, then for $\sigma_0 = 1$, the ordinate of the distribution curves will not differ by an amount greater than 0.08.

## 4. *Student's Distribution.*

A similar distribution is used for estimating the probability of deviations of sample means of a general average set that obeys a normal distribution law. V. I. Romanovskii used Student's distribution in the theory of errors for problems involving a small number of observations. The probability density in Student's distribution is of the form

$$p(t) = C(n)\left(1 + \frac{t^2}{n-1}\right)^{-\frac{n}{2}}, \qquad (11.50)$$

where $n$ is the number of objects in the sample (in particular, the number of observations). The remaining quantities are determined by the formulas

$$\bar{x} = \frac{x_1 + x_2 + \ldots + x_n}{n},$$

$$\bar{\sigma} = \sqrt{\frac{\sum_{k=1}^{n} (x_k - \bar{x})^2}{n-1}}, \quad \sigma_{\bar{x}} = \frac{\bar{\sigma}}{\sqrt{n}},$$

$$t = \frac{\bar{x} - x_0}{\sigma_{\bar{x}}},$$

Here, $C$ depends only on $n$; $x_1, x_2, \ldots, x_n$ are sample values of the variable; $x_0$ is the mean value in the entire (general) set. It is sensible to use Student's distribution when the number of observations does not exceed twenty since, for $n = 20$, the distribution varies only slightly from a normal distribution.

Chapter 12

# JOINT PROBABILITY DISTRIBUTION OF TWO CONTINUOUS RANDOM VARIABLES

## 61. THE JOINT PROBABILITY DENSITY OF TWO VARIABLES

Let us consider two continuous random variables $X$ and $Y$ together. The basic problem for us is to compute the probability that $X$ will assume a value in a given interval $(x_1, x_2)$ and $Y$ will assume a value in an interval $(y_1, y_2)$, that is, that

$$x_1 < X < x_2; \quad y_1 < Y < y_2.$$

If these events (that is satisfaction of these inequalities) are independent, the random variables are said to be *independent* and the probability that we are interested in will be the product of the probabilities of the two inequalities:

$$P\left\{\begin{matrix} x_1 < X < x_2 \\ y_1 < Y < y_2 \end{matrix}\right\} = P(x_1 < X < x_2)\, P(y_1 < Y < y_2).$$

If the probability that one of these variables will take a value in an arbitrary interval depends on the value of the other variable, these variables are said to be *correlated* (or we may say that there is a *correlation* between $X$ and $Y$). The correlation is completely determined from the point of view of probability theory if we know the law determining the probability of the simultaneous satisfaction of the above inequalities for arbitrary values of $x_1$, $x_2$, $y_1$, and $y_2$. Such a law may be either a function of the joint distribution of the two random variables or it may be the probability density. We can introduce the concept of probability density in the following manner:

Suppose that we know the probability

$$P\left\{\begin{matrix} x < X < x + \Delta x \\ y < Y < y + \Delta y \end{matrix}\right\}$$

that $X$ will assume a value in the interval from $x$ to $x+\Delta x$ and that $Y$ will simultaneously take a value from $y$ to $y+\Delta y$ (for $\Delta x > 0$ and $\Delta y > 0$). In general, this probability depends on $x$, $y$, $\Delta x$, and $\Delta y$. The number

$$\frac{P\left\{\begin{matrix} x < X < x+\Delta x \\ y < Y < y+\Delta y \end{matrix}\right\}}{\Delta x\,\Delta y} \tag{12.1}$$

may be called the *mean probability density* in the intervals $(x,\ x+\Delta x)$ and $(y,\ y+\Delta y)$. Let us find

$$\lim_{\substack{\Delta x \to 0 \\ \Delta y \to 0}} \frac{P\left\{\begin{matrix} x < X < x+\Delta x \\ y < Y < y+\Delta y \end{matrix}\right\}}{\Delta x\,\Delta y}. \tag{12.2}$$

If this limit exists, it will, in general, be a function of $x$ and $y$. We denote it by $f(x,\ y)$ and call it the *joint probability density* of two random variables.* From the definition, we have the approximate equality:

$$P\left\{\begin{matrix} x < X < x+\Delta x \\ y < Y < y+\Delta y \end{matrix}\right\} = f(x,\ y)\,\Delta x\,\Delta y, \tag{12.3}$$

if $\Delta x$ and $\Delta y$ are sufficiently small.

If the probability density of a set of two random variables is given, the probability that they will take values in the intervals from $x_1$ to $x_2$ and from $y_1$ to $y_2$ is determined from the obvious exact formula representing a generalization of the analogous formula for the one-dimensional problem:

$$P\left\{\begin{matrix} x_1 < X < x_2 \\ y_1 < Y < y_2 \end{matrix}\right\} = \int_{y_1}^{y_2}\int_{x_1}^{x_2} f(x,\ y)\,dx\,dy. \tag{12.4}$$

We might pose the more general problem of the probability that the variables will take values in some two-dimensional region $S$. This problem is solved by the formula

$$P\left\{\begin{matrix} X \\ Y \end{matrix}(S)\right\} = \iint_S f(x,\ y)\,dx\,dy. \tag{12.5}$$

Suppose that all combinations of values of the random variables $X$ and $Y$ are contained in a two-dimensional region $\Sigma$. Since our variables will certainly take some value or other in this region $\Sigma$, we have, from the last formula,

$$\iint_\Sigma f(x,\ y)\,dx\,dy = 1. \tag{12.6}$$

*This function is also called the *differential distribution function.*

This formula expresses the basic property of a two-dimensional probability density, which, in analogy with the corresponding property in the case of the one-dimensional problem, we may call the condition of normalization of probability density.

It follows from the definition of probability density that $f(x, y) = 0$ outside the region $\Sigma$.. Therefore, the condition of normalization can always be written in the form

$$\int_{-\infty}^{+\infty}\int_{-\infty}^{+\infty} f(x, y)\,dx\,dy = 1. \tag{12.7}$$

We can determine the theoretical mean value (the expectation) for each of the variables $X$ and $Y$ from the following formulas:

$$\bar{x} = E(X) = \int_{-\infty}^{+\infty}\int_{-\infty}^{+\infty} xf(x, y)\,dx\,dy, \tag{12.8}$$

$$\bar{y} = E(Y) = \int_{-\infty}^{+\infty}\int_{-\infty}^{+\infty} yf(x, y)\,dx\,dy. \tag{12.9}$$

The point with coordinates $(\bar{x}, \bar{y})$ is called the *center of distribution*. A generalization of these concepts is the concept of the expectation of the function $\Psi(X, Y)$ of the variables in question:

$$E[\Psi(X, Y)] = \int_{-\infty}^{+\infty}\int_{-\infty}^{+\infty} \Psi(X, Y) f(x, y)\,dx\,dy. \tag{12.10}$$

The reader can independently define the initial and central moments of various orders for a set of two variables.

## 62. CONDITIONAL PROBABILITY DENSITY

In this section, we shall study the relationship between the joint probability density $f(x, y)$ of the two variables $X$ and $Y$ and the probability densities $f_1(x)$ and $f_2(y)$ of the two individual variables.

This relationship is found most simply for independent variables. For if $X$ and $Y$ are independent, then, for arbitrary $\Delta x > 0$ and $\Delta y > 0$,

$$P\begin{Bmatrix} x < X < x + \Delta x \\ y < Y < y + \Delta y \end{Bmatrix} = P(x < X < x + \Delta x)\,P(y < Y < y + \Delta y).$$

If we divide this equation by the product $\Delta x\,\Delta y$ and take the limit as $\Delta x$ and $\Delta y$ approach 0, we obtain the joint probability density of $X$ and $Y$ on the left side and the product of the individual probability densities of the variables $X$ and $Y$ on the right:

$$f(x, y) = f_1(x) f_2(y). \tag{12.11}$$

Let us turn now to two *correlated* variables. From the theorem on multiplication of probabilities, we have the exact equations

$$P\left\{\begin{matrix} x < X < x+\Delta x \\ y < Y < y+\Delta y \end{matrix}\right\} =$$
$$= P(x < X < x+\Delta x)\, P(y < Y < y+\Delta y \mid x < X < x+\Delta x),$$

in which the second factor on the right is the conditional probability that the variable $Y$ will take a value in the interval from $y$ to $y+\Delta y$, if it is known that the variable $X$ takes a value from $x$ to $x+\Delta x$. If we divide both sides of this equation by $\Delta x\, \Delta y$ and take the limit as $\Delta x$ and $\Delta y$ approach 0, the left side will give the joint probability density $f(x, y)$ of the two variables $X$ and $Y$. The first factor on the right, when divided by $\Delta x$, will, in the limit, give the probability density $f_1(x)$ of the variable $X$. The second factor on the right, when divided by $\Delta y$ will give a function of $y$ containing $x$ as a parameter and not containing $\Delta x$ or $\Delta y$. We denote this function by $\varphi_2(y \mid x)$ and call it the *conditional probability density* of the variable $Y$ for a given value of $x$. This conditional probability is formally defined by the equation

$$\varphi_2(y \mid x) = \lim_{\Delta x \to 0,\ \Delta y \to 0} \frac{P(y < Y < y+\Delta y \mid x < X < x+\Delta x)}{\Delta y}.$$

If we take the limit in the expression for the probability, we get the equation

$$f(x, y) = f_1(x) \cdot \varphi_2(y \mid x). \tag{12.12}$$

In an analogous fashion, we obtain the equation

$$f(x, y) = f_2(y) \cdot \varphi_1(x \mid y), \tag{12.13}$$

in which $\varphi_1(x \mid y)$ is the conditional probability density of the random variable $X$ given that $Y$ takes the value $y$. This function is determined by the formula

$$\varphi_1(x \mid y) = \lim_{\Delta x \to 0,\ \Delta y \to 0} \frac{P(x < X < x+\Delta x \mid y < Y < y+\Delta y)}{\Delta x}.$$

From these relationships between the conditional and unconditional probability densities it follows that only three of the five can be given to some degree arbitrarily. The other two can be calculated from the formulas that we have obtained. Also, our choice is limited by the normalization conditions of the five probability densities:

$$\int_{-\infty}^{\infty}\int_{-\infty}^{\infty} f(x, y)\, dx\, dy = 1, \qquad \int_{-\infty}^{\infty} f_1(x)\, dx = 1; \qquad \int_{-\infty}^{\infty} f_2(y)\, dy = 1;$$

$$\int_{-\infty}^{\infty} \varphi_1(x \mid y)\, dx = 1, \qquad \int_{-\infty}^{\infty} \varphi_2(y \mid x)\, dy = 1.$$

Equations (12.12) and (12.13) make it possible to obtain a simple differential relationship between the two conditional probability densities. From these equations, we have

$$f_1(x)\varphi_2(y \mid x) = f_2(y)\varphi_1(x \mid y). \tag{12.14}$$

If we take the logarithms of both sides of this equation, we obtain

$$\ln f_1(x) + \ln \varphi_2(y \mid x) = \ln f_2(y) + \ln \varphi_1(x \mid y).$$

Let us differentiate this equation once with respect to $x$ and once with respect to $y$. The derivatives of the first terms on each side of this equation are equal to 0 and we have the desired relationship:

$$\frac{\partial^2 [\ln \varphi_1(x \mid y)]}{\partial x\, \partial y} = \frac{\partial^2 [\ln \varphi_2(y \mid x)]}{\partial x\, \partial y}. \tag{12.15}$$

It follows from equations (12.12) and (12.13) that the joint probability density of two random variables is a function in which the probability density of each of the individual variables occurs as a separate factor. Consequently, we can write $f(x, y)$ in the following form:

$$f(x, y) = f_1(x) f_2(y) \varphi(x, y). \tag{12.16}$$

It follows from (12.11) and (12.16) that the function $\varphi(x, y)$ is identically equal to unity in the case of independent variables. It is not difficult to show that the converse is also true. If the variables $X$ and $Y$ are mutually independent, then, for arbitrary values of $x_1$, $x_2$, $y_1$, and $y_2$, we may write for a rectangular region:

$$P\left\{\begin{matrix} x_1 < X < x_2 \\ y_1 < Y < y_2 \end{matrix}\right\} = \int_{y_1}^{y_2}\int_{x_1}^{x_2} f_1(x) f_2(y)\, dx\, dy = \int_{y_1}^{y_2} f_2(y)\, dy \int_{x_1}^{x_2} f_1(x)\, dx, \tag{12.17}$$

or

$$P\left\{\begin{matrix} x_1 < X < x_2 \\ y_1 < Y < y_2 \end{matrix}\right\} = P(x_1 < X < x_2) \cdot P(y_1 < Y < y_2).$$

This last equation shows that our variables are independent.

Thus, the variables $X$ and $Y$ are mutually independent if and only if

$$\varphi(x, y) \equiv 1. \tag{12.18}$$

Consequently, the nature of the correlation is completely given by the function $\varphi(x, y)$.

One of the characteristics of the conditional distribution of $X$ for a given value of $Y=y$ is the *conditional expectation* (conditional mean value) given by the formula

$$m_1(y)=\int_{-\infty}^{+\infty} x\varphi_1(x \mid y)\,dx. \tag{12.19}$$

The other conditional mean value is given by the analogous formula

$$m_2(x)=\int_{-\infty}^{+\infty} y\varphi_2(y \mid x)\,dy. \tag{12.20}$$

The lines in the $xy$-plane corresponding to the equations $x=m_1(y)$ and $y=m_2(x)$ are called the *lines of regression* and their equations are called the *equations of regression*.

From the definitions of the joint mean values of $\bar{x}$ and $\bar{y}$ and the conditional mean values $m_1(y)$ and $m_2(x)$, we have the relations

$$\left.\begin{aligned} \bar{x}&=\int_{-\infty}^{+\infty} f_2(y)\,m_1(y)\,dy,\\ \bar{y}&=\int_{-\infty}^{+\infty} f_1(x)\,m_2(x)\,dx. \end{aligned}\right\} \tag{12.21}$$

## 63. THE NORMAL DISTRIBUTION OF TWO RANDOM VARIABLES

The distribution of two random variables is said to be *normal* if each of them obeys Gauss' law when the value of the other lies within an arbitrarily small interval. This definition assumes that the functions $\varphi_1(x \mid y)$ and $\varphi_2(y \mid x)$, which we called the conditional probability densities of the variables $X$ and $Y$, are densities of normal distributions. Since the quantity $y$ is a parameter for the function $\varphi_1(x \mid y)$, it is natural to assume in the general case that the mean value and the mean square deviation, which appear in the density of a normal distribution, depend on $y$. Therefore, the function $\varphi_1(x \mid y)$ must take the form

$$\varphi_1(x \mid y)=\frac{1}{\sqrt{2\pi}\,s_1(y)}\exp\left\{-\frac{[x-m_1(y)]^2}{2s_1^2(y)}\right\}. \tag{12.22}$$

Here, $m_1(y)$ is the conditional mean value (expectation) of the variable $X$ for given $y$ and $s_1(y)$ is the conditional mean square deviation of $X$. For the same reasons, we may write

$$\varphi_2(y \mid x)=\frac{1}{\sqrt{2\pi}\,s_2(x)}\exp\left\{-\frac{[y-m_2(x)]^2}{2s_2^2(x)}\right\}, \tag{12.23}$$

where $m_2$ and $s_2$ have the same meanings for the variable $Y$ as $m_1$ and $s_1$ have for $X$.

Let us use equation (12.15) to determine the dependence between the functions $s_1(y)$, $s_2(x)$, $m_1(y)$ and $m_2(x)$. This relationship will make possible the determination of the form of these functions. We introduce the notation

$$k_1(y) = \frac{1}{s_1^2(y)}, \qquad k_2(x) = \frac{1}{s_2^2(x)}. \tag{12.24}$$

Then,

$$\ln \varphi_1(x \mid y) = -\ln \sqrt{2\pi} + \ln \sqrt{k_1(y)} - \frac{1}{2} k_1(y)[x - m_1(y)]^2,$$
$$\ln \varphi_2(x \mid y) = -\ln \sqrt{2\pi} + \ln \sqrt{k_2(x)} - \frac{1}{2} k_2(x)[y - m_2(x)]^2.$$

If we differentiate once with respect to $x$ and once with respect to $y$, the first two terms on the right sides of these equations vanish. Therefore, according to (12.15),

$$xk_1'(y) - m_1'(y)\,k_1(y) - m_1(y)\,k_1'(y) = \\ = yk_2'(x) - m_2'(x)\,k_2(x) - m_2(x)\,k_2'(x). \tag{12.25}$$

We now differentiate equation (12.25) once with respect to $y$ and once with respect to $x$. Since the second and third terms on the left depend only on $y$, their derivatives with respect to $x$ are equal to 0. For the same reason, the derivatives of the second and third terms on the right are equal to 0. As a result, we have

$$k_1''(y) = k_2''(x).$$

Since $x$ and $y$ are not functionally related, this identity is possible only when

$$k_1''(y) = 2C \text{ and } k_2''(x) = 2C,$$

where $C$ is an arbitrary constant. If we twice integrate each of these equations, we obtain

$$k_1(y) = Cy^2 + d_1 y + f_1,$$
$$k_2(y) = Cx^2 + d_2 x + f_2,$$

where $d_1$, $d_2$, $f_1$, and $f_2$ are arbitrary constants resulting from the integration. The form that we have obtained for the function $k_1(y)$ is such that $k_1(y)$ approaches $\infty$ as $y$ approaches $\infty$ provided $C$ and $d_1$ are not both equal to 0. Since, by (12.24),

$$k_1(y) = \frac{1}{s_1^2(y)},$$

under these conditions $s_1(y)$ approaches 0.

o

The function $s_1(y)$ represents the mean square deviation of the normal distribution of $X$ when $Y=y$. If $s_1(y)$ is very small for large values of $y$, this means that small deviations from the mean $m_1(y)$ are extremely unlikely.

In most applications of the theory of correlation, a relationship of this nature is not of great interest since it would indicate stability (constancy almost) of the values of $X$ for large values of $Y$. The same may be said about the function $k_2(x)$. Therefore, to exclude these special forms of distributions, we set

$$C=d_1=d_2=0,$$

so that

$$k_1(y)=f_1, \quad k_2(x)=f_2.$$

Therefore,

$$k_1(y)=\frac{1}{s_1^2} \text{ and } k_2(x)=\frac{1}{s_2^2},$$

where $s_1$ and $s_2$ are now constants. If we substitute these values of $k_1$ and $k_2$ into equation (12.23), we obtain

$$\frac{m_1'(y)}{s_1^2}=\frac{m_2'(x)}{s_2^2}. \tag{12.26}$$

Since $x$ and $y$ are not functionally related, this equality is possible only if each of the functions appearing on the two sides of (12.24) is a constant, that is, only if

$$\frac{m_1'(y)}{s_1^2}=m, \quad \frac{m_2'(x)}{s_2^2}=m,$$

where $m$ is an arbitrary constant. If we integrate these two equations, we obtain

$$m_1(y)=ms_1^2y+p_1, \quad m_2(x)=ms_2^2x+p_2, \tag{12.27}$$

where $p_1$ and $p_2$ are arbitrary constants resulting from the integration. If we substitute these values of $m_1(y)$ and $m_2(x)$ into the expressions (12.22) and (12.23) for the conditional densities, we obtain

$$\varphi_1(x \mid y)=\frac{1}{s_1\sqrt{2\pi}} \exp\left\{-\frac{[x-(ms_1^2y+p_1)]^2}{2s_1^2}\right\}, \tag{12.28}$$

$$\varphi_2(y \mid x)=\frac{1}{s_2\sqrt{2\pi}} \exp\left\{-\frac{[y-(ms_2^2x+p_2)]^2}{2s_2^2}\right\}. \tag{12.29}$$

The quantity $ms_1^2y+p_1$ in equation (12.28) is the theoretical mean value of the variable $X$ corresponding to the given value of

$y$ and the quantity $ms_2^2x + p_2$ in equation (12.29) is the theoretical mean value of $Y$ corresponding to the given value of $x$. The mean square deviations $s_1$ and $s_2$ of the conditional distributions are then constants.

Thus, in the case of a normal correlation, the mean of those values of each variable which correspond to a definite value of the other variable is a linear function of that value. In other words, the lines of regression are straight. The equations corresponding to these lines are of the form

$$\left.\begin{aligned} x &= ms_1^2 y + p_1, \\ y &= ms_2^2 x + p_2. \end{aligned}\right\} \tag{12.30}$$

The coefficients $ms_1^2$ and $ms_2^2$ in these equations are called the *coefficients of regression*. Let us denote by $\bar{x}$ and $\bar{y}$ the coordinates of the point of intersection of the lines of regression. Obviously,

$$p_1 = \bar{x} - ms_1^2\bar{y},$$
$$p_2 = \bar{y} - ms_2^2\bar{x}.$$

Therefore, the conditional probability densities and the equations of regression can be written in the form

$$\varphi_1(x \mid y) = \frac{1}{s_1\sqrt{2\pi}} \exp\left\{-\frac{\left[(x-\bar{x}) - ms_1^2(y-\bar{y})\right]^2}{2s_1^2}\right\},$$
$$\varphi_2(y \mid x) = \frac{1}{s_2\sqrt{2\pi}} \exp\left\{-\frac{\left[(y-\bar{y}) - ms_2^2(x-\bar{x})\right]^2}{2s_2^2}\right\};$$
$$x - \bar{x} = ms_1^2(y - \bar{y}),$$
$$y - \bar{y} = ms_2^2(x - \bar{x}).$$

## 64. THE PROBABILITY DENSITY OF A NORMAL DISTRIBUTION

To derive a formula for the probability density of a normal distribution, we move the coordinate origin to the point of intersection $(\bar{x}, \bar{y})$ of the lines of regression.

Then, the equations of the lines of regression for the new (displaced) random variables $U$ and $V$ are of the form

$$\left.\begin{aligned} u &= ms_1^2 v, \\ v &= ms_2^2 u, \end{aligned}\right\} \tag{12.31}$$

and the conditional probability densities are written in the form

$$\left.\begin{aligned} \varphi_1(u \mid v) &= \frac{1}{s_1\sqrt{2\pi}} \exp\left\{-\frac{u^2 - 2ms_1^2uv + m^2s_1^4v^2}{2s_1^2}\right\}, \\ \varphi_2(u \mid v) &= \frac{1}{s_2\sqrt{2\pi}} \exp\left\{-\frac{v^2 - 2ms_2^2uv + m^2s_2^4u^2}{2s_2^2}\right\}. \end{aligned}\right\} \tag{12.32}$$

If we substitute these values of $\varphi_1$ and $\varphi_2$ into equation (12.14), we obtain

$$f_1(u)\frac{1}{s_2\sqrt{2\pi}}\exp\left\{-\frac{v^2}{2s_2^2}+muv-\frac{m^2s_2^2u^2}{2}\right\}=$$

$$=f_2(v)\frac{1}{s_1\sqrt{2\pi}}\exp\left\{-\frac{u^2}{2s_1^2}+muv-\frac{m^2s_1^2v^2}{2}\right\},$$

where $f_1(u)$ and $f_2(v)$ are as yet unknown probability densities of the distribution of the two individual variables.

Let us now cancel $e^{muv}$ and let us rewrite the equation so that on one side we have factors depending only on $u$ and on the other side factors depending only on $v$:

$$\frac{1}{s_2}f_1(u)\exp\left[-\frac{1}{2}\left(m^2s_2^2-\frac{1}{s_1^2}\right)u^2\right]=$$

$$=\frac{1}{s_1}f_2(v)\exp\left[-\frac{1}{2}\left(m^2s_1^2-\frac{1}{s_2^2}\right)v^2\right].$$

Since $u$ and $v$ are not functionally related, this equation is possible only if

$$\left.\begin{aligned}\frac{1}{s_2}f_1(u)\exp\left[-\frac{1}{2}\left(m^2s_2^2-\frac{1}{s_1^2}\right)u^2\right]=C,\\ \frac{1}{s_1}f_2(v)\exp\left[-\frac{1}{2}\left(m^2s_1^2-\frac{1}{s_2^2}\right)v^2\right]=C,\end{aligned}\right\}\qquad(12.33)$$

where $C$ is an arbitrary constant. Consequently,

$$\left.\begin{aligned}f_1(u)=Cs_2\exp\left[-\frac{1}{2}\left(\frac{1}{s_1^2}-m^2s_2^2\right)u^2\right],\\ f_2(v)=Cs_1\exp\left[-\frac{1}{2}\left(\frac{1}{s_2^2}-m^2s_1^2\right)v^2\right].\end{aligned}\right\}\qquad(12.34)$$

From the forms of the functions $f_1(u)$ and $f_2(v)$, we conclude that in the case of a normal correlation the distribution of each variable obeys a normal law separately.

Let us write these probability densities in the usual form:

$$\left.\begin{aligned}f_1(u)=\frac{1}{\sigma_u\sqrt{2\pi}}e^{-\frac{u^2}{2\sigma_u^2}},\\ f_2(v)=\frac{1}{\sigma_v\sqrt{2\pi}}e^{-\frac{v^2}{2\sigma_v^2}}.\end{aligned}\right\}\qquad(12.35)$$

If we equate these formulas with the preceding ones, we obtain

$$\sigma_u^2 = \frac{s_1^2}{1 - m^2 s_1^2 s_2^2}, \qquad \sigma_v^2 = \frac{s_2^2}{1 - m^2 s_1^2 s_2^2}. \qquad (12.36)$$

Let us define

$$R^2 = m^2 s_1^2 s_2^2. \qquad (12.37)$$

Then,

$$s_1^2 = \sigma_u^2 (1 - R^2), \qquad s_2^2 = \sigma_v^2 (1 - R^2),$$

$$m s_1^2 = R \frac{\sigma_u}{\sigma_v}, \qquad m s_2^2 = R \frac{\sigma_v}{\sigma_u}.$$

If we substitute the expressions (12.34) and (12.32) that we have found for the functions $f_1(u)$ and $\varphi_2(v \mid u)$ into equation (12.12) with $x$ and $y$ replaced by $u$ and $v$, we obtain the probability density of a normal distribution of the variables $U$ and $V$:

$$f(u, v) = \frac{1}{\sqrt{2\pi}\sqrt{1 - R^2}\,\sigma_u \sigma_v} \times$$
$$\times \exp\left\{-\frac{1}{2(1 - R^2)}\left[\frac{u^2}{\sigma_u^2} - 2R\frac{u}{\sigma_u}\frac{v}{\sigma_v} + \frac{v^2}{\sigma_v^2}\right]\right\}. \qquad (12.38)$$

The equations of regression with the new variables ($R$ instead of $m$ and $\sigma_u$, $\sigma_v$ instead of $s_1$, $s_2$) are of the form

$$u = R \frac{\sigma_u}{\sigma_v} v, \qquad v = R \frac{\sigma_v}{\sigma_u} u. \qquad (12.39)$$

Let us now find the center of a normal distribution. In the present case,

$$m_1(v) = R \frac{\sigma_u}{\sigma_v} v, \qquad m_2(u) = R \frac{\sigma_v}{\sigma_u} u.$$

Therefore, from formulas (12.21),

$$\bar{u} = \frac{R\sigma_u}{\sqrt{2\pi}} \int_{-\infty}^{+\infty} v e^{-\frac{v^2}{2\sigma_v^2}} dv, \qquad \bar{v} = \frac{R\sigma_v}{\sqrt{2\pi}} \int_{-\infty}^{+\infty} u e^{-\frac{u^2}{2\sigma_u^2}} du.$$

The integrals on the right sides of these equations are obviously equal to 0 and, consequently,

$$\bar{u} = 0, \qquad \bar{v} = 0. \qquad (12.40)$$

Remembering that *our coordinate origin is situated at the point of intersection of the lines of regression, we conclude that in the case* *of a normal distribution of two random variables, the point of intersection of the lines of regression coincides with the center of distribution.**

To find a "probabilistic expression" for the variable $R$, let us calculate the expectation of the product of the random variables $U$ and $V$. If we substitute the value of $f(u, v)$ given by equation (12.38) into the equation

$$E(UV) = \int_{-\infty}^{+\infty}\int_{-\infty}^{+\infty} uvf(u, v)\,du\,dv,$$

we obtain

$$E(UV) = \int_{-\infty}^{\infty} \frac{u}{\sigma_u\sqrt{2\pi}} e^{-\frac{u^2}{2\sigma_u^2}} \int_{-\infty}^{\infty} \frac{v}{\sigma_v\sqrt{1-R^2}\sqrt{2\pi}} \exp\left[-\frac{\left(v - R\frac{\sigma_v}{\sigma_u}u\right)^2}{2(1-R^2)\sigma_v^2}\right] dv\,du.$$

To evaluate the inner integral, we make the substitution

$$\frac{v - R\frac{\sigma_v}{\sigma_u}u}{\sigma_v\sqrt{1-R^2}} = z.$$

Then,

$$dv = \sigma_v\sqrt{1-R^2}\,dz, \qquad \frac{v}{\sigma_v\sqrt{1-R^2}} = z + \frac{Ru}{\sigma_u\sqrt{1-R^2}};$$

Here, $u$ is considered a constant.

The integral with respect to $v$ takes the form

$$\int_{-\infty}^{\infty} z\frac{1}{\sqrt{2\pi}} e^{-\frac{z^2}{2}} \sigma_v\sqrt{1-R^2}\,dz + \int_{-\infty}^{\infty} R\frac{\sigma_v}{\sigma_u}u\frac{1}{\sqrt{2\pi}} e^{-\frac{z^2}{2}}\,dz.$$

The first of these integrals vanishes since the integrand is an odd function of $z$. The second is equal to $R(\sigma_v/\sigma_u)u$ because

$$\int_{-\infty}^{\infty} \frac{1}{\sqrt{2\pi}} e^{-\frac{z^2}{2}}\,dz = 1.$$

Consequently,

$$E(UV) = R\frac{\sigma_v}{\sigma_u}\int_{-\infty}^{\infty} u^2\frac{1}{\sigma_u\sqrt{2\pi}} e^{-\frac{u^2}{2\sigma_u^2}}\,du.$$

Since $\bar{u} = 0$, the integral on the right is the variance of the variable $u$, which is equal to $\sigma_u^2$. Therefore,

*We note that in the present case the coordinates of the center of distribution coincide with the theoretical means of each of the two *individual* variables.

$$E(UV) = R\sigma_u\sigma_v,$$

or

$$R = \frac{E(UV)}{\sigma_u\sigma_v}. \tag{12.41}$$

Let us go back to the original variables $x$ and $y$ in the equations that we obtained for the probability density (12.38), the regression equations (12.39), and the coefficient $R$(12.41). Since $x$ and $y$ were replaced by $u$ and $v$ by means of a displacement of the origin,

$$u = x - \bar{x}, \quad v = y - \bar{y},$$

Therefore, $\sigma_u = \sigma_x$ and $\sigma_v = \sigma_y$. The expression for the probability density therefore takes the form

$$f(x, y) = \frac{1}{2\pi\sigma_x\sigma_y\sqrt{1-R^2}} \exp\left\{-\frac{1}{2(1-R^2)}\left[\frac{(x-\bar{x})^2}{\sigma_x^2} - \right.\right.$$
$$\left.\left. - 2R\frac{x-\bar{x}}{\sigma_x} \cdot \frac{y-\bar{y}}{\sigma_y} + \frac{(y-\bar{y})^2}{\sigma_u^2}\right]\right\}. \tag{12.42}$$

The regression equations are then written

$$y - \bar{y} = R\frac{\sigma_y}{\sigma_x}(x - \bar{x}), \quad x - \bar{x} = R\frac{\sigma_x}{\sigma_y}(y - \bar{y}), \tag{12.43}$$

where the $y$ and $x$ on the left sides of these equations represent the mean values obtained in the case of the definite values of $x$ and $y$ given on the right sides. Therefore, the $y$ and $x$ that appear on the left are sometimes denoted by $\bar{y}_x$ and $\bar{x}_y$. For the coefficient $R$, we obtain the expression

$$R = \frac{E\{(x-\bar{x})(y-\bar{y})\}}{\sigma_x\sigma_y} = \frac{E(XY) - \bar{x}\bar{y}}{\sigma_x\sigma_y}. \tag{12.44}$$

The product $R\sigma_x\sigma_y$ is called the *covariance*. If we denote by $\rho_{yx}$ and $\rho_{xy}$ the coefficients of regression, we have

$$\rho_{yx} = R\frac{\sigma_y}{\sigma_x}, \quad \rho_{xy} = R\frac{\sigma_x}{\sigma_y}. \tag{12.45}$$

The quantities $\bar{x}$, $\bar{y}$, $\sigma_x$, and $\sigma_y$ that appear in these formulas are the theoretical mean values and mean square deviations of each of the separate variables $X$ and $Y$. The point $(\bar{x}, \bar{y})$ is the center of distribution and at the same time the intersection point of the lines of regression. The significance of the quantity $R$ from a probability standpoint is given by the following theorem:

*For two variables obeying a normal law to be mutually independent, it is necessary and sufficient that $R = 0$.*

Proof: We write $f(x, y)$ in the form

$$f(x, y) = \left\{\frac{1}{\sigma_x\sqrt{2\pi}} \exp\left[-\frac{(x-\bar{x})^2}{2\sigma_x^2}\right]\right\}\left\{\frac{1}{\sigma_y\sqrt{2\pi}} \exp\left[-\frac{(y-\bar{y})^2}{2\sigma_y^2}\right]\right\} \times$$
$$\times\left\{\frac{1}{\sqrt{1-R^2}} \exp\left\{-\frac{R}{2(1-R^2)}\left[\frac{R(x-\bar{x})^2}{\sigma_x^2} - \frac{2(x-\bar{x})}{\sigma_x}\frac{(y-\bar{y})}{\sigma_y} + \frac{R(y-\bar{y})^2}{\sigma_y^2}\right]\right\}\right\}.$$

In the preceding section (see formula (12.16)), the last factor was denoted by $\varphi(x, y)$ and it was shown that the function $\varphi(x, y)$ completely determines the nature of the correlation; specifically, if the variables are independent, $\varphi(x, y)$ must be identically equal to unity and conversely. From the last formula, it is clear that in the case of a normal correlation, the last factor will be identically equal to unity only if $R=0$.

It follows from the expressions for $s_1^2$ and $s_2^2$ that $|R| \leqslant 1$. If $|R| = 1$, then $s_1 = s_2 = 0$. Since $s_1$ and $s_2$ are the mean square deviations of the conditional distributions, there corresponds in this case only one value of $x$ (coinciding with the mean value $\bar{x}$) to each value of $y$ and conversely; that is, $x$ and $y$ are each single-valued functions of the other. For, as $s_1 \to 0$, Gauss' curve characterizing the distribution of $X$ for a given constant value of $Y=y$ tends to coincide with the ordinate; in other words, the probability of any deviation from the mean approaches 0. Since the theoretical lines of regression are straight, the uniquely determined dependence between $X$ and $Y$ will be linear when $|R| = 1$.

Thus, this number $R$ characterizes the deviation of the correlation from a linear functional relationship. The number $R$ is called the *correlation coefficient*.

It follows from formulas (12.45) that

$$R^2 = \rho_{yx}\rho_{xy}$$

Thus, the square of the correlation coefficient is equal to the product of the coefficients of regression.

As we have noted, in the case of a normal distribution of two random variables, the mean value of each of these variables when the other is held constant is a linear function of the value at which the other variable is fixed. A correlation of this kind is called a *linear correlation*. On the basis of the linearity that we have shown for the equations of regression, we may say that the assumption of a linear correlation between two variables can be considered justified if there is a reason for assuming that the random variables in question obey a two-dimensional normal law of distribution. When this is the case, the set of two random variables is completely characterized by five numbers: the individual mean values of the two variables, their mean square deviations, and the correlation coefficient.

## Ellipses of Equal Probabilities.

From the general form of the probability density of two random variables, it follows that the probability density is constant at all points of the $xy$-plane at which

$$\frac{(x-\bar{x})^2}{\sigma_x^2} - 2r\frac{(x-\bar{x})(y-\bar{y})}{\sigma_x\sigma_y} + \frac{(y-\bar{y})^2}{\sigma_y^2} = \lambda^2,$$

where $\lambda$ is an arbitrary constant and $r$ is the correlation coefficient.

The curve in the $xy$-plane described by this equation is an ellipse, a fact that is easily verified by the methods of the theory of second-degree curves. Such an ellipse is called an ellipse of equal probability, since at every point on it the probabilities are equal for falling on equal elementary areas. We call such an ellipse a $\lambda$-ellipse and denote the region in the $xy$-plane encircled by it with the letter $\Lambda$; we denote the probability that a point will fall in the region by $P(\lambda)$.

For brevity in writing, we convert to the arguments $u$ and $v$, that is, to the deviations of our variables from their expectations. The equation of a $\lambda$-ellipse in the new variables takes the form

$$\frac{u^2}{\sigma_u^2} - 2r\frac{uv}{\sigma_u \sigma_v} + \frac{v^2}{\sigma_v^2} = \lambda^2;$$

$$\sigma_u = \sigma_x, \qquad \sigma_v = \sigma_y.$$

By the definition of probability density, we have

$$P(\lambda) = \int\int_{\Lambda} p(u, v)\, du\, dv,$$

where $p(u, v)$ denotes the probability density.

Let us use the polar coordinates

$$u = \rho \cos \theta, \quad v = \rho \sin \theta.$$

By a transformation of the integral, we obtain

$$P(\lambda) = \frac{1}{2\pi\sigma_u\sigma_v\sqrt{1-r^2}} \int_0^{2\pi} d\theta \int_0^{\frac{\lambda}{s\sqrt{1-r^2}}} e^{-\frac{\rho^2 s^2}{2}} \rho\, d\rho,$$

where

$$s^2 = \left[\frac{\cos^2\theta}{\sigma_u^2} - 2r\frac{\cos\theta \sin\theta}{\sigma_u\sigma_v} + \frac{\sin^2\theta}{\sigma_v^2}\right] \cdot \frac{1}{1-r^2}.$$

Integrating with respect to $\rho$, we have

$$P(\lambda) = \frac{1}{2\pi\sigma_u\sigma_v\sqrt{1-r^2}}\left[1 - e^{-\frac{\lambda^2}{2(1-r^2)}}\right]\int_0^{2\pi}\frac{d\theta}{s^2}.$$

To simplify the evaluation of the integral with respect to $\theta$, we assume that the ellipse encompasses the entire plane as $\lambda$ approaches $\infty$. In other words, $P(\infty) = 1$. On the other hand, from this formula we obtain

$$P(\infty) = \frac{1}{2\pi\sigma_u\sigma_v\sqrt{1-r^2}}\int_0^{2\pi}\frac{d\theta}{s^2}.$$

Therefore,

$$P(\lambda) = 1 - \exp\frac{\lambda^2}{2(1-r^2)}.$$

In particular, if the variables are mutually independent, $r$ will be equal to 0. In this case, for example,

$$P(2) = 0.865, \qquad P(3) = 0.989.$$

The semi-axes of the corresponding ellipses are respectively equal to twice and three times the mean square deviation. Such ellipses may be called confidence limits in analogy with the concept of the one-dimensional problem and the corresponding probabilities may also be called confidence probabilities.

# Part IV

# FUNDAMENTALS OF THE THEORY OF RANDOM MEASUREMENT ERRORS

## (The method of least squares)

Chapter 13

# GENERAL REMARKS ON MEASUREMENT ERRORS

## 65. TYPES OF MEASUREMENT ERRORS

All measurements contain errors of various origins. It is customary to classify these errors as:

(1) systematic,
(2) random,
(3) personal, and
(4) gross.

### 1. *Systematic errors*

The most important class of systematic errors is instrumental errors. The instruments used to make measurements cannot be constructed so as to be perfectly accurate. In the simplest case of a direct measurement made on a calibrated instrument, the spaces between the dividing lines are somewhat wider or narrower than the nominal distance (for example, the space between dividing lines may be 0.999 mm at one point on a ruler and 1.002 mm at another point, etc.). Scale errors may appear when we measure the intervals with a precision instrument. The original instrument can then be used along with a rating plate giving the error in terms of the measured quantity (an interval, an angle, etc.).

Sometimes, rather than measure the error, we may be able to organize the measurements in such a way that the error will be eliminated. A very familiar example is that of the error due to the eccentricity of a protractor. It is rarely possible to make the instrument in such a way that the geometric center of the circle divided into degrees will coincide sufficiently closely with the center of rotation of the circle. Therefore, the calibrated arc does not measure the required angle (error of eccentricity). To measure and allow for the error due to eccentricity would be quite tedious. However, it is easy to eliminate this error by rotating the circle 180° and taking another reading. From geometric considerations, it is clear that the arithmetic mean of the two readings will give the exact value of the angle, regardless of the eccentricity.

Another very simple instrumental error is that of taking the wrong point as the zero point of a reading. As a result of such an error, all measurements will differ from the exact values by the same amount, which may be positive or negative.

The errors connected with the instruments used in astronomy must be studied; they must be measured for each individual device, and they must be eliminated from the results of the measurements. When possible, measurements should be made in such a way that the error is excluded by a combination of two or more measurements.

Instrumental errors appear in every measurement result. They may be constant or they may depend in some definite way on other quantities, in particular, on the measured quantity itself. This is the reason for such errors being called systematic errors.

Instrumental errors are not the only kind of systematic errors. For example, in the differential determination of the coordinates of heavenly bodies (e.g., of small planets) from photographs, the positions of these bodies are measured with respect to base stars. Since the coordinates of the base stars, which are taken from catalogues, contain systematic errors (catalogue errors), the evaluated coordinates of the heavenly bodies in question will contain the same errors. These errors, like the instrumental errors, must be investigated and eliminated from the results of measurements.

We may take as the general criterion for systematic errors the theoretical possibility of studying them and eliminating them from the results of measurements. Methods of allowing for systematic errors are considered in the various fields of astronomy which depend on the results of observations.

## 2. *Random errors*

Experiment has shown that successive measurements of a single fixed quantity, made with the greatest possible care, give different numerical values even after all the known systematic errors are allowed for. This fact shows that physical causes of some sort have an effect on the results of measurements—causes for which we cannot make allowance. For example, suppose that an object is being weighed on sufficiently accurate and sensitive scales. If a door were to be slammed in the same building at the instant that the measurement is taken, the needle of the scale would fluctuate in a direction not predictable and the number obtained would differ from the exact value. If a heavy truck were to pass by at the instant of another measurement, the new jolt would differ from the preceding one and the result would be changed again. If the measurements are not completely mechanical, if any human being takes part in them, the random changes in the state of those organs that he uses to make the measurements will have an effect on the result.

A whole series of similar random causes may produce deviations from an exact value. In each case, the deviation is slight: otherwise it would be noticed and investigated. However, the total effect of all these causes can yield significant deviations.

The theory of errors usually has to do with the theory of random errors. For the construction of such a theory, the very nature of random errors suggests the apparatus of probability theory.

### 3. *Personal errors.*

Experience in astronomical observations has shown that the results of measurements depend to some degree on the physical peculiarities of the observer (under otherwise equal conditions). For example, in recording the instant of a phenomenon, one observer may regularly notice a phenomenon somewhat sooner than will another. Repeated study of the personal errors of different observers has shown that these errors can be both systematic and random. It is known that some average amount of personal error is associated with an observer, and this error should be considered systematic and taken into consideration in the analysis of the observations. However, in individual observations, the personal error is a random quantity that varies for different reasons (the physical condition of the observer, external conditions, etc.). Observations are made to determine the personal errors and the results of these observations are analyzed in much the same way as in the case of random errors, in order to obtain their average value.

### 4. *Gross errors.*

In the analysis of observations, we need to allow for the possibility of blunders or external influences that cause completely inaccurate results. One of the simplest of these will be for an observer to read twenty and write down thirty, for example. A very simple example of an external cause of a large error that might not be noticed by the observer is a jolt that would distort the result. The presence of gross errors is detected by the fact that in a succession of comparatively close results only one or only a few values will differ appreciably from the general level of values; that is, these results stand out. If the discrepancy is great enough for us to be sure that it is the result of an error, the measurement can be disregarded. However, the situation is rarely that simple. If we keep in mind that a random error represents the sum of a large number of small random errors, we may conceive of an unfavorable combination of constituent small errors that will give a random error that is large in absolute value. It is true that the probability of such an unfavorable combination is very small, but it is not equal to 0; that is, such a combination is theoretically possible. Therefore, we may not as a rule immediately call an observation a gross error merely because of a sharp discrepancy. We shall consider gross errors from a probability standpoint later on.

## 66. THE BASIC HYPOTHESIS IN THE THEORY OF RANDOM ERRORS. METHODS OF EVALUATING ERRORS

The necessity of applying probability theory to the study of random errors is rather obvious. Since a random measuring error is a continuous random variable, in order to construct the theory we must have the probability density or the distribution function.

Let us denote the unknown exact value of the quantity measured by $a$ and let us denote an arbitrary measurement of this quantity by $x$. We apply the term "error" to the quantity

$$\delta = x - a. \tag{13.1}$$

This error is considered random and consequently the values of $x$ are also random.

We make the following *assumption:* The random errors obey a normal law of distribution with center equal to 0. According to this assumption, the probability density of the random variables is determined by the formula

$$p(\delta) = \frac{1}{\sigma\sqrt{2\pi}} e^{-\frac{\delta^2}{2\sigma^2}}, \tag{13.2}$$

from which it immediately follows that the probability density of random measuring results is expressed by

$$\varphi(x) = \frac{1}{\sigma\sqrt{2\pi}} e^{-\frac{(x-a)^2}{2\sigma^2}}. \tag{13.3}$$

As we know, $\sigma^2$ in this expression is the variance of the random errors. In what follows, we shall call the quantity $\sigma$ the mean square error of a measurement. It is a numerical characteristic of the quality of the set of measurements for which it is given or calculated. The probabilistic significance of the quantity $\sigma$ is known from the general theory of a normal distribution. As we have seen,

$$P(|\delta| < \sigma) \approx 0.68; \qquad P(|\delta| < 3\sigma) \approx 0.9973 \text{ etc.}$$

The greater the value of $\sigma$, the poorer is the quality of the measurements.

We use three other quantities to describe the quality of the measurements:

(a) The probable error

$$r \approx \frac{2}{3}\sigma,$$

which is determined by the condition that $P(|\delta| < r) = 0.5$,

(b) The absolute error

$$m = E(|\delta|)$$

that is, the expectation of the absolute value of the error (it may be shown* that $m \approx 0.8\sigma$),

(c) the modulus of precision:

$$h = \frac{1}{\sigma\sqrt{2}} \approx \frac{0,7}{\sigma}.$$

The probable and absolute errors are great when the quality of the measurements is poor. The modulus of precision increases with increasing accuracy of measurements.

The assumption of a normal law of distribution can be justified by Lyapunov's limit theorem if we accept the view stated above with regard to the net effect of a large number of small errors. It also follows from the conditions of Lyapunov's theorem that the assumption of a normal law indicates that the constituent errors must be of approximately the same order. If, from physical considerations, we may expect that there is a single outstanding error, a supplementary assumption must be made with regard to the distribution law of the predominant error, retaining the assumption of the normal law for the set of the other constituent errors. Then we must derive a distribution law for the sum of the variables.**

The assumption of a normal law can be verified by observations. Let us suppose that we have found an approximate value of the quantity in question with a sufficient accuracy to take it as the exact value (with a very small error). In practice, such a value can be dervied from a very large number of observations.

---

*From the definition of expectation,

$$m = \frac{1}{\sigma\sqrt{2\pi}} \int_{-\infty}^{+\infty} |\delta| e^{-\frac{\delta^2}{2\sigma^2}} d\delta$$

or

$$m = \frac{2}{\sigma\sqrt{2\pi}} \int_0^{\infty} \delta e^{-\frac{\delta^2}{2\sigma^2}} d\delta.$$

If we make the change of variable $\frac{\delta^2}{2\sigma^2} = z$, we obtain

$$m = \sqrt{\frac{2}{\pi}}\,\sigma \int_0^{\infty} e^{-z}\, dz = \sqrt{\frac{2}{\pi}}\,\sigma \approx 0.8\sigma.$$

**A question similar to this one is examined in the book by V. L. Goncharov.

P

The quantity $\sigma$ can then be evaluated by taking the square root of the sum of the squares of the deviations of the results from the "exact" value and dividing by the number of measurements.

Consequently, we shall assume that $u$ and $\sigma$ are exact. From a property of the normal law, we can compute the probability that the absolute value of the error will lie within arbitrary given bounds,

$$P(|\delta| < \alpha\sigma) = 2\Phi(\alpha), \qquad \alpha > 0,$$

where $\Phi(z)$ is a tabulated function (see Chapter 11). (Here, the bounds are taken in units of $\sigma$.) Let us assign various values to $\alpha$ within the limits between 0 and 3 and let us calculate the number $n_\alpha$ of values of $\delta$ that satisfy the above inequality. We may also calculate the theoretical number of such values

$$n'_\alpha = n \cdot 2\Phi(\alpha),$$

where $n$ is the total number of observations. Comparison of the table of values of $n'_\alpha$ and $n_\alpha$ gives an indication of the acceptability or inacceptability of a normal law. Such a check has been made and its results are given in the book by A. N. Krylov *Lektsii o priblizhennykh vychisleniyakh* (Lectures on Approximate Calculations). The above text also presents various derivations of the normal law, on the basis of different types of hypotheses.

As with every mathematical theory, it is possible, in this case, to begin with basic assumptions other than that of a normal distribution. Thus, for example, in one of Gauss' works, the theory of random errors is based on the assumption that the most probable value of a measured quantity is the arithmetic mean of the values obtained in a number of equally accurate measurements. With this postulate, it is possible to show that the errors obey a normal distribution law.

Let us now consider a method of eliminating gross errors, under the assumption of a normal distribution law of random errors. Let us suppose that as a result of several measurements, we have found an approximate value of the measured quantity $\bar{x}$ and of the mean square error $\sigma$ of a single measurement. Let us determine the approximate value of the error of each measurement:

$$\varepsilon_k = x_k - \bar{x} \approx \delta_k.$$

Because of the normal distribution,

$$P(|\delta| < 3\sigma) = 0.9973,$$

and consequently,

$$P(|\delta| > 3\sigma) = 0.0027.$$

It is usually assumed to be unlikely that the absolute value of the error will exceed $3\sigma$. Therefore, if we find that the absolute value of any of the $\varepsilon_k$ exceeds $3\sigma$, the corresponding measurement is assumed to contain a gross error and is discarded. In certain types of problems, the conditions under which measurements for which $|\varepsilon_k| > 2\sigma$ are discarded are considered. After such observations are discarded, it is necessary to recalculate both the approximate value $\bar{x}$ and the number $\sigma$.

Chapter 14

# ANALYSIS OF EQUALLY PRECISE MEASUREMENTS OF A FIXED QUANTITY

## 67. THE PROBLEM OF ANALYZING MEASUREMENTS OF A FIXED QUANTITY

Suppose that $n$ measurements are made of an unknown quantity $a$ and that the results of these measurements are $x_1, x_2, \ldots, x_n$. From this set of numbers, we must derive the approximate value of $a$ that is (in some specified sense) the most acceptable, and also the approximate value of the mean square error of an individual measurement. The expression "most acceptable" value usually means the most probable value. The value taken for $a$ is a function of the random numbers $x_1, x_2, \ldots, x_n$. Therefore, it too should be considered random. We then have the problem of a probable estimate of the accuracy of the result. In other words, in addition to the mean square error of an individual measurement, we must also compute the mean square error of the most probable value of the measured quantity.

However, we first need to introduce the concept of *equal precision of measurements*. This is the probabilistic expression of the "ordinary" concept of equal accuracy of all the results $x_1, x_2, \ldots, x_n$ of measurements of the quantity in question. The $k$th measurement (for $(k = 1, 2 \ldots)$ gives a random result $x_k$. The randomness appears in the fact that when such a series of measurements is repeated, the $k$th measurement will give a new value $x'_k$ different, as a rule, from $x_k$. The set of all possible results of the $k$th measurement is determined in the general case by the probability density with parameter $\sigma_k$. The formal test of equal precision of measurements is the equality of all the $\sigma_k$, independent of the subscript $k$. (We indicate the common value of the $\sigma_k$ by $\sigma$.)

## 68. THE MOST PROBABLE VALUE OF A MEASURED QUANTITY. THE METHOD OF LEAST SQUARES

Suppose that $n$ equally precise measurements $x_1, x_2, \ldots, x_n$ of a fixed quantity $a$ are made. Let us also suppose that the quantity $a$

is known. Then, we may determine the errors of the individual measurements

$$\delta_k = x_k - a. \tag{14.1}$$

We also assume (in the present section) that the mean square error of a single measurement $\sigma$ is known. By using the properties of probability density, we can write an approximate expression for the probability that the error in the $k$th measurement will be close to that obtained:

$$P_k(\delta_k < \delta < \delta_k + \Delta\delta) \approx \frac{1}{\sigma\sqrt{2\pi}} e^{-\frac{\delta_k^2}{2\sigma^2}} \Delta\delta \qquad (k = 1, 2, \ldots, n), \tag{14.2}$$

where $\Delta\delta$ is an arbitrary small positive number. We adopt the following notation to write this equation more briefly:

$$P_k(\delta \approx \delta_k) \approx \frac{1}{\sigma\sqrt{2\pi}} e^{-\frac{\delta_k^2}{2\sigma^2}} \Delta\delta.$$

Now, let us drop the assumption that the quantity $a$ is exactly known and let us make various hypotheses about the value of the quantity $a$. To each such hypothesis, there corresponds a set of numbers $\delta_k$ and a corresponding set of probabilities $P_k$. The conditional probability $P_k$ of the event that $\delta \approx \delta_k$ in the $k$th measurement, given an arbitrary hypothesis as to the value of $a$, is given by the equation

$$P_k(\delta \approx \delta_k \mid a) \approx \frac{1}{\sigma\sqrt{2\pi}} e^{-\frac{\delta_k^2}{2\sigma^2}} \Delta\delta, \tag{14.3}$$

The left side of this equation should be read "the probability that the error in the $k$th measurement will be approximately equal to $\delta_k$ (i.e., between $\delta_k$ and $\delta_k + \Delta\delta$), under the hypothesis in question with regard to the quantity $a$."

Analogous equations may be written for all the measurements. Each of them determines the probability of the event referred to. Let us assume that the measurements are mutually independent, that is, that the probability of each value of the error in the $k$th measurement is independent of the value of the errors made in the other measurements. The corresponding events (the occurrence of errors of different magnitude) are also mutually independent.

Let us now calculate the conditional probability of obtaining a definite set of errors $\delta_1, \delta_2, \ldots, \delta_n$, given a particular hypothesis with regard to the quantity $a$. This probability can be denoted by $P(\delta \approx \delta_1, \delta_2, \ldots, \delta_n \mid a)$. Since we have a set of mutually independent events (errors), the probability that we are seeking can be found by using the theorem on multiplication of probabilities for mutually independent events. By use of (14.3), we obtain

$$P(\delta \approx \delta_1, \delta_2, \ldots, \delta_n \mid a) \approx \left(\frac{\Delta\delta}{\sigma\sqrt{2\pi}}\right)^n \exp\left\{-\frac{\sum_{k=1}^{n} \delta_k^2}{2\sigma^2}\right\}. \tag{14.4}$$

Since, by (14.1), $\delta_k = x_k - a$, we have

$$P(X \approx x_1, x_2, \ldots, x_n \mid a) \approx \left(\frac{\Delta\delta}{\sigma\sqrt{2\pi}}\right)^n \exp\left\{-\frac{\sum_{k=1}^{n} (x_k - a)^2}{2\sigma^2}\right\}. \tag{14.5}$$

The right side of this equation is a function of the quantity $a$. If we assign different values to $a$, we shall obtain different probabilities.

Let us now suppose that all the hypotheses concerning the variable $a$ in some arbitrary region are equally precise. Then, from the corollary to Bayes' formula, the probabilities of the different hypotheses, after the occurrence of the event, are proportional to the conditional probabilities of the event under these hypotheses. In the present case, the event is the occurrence of the numbers $x_1, x_2, \ldots, x_n$. Therefore, we may write

$$P(a \mid x_1, x_2, \ldots, x_n) = C\left(\frac{\Delta\delta}{\sigma\sqrt{2\pi}}\right)^n \exp\left\{-\frac{\sum_{k=1}^{n} (x_k - a)^2}{2\sigma^2}\right\}, \tag{14.6}$$

where $C$ is a proportionality constant.

From equation (14.6), the probability of a hypothesis concerning the variable $a$ depends on the value of $a$ that appears in the exponent on the right. It is easy to see that the probability $P$ has its greatest value when the quantity

$$S(a) = \sum_{k=1}^{n} (x_k - a)^2 \tag{14.7}$$

is smallest. The problem of determining the most probable value of $a$ is thus reduced to finding that value of $a$ at which $S(a)$ is minimum. As we know from analysis, a necessary condition for an extremum of $S(a)$ is that

$$\frac{dS}{da} = -2\sum_{k=1}^{n} (x_k - a) = 0.$$

Since $S(a)$ is a positive-definite quadratic form in $a$, $S$ can have only one extremum and that one must be a minimum. When we set the first derivative equal to 0, we obtain the most probable value of the unknown variable $a$:

$$a_{\text{prob}} = \frac{\sum_{k=1}^{n} x_k}{n}. \tag{14.8}$$

Thus, we arrive at the following conclusion: The most probable value of a fixed quantity on which equally precise measurements have been made is the arithmetic mean of these measurements.

Henceforth, instead of $a_{\text{prob}}$, we shall use the notation $\bar{x}$:

$$\bar{x} = \frac{\sum_{k=1}^{n} x_k}{n}. \tag{14.9}$$

This method of calculating an approximate value of the variable $a$ is called "the method of least squares," since we use the condition that the sum of the squares of the errors $S(a)$ be minimized.

From (14.3) we have the following property of the arithmetic mean, which we shall find useful in the future: the sum of all the deviations from the arithmetic mean is equal to 0. This is true because, according to (14.9),

$$\sum_{k=1}^{n} (x_k - \bar{x}) = \sum_{k=1}^{n} x_k - n\bar{x} = 0. \tag{14.10}$$

## 69. THE MEAN SQUARE ERROR OF THE ARITHMETIC MEAN

In a given set of $n$ observations, the arithmetic mean $\bar{x}$ is a linear function of the results $x_1, x_2, \ldots, x_n$ of these observations (cf. equation (14.8)). If we again make a set of $n$ measurements, the values $x_k$ will, because of random influences, differ from those obtained the first time. Therefore, the value of $\bar{x}$ will be different. The same will be true of all subsequent sets of measurements. Therefore, the number $\bar{x}$ that we obtain as a result of one set of measurements is a random approximate value of the desired quantity. To get an idea of the possible deviations of $\bar{x}$ from the desired exact value, we need to calculate the mean square error of the arithmetic mean. To keep in mind just what it is that we are doing here, we should note that the mean square error of the arithmetic mean is a probability characteristic of the set of all possible values of the arithmetic mean that can be obtained from the $n$ measurements.

Since the results of the measurements are assumed to represent mutually independent random variables, application of the theorem on the variance of a linear function of such variables yields

$$\operatorname{var} x = \sum_{k=1}^{n} \frac{D(x_k)}{n^2}.$$

Since the measurements are assumed to be equally precise,

$$\operatorname{var} x_k = \sigma^2$$

for all $k$. Therefore

$$\operatorname{var} \bar{x} = \frac{n\sigma^2}{n^2} = \frac{\sigma^2}{n}$$

and

$$\sigma_{\bar{x}} = \frac{\sigma}{\sqrt{n}}. \tag{14.11}$$

It should be noted that this formula is *precise*, but the quantity $\sigma$ itself is unknown.

We may consider as exceptional the rare cases in which experimental measurements are made with very small random errors. In the case of such high accuracy measurements, the results will be expressed as many-digit numbers with a large number of initial digits in common. Such measurements, for example, might be 3.48754, 3.48733, 3.48761, etc. In such a case, we may take the common part of all the results as the exact value of the measured quantity. In the present example, this would be 3.487, which has four significant figures. If measurements of lower accuracy are made, the individual measurements will not all yield four reliable digits. For example, we may obtain 3.485, 3.488, etc. Deviations from the "exact" value can be considered exact errors ("exact" in a conventional sense, specifically, having a specified number of significant figures). The mean square error of a single measurement, on the basis of $n$ measurements under these conditions, is defined as the square root of the sum of the squares of the errors divided by the number of measurements. However, it should be noted that we still do not obtain the "exact" value of $\sigma$. The quantity $\sigma$ is a parameter of the normal distribution law of the errors. To find its value with a sufficient degree of reliability, we would have to make many similar measurements and deduce the value of $\sigma$ from them.

## 70. THE MOST PROBABLE VALUE OF THE MEAN SQUARE ERROR OF AN INDIVIDUAL MEASUREMENT

In the derivation of the most probable value of a measured quantity, it was assumed that the quantity $\sigma$ was known. Therefore, the probability of obtaining a certain set of errors (which is equal to the probability of obtaining a certain set of measurement results) depended only on the hypothesis made regarding the variable $a$.

Let us now assume that the quantity $\sigma$ is also unknown. To examine the probability of the set of errors, we now need to make hypotheses regarding the values of both $a$ and $\sigma$. Just as was the case in Section 68, the probability of obtaining the results $x_1, x_2, \ldots, x_n$ under these hypotheses is given by the formula

$$P(X \approx x_1, x_2, \ldots, x_n \mid a, \sigma) = \left(\frac{\Delta\delta}{\sqrt{2\pi}}\right)^n \sigma^{-n} \exp\left[-\frac{S(a)}{2\sigma^2}\right], \tag{14.12}$$

where

$$S(a) = \sum_{k=1}^{n} (x_k - a)^2. \tag{14.13}$$

Let us rewrite the quantity $S(a)$ as follows:

$$S(a) = \sum_{k=1}^{n}(x_k - a)^2 = \sum_{k=1}^{n} [(x_k - \bar{x}) + (\bar{x} - a)]^2 =$$
$$= \sum_{k=1}^{n}(x_k - \bar{x})^2 + 2(\bar{x} - a)\sum_{k=1}^{n}(x_k - \bar{x}) + n(\bar{x} - a)^2.$$

From property (14.10) of an arithmetic mean, we have the exact equation

$$\sum_{k=1}^{n}(x_k - \bar{x}) = 0$$

(if $\bar{x}$ is exactly computed). Therefore,

$$S(a) = \sum_{k=1}^{n}(x_k - \bar{x})^2 + n(\bar{x} - a)^2.$$

The probability of the set of measurements can then be written in the form

$$P(X \approx x_1, x_2, \ldots, x_n \mid a, \sigma) =$$
$$= \left(\frac{\Delta\delta}{\sqrt{2\pi}}\right)^n \frac{\sqrt{2\pi}}{\sqrt{n}} \sigma^{-n+1} \exp\left[-\frac{\sum_{k=1}^{n}(x_k - \bar{x})^2}{2\sigma^2}\right] \times$$
$$\times \left\{\frac{1}{\sqrt{2\pi}\frac{\sigma}{\sqrt{n}}} \exp\left[-\frac{(a - \bar{x})^2}{2\left(\frac{\sigma}{\sqrt{n}}\right)^2}\right]\right\}. \tag{14.14}$$

Here, the desired probability is a function of the two independent parameters $a$ and $\sigma$.

To obtain a rule for finding the most probable value of $\sigma$ that is suitable for all values of $a$, let us assume that all values of $a$ are equally probable in some region from $-\alpha$ to $\alpha$ that is large enough for us to be able to consider it as practically equivalent to the interval from $-\infty$ to $+\infty$. For this, it is sufficient that $\alpha$ be a magnitude of the order of $3-4\sigma$.

Let us multiply both sides of this equation by $da$ and let us integrate with respect to $a$ from $-\infty$ to $+\infty$. From the generalized theorem on the addition of probabilities, we obtain on the left the probability of the set of measurements for all values of $a$ with fixed $\sigma$. On the right side, we need to integrate only the last factor since it is the only one containing $a$. Formally, this factor is the normal probability density of the "random variable" $a$. Therefore, its integral from $-\infty$ to $+\infty$ is unity, and we obtain

$$P(X \approx x_1, x_2, \ldots, x_n | \sigma) = \left(\frac{\Delta\delta}{\sqrt{2\pi}}\right)^n \frac{\sqrt{2\pi}}{\sqrt{n}} \exp\left(-\frac{\overline{S}}{2\sigma^2}\right) \sigma^{-n+1}, \tag{14.15}$$

where

$$\overline{S} = \sum_{k=1}^{n} (x_k - \overline{x})^2. \tag{14.16}$$

Our reasoning now proceeds along the same lines as in Section 68. We have the probability of the occurrence of our measurement results under the chosen hypothesis regarding the quantity $\sigma$ and with arbitrary values of $a$. This is the conditional probability of the event $(X \approx x_1, x_2, \ldots, x_n)$ under the hypothesis regarding the quantity $\sigma$. Let us suppose that prior to the observations, all the hypotheses regarding the quantity $\sigma$ are equally likely. From the corollary to Bayes' formula, the probabilities of the hypotheses regarding the value of $\sigma$ after the occurrence of the event $x_1, x_2, \ldots, x_n$ are proportional to the conditional probabilities of the event under these hypotheses. Therefore,

$$P(\sigma | x_1, x_2, \ldots, x_n) = C\sigma^{-n+1} e^{-\frac{\overline{S}}{2\sigma^2}}, \tag{14.17}$$

where the coefficient $C$ includes the proportionality constant appearing in the corollary of Bayes' formula as well as all the factors that do not depend on $\sigma$.

Let us now determine the most probable value of $\sigma$ (that is, of the mean square error of an individual measurement) that can be obtained from a given set of measurements. For this, we need to find that value of $\sigma$ at which the function

$$P(\sigma) = \sigma^{-n+1} e^{-\frac{\overline{S}}{2\sigma^2}}$$

has a maximum. If we take the logarithm of both sides and then differentiate twice with respect to $\sigma$, we obtain

$$\ln P = (1-n) \ln \sigma - \frac{\overline{S}}{2\sigma^2},$$

$$\frac{1}{P} \frac{dP}{d\sigma} = \frac{1-n}{\sigma} + \frac{\overline{S}}{\sigma^3},$$

$$-\frac{1}{P^2} \frac{dP}{d\sigma} + \frac{1}{P} \frac{d^2P}{d\sigma^2} = \frac{n-1}{\sigma^2} - \frac{3\overline{S}}{\sigma^4}.$$

If we set the first derivative equal to 0, we obtain

$$\sigma^2_{\text{prob}} = \frac{\overline{S}}{n-1}. \tag{14.18}$$

If we substitute these values of $\sigma$ into the equation containing the second derivative and remember that $\left(\frac{dP}{d\sigma}\right) = 0$ at $\sigma = \sigma_{\text{prob}}$, we obtain

$$\left(\frac{1}{P}\frac{d^2P}{d\sigma^2}\right)_{\sigma=\sigma_{\text{prob}}} = -2\frac{(n-1)^2}{\overline{S}} < 0, \tag{14.19}$$

which confirms that the value obtained for $\sigma$ is the most probable one.

Henceforth, instead of $\sigma_{\text{prob}}$ we shall write simply $\sigma$. If we substitute into (14.18) the value of $\overline{S}$ given by (14.16), we obtain

$$\sigma = \sqrt{\frac{\sum_{k=1}^{n}(x_k - \overline{x})^2}{n-1}}. \tag{14.20}$$

After computing $\overline{x}$ and $\sigma$, we need to look through a table of values of $\varepsilon_k = x_k - \overline{x}$. If any of these numbers have absolute values exceeding $3\sigma$, they should be discarded and $\overline{x}$ and $\sigma$ must be recomputed.

## 71. A SECOND DERIVATION OF THE APPROXIMATE VALUE OF A MEASURED QUANTITY AND OF THE APPROXIMATE VALUE OF THE MEAN SQUARE ERROR OF AN INDIVIDUAL MEASUREMENT

Let us consider the set of measurements as a sample of $n$ items out of the infinitely many results that are possible due to random errors. We base the theory on the following two hypotheses:

(1) The expectation of each measurement result is equal to the exact value of the measured quantity;

(2) The variance of each measurement result is the same for all measurements.

The first of these can be considered natural. The second means that we are dealing with equally precise measurements. We make no assumption as to the law of distribution of the random errors of the measurements.

According to the corollary to Chebyshev's theorem, if a sufficiently large number of measurements are made, we may assert with probability arbitrarily close to unity that the exact value and the arithmetic mean of the sample values will be arbitrarily close. This provides the basis for taking the arithmetic mean as the approximate value of the measured quantity. Consequently, we postulate the approximate equation

$$a \approx \overline{x} = \frac{\sum_{k=1}^{n} x_k}{n}.$$

When a large number of observations are made, such an approximation is, to a certain extent, justified by Chebyshev's theorem. When a small number of observations are made, we can consider it only a convention.

However, we may apply a criterion proposed by A. A. Markov for an approximation that does not contain systematic errors. We denote by $\xi$ an arbitrary approximation of the quantity $a$. This approximation will not contain systematic errors if the expectation of the approximation is equal to the expectation of the approximated quantity (which, in the present case, is the exact value). We denote the random results of the measurements by $\xi_1, \xi_2, \ldots, \xi_n$. Their arithmetic mean is

$$\overline{\xi} = \frac{\xi_1 + \xi_2 + \ldots + \xi_n}{n}.$$

From the first assumption,

$$E(\bar{\xi}) = \frac{a + a + \ldots + a}{n} = a.$$

Thus, if we take the arithmetic mean of the measured values as the approximate value, we satisfy Markov's criterion.

To get an approximate value of the mean square error of a single measurement, we proceed as follows. For the items in our sample, we find the expectation of the sum of the square of the deviations of the individual values from their arithmetic mean; that is, we find the quantity

$$\bar{\Sigma} = E\left\{ \sum_{k=1}^{n} (\xi_k - \bar{\xi})^2 \right\}.$$

We expand the expression in the braces and apply the equation $\sum \xi_k = n\bar{\xi}$. We then obtain

$$\bar{\Sigma} = E\left\{ \sum_{k=1}^{n} \xi_k^2 - n\bar{\xi}^2 \right\} = \sum_{k=1}^{n} E\left(\xi_k^2\right) - nE(\bar{\xi}^2).$$

Since $a = E(\xi_k) = E(\bar{\xi})$, from the property of the variance, for the random variables $\xi_k$ $(k = 1, 2, \ldots, n)$ we have

$$E\left(\xi_k^2\right) = \sigma^2 + a^2,$$
$$E(\bar{\xi}^2) = \sigma_{\bar{\xi}}^2 + a^2.$$

The quantity $\sigma_{\bar{\xi}}^2$ is determined from the theorem on the variance of a linear function:

$$\bar{\xi} = \sum \frac{\xi_k}{n};$$

hence,

$$\sigma_{\bar{\xi}}^2 = \sum \frac{n\sigma^2}{n^2} = \frac{\sigma^2}{n}.$$

Therefore,

$$E(\bar{\xi}^2) = \frac{\sigma^2}{n} + a^2,$$

$$\bar{\Sigma} = n(\sigma^2 + a^2) - n\left(\frac{\sigma^2}{n} + a^2\right) = (n - 1)\sigma^2.$$

Thus, we come to the exact formula: the expectation of the sum of the squares of the deviations (of the sample random values) from the arithmetic mean of these values is equal to the variance of a single measurement times $n - 1$, where $n$ is the number of elements in the sample.

The expectation of the sum of the squares of the deviations from the arithmetic mean is the mean value of this quantity as obtained from all possible samples. Instead of the mean value of the sum of the squares of the deviations, we substitute into the exact formula that value that is obtained for one sample. We then obtain an approximate formula for calculating the variance of a single measurement:

$$\sigma^2 = \frac{\sum_{k=1}^{n} (x_k - \bar{x})^2}{n - 1}$$

(instead of $\xi_k$ and $\bar{\xi}_k$, we write $x_k$ and $\bar{x}$). Note that in the derivation of this formula no assumptions were made as to the distribution law of the random errors.

## 72. AN EXAMPLE OF THE ANALYSIS OF EQUALLY PRECISE MEASUREMENTS OF A SINGLE FIXED QUANTITY

The geographic latitude of the Tashkent observatory has been determined from the observations of fourteen stars. The results are given in column II of the following table:

| I | II | III | IV | V | VI |
|---|---|---|---|---|---|
| No. | $\varphi_k$ | $x_k$ | $x_k - \bar{x}$ | $(x_k - \bar{x})^2$ | |
| 1 | 41°19′33.10″ | +3.10″ | +1.68″ | 2.82 | $\varphi_0 = 41°19'30''$; |
| 2 | 32.96 | +2.96 | +1.54 | 2.37 | |
| 3 | 28.95 | −1.05 | −2.47 | 6.10 | $x_k = \varphi_k - \varphi_0$; |
| 4 | 30.08 | +0.08 | −1.34 | 1.80 | $\bar{x} = 19.87'' : 14 = 1.42''$; |
| 5 | 28.81 | −1.19 | −2.61 | 6.81 | $\bar{\varphi} = 41°19'30'' + 1.42'' =$ |
| 6 | 31.16 | +1.16 | −0.26 | 0.068 | $= 41°19'31.42''$; |
| 7 | 31.38 | +1.38 | −0.04 | 0.002 | |
| 8 | 32.15 | +2.15 | +0.73 | 0.53 | $\sigma^2 = 50.28 : (14-1) =$ |
| 9 | 34.89 | +4.89 | +3.47 | 12.04 | $= 3.87;\ \sigma = 1.97''$; |
| 10 | 33.34 | +3.34 | +1.92 | 3.69 | $\sigma_{\bar{\varphi}} = 1.97'' : \sqrt{14} = 0.53''$; |
| 11 | 32.39 | +2.39 | +0.97 | 0.94 | |
| 12 | 31.51 | +1.51 | +0.09 | 0.008 | $\varphi - 41°19'31.42'' \pm 0.53''$; |
| 13 | 31.35 | +1.35 | −0.07 | 0.005 | $\varphi = 41°19'31.4'' \pm 0.5''$ |
| 14 | 27.80″ | −2.20″ | −3.62″ | 13.10 | |
| | | +19.87″ | (−0.01″) | 50.28 | |

Since the observations were made under approximately equal conditions, they may be considered equally precise. Column III gives the deviations of the values obtained for the latitude from the value 41°19′30″; these deviations are denoted by the symbol $x_k$ (for $k = 1, 2, \ldots, 14$). This was done only to simplify the calculations. The use of these numbers instead of the $\varphi_k$ is equivalent to changing the origin from which the latitudes are calculated. It is necessary to take this into consideration only in deriving the most probable value of the latitude from all the observations. The new origin is not involved in the calculation of the mean square errors because, as can easily be seen, the displacement of the origin does not change the deviation from the mean. Column IV gives the deviations of the values of $x_k$ from the mean $\bar{x}$. For the reasons just given, these numbers represent the deviations of the numbers $\varphi_k$ from their mean value. The sum of the numbers in column IV can be calculated as a check: if the mean $\bar{x}$ were formally calculated exactly (when $\sum x_k$ can be divided evenly by $n$, with the same number of digits after the decimal point as are taken in the calculations), this sum would have to be exactly equal to 0. Usually, the mean is calculated with a limiting error equal to one half the unit of the last digit. In this checking operation, the numbers $x_k$ should be assumed exact. Therefore, the sum of the numbers in column IV must not exceed the product of one half the unit of the last digit in $\bar{x}$ and the number of measurements.

Column V gives the squares of the deviations. Their sum is necessary for calculating the mean square errors. In practice, instead of writing out the squares of the individual deviations, we may obtain the entire sum of the squares of the deviations on a calculating machine by the method of "accumulation." If we do this, however, we do not have the sum-of-squares check and, therefore, the check must be made in another manner, namely, by using the following identity, which is a consequence of the formula for calculating the variance:

$$\sum_{k=1}^{n} (x_k - \bar{x})^2 = \sum_{k=1}^{n} x_k^2 - \bar{x}^2 n.$$

This identity is satisfied almost exactly because, in the calculation of the sum of the squares on the calculating machine, all the digits formally obtained are usually used and there will only be the discrepancy resulting from the inexactness of the mean $\bar{x}$. In each particular case, we may calculate the limiting value of the difference between the two sides of the identity.

We now make some clarifying remarks about the calculations in the last column.

All the calculations of the most probable value of the latitude and of the mean square errors appear in column VI. The number $\varphi_0$, referred to above, is written first. The mean value $\bar{x}$ is then computed. When this number is added to $\varphi_0$, we obtain the arithmetic mean, that is, the most probable value of the latitude. If we divide the sum of the squares of the deviations from the mean by the number of measurements minus 1, we find the square of the most probable value of the mean square error of a single measurement. If we divide $\sigma$ by the square root of the number of measurements, we get the mean square error of the result. The result is usually written as shown in the next-to-the-last row of column VI. Sometimes, the probable (instead of the mean square) error is given. Therefore, it should be stated what kind of error is given in the result.

It is clear from the value of the mean square error of the mean value that the hundredths of a second are completely unreliable in the result. Therefore, it would be better to give the final result only up to the tenths of a second, as was done in the last row of column VI. The probabilistic meaning of the result follows from the properties of the normal distribution. The actual value of the latitude lies between $41°19'30.9''$ and $41°19'31.9''$ with probability 0.68; it lies between $41°19'29.9''$ and $41°19'32.9''$ with probability 0.9973.

Since a reliable knowledge of the sum of the squares of the deviations is necessary for the determination of the mean errors, we shall check it by means of the identity given above. We obtain

$$\sum_{k=1}^{n} (x_k - \bar{x})^2 = 78.49 - 28.23 = 50.26.$$

This difference between the initial value and the check is insignificant. Therefore, we may be sure of the accuracy of the calculations.

Finally, by using the mean square error of a single measurement $\sigma$, we may see whether there are gross errors in the measurements or not. To do this, we take the deviation from the mean $x_k - \bar{x}$ (for $k = 1, 2 \ldots, 14$) of greatest absolute value and we find the ratio of this deviation to the mean square error of a single measurement. In the present example, we have $3.62/1.97 = 1.84$. Since this number is less than 3, we may assume that there are no gross errors.

Chapter 15

# ANALYSIS OF MEASUREMENTS WHICH ARE NOT EQUALLY PRECISE

## 73. THE CONCEPT OF UNEQUALLY PRECISE MEASUREMENTS. WEIGHTED MEASUREMENTS

In practice, we often can get the most reliable determination of some quantity or other by comparing measurements made on different instruments and by different techniques. This is especially true of the fundamental astronomic constants. One of these fundamental constants is the average distance between the earth and the sun or, equivalently, the parallax of the sun. The solar parallax is determined in a number of ways, which give slightly different results.

The simplest example of unequally precise measurements is the case of a set of values that are not directly measured but that are deduced from equally precise measurements, the number of which is different in the case of different deductions.

Suppose that we have made $m_1$ equally precise measurements and that we have found the most probable value $x_1$ of the quantity being measured. Suppose that we now make a second series of $m_2$ measurements of the same quantity, either at the same or at another observatory, and that these measurements give a number $x_2$. Suppose that a third set of $m_3$ measurements gives the result $x_3$, etc. We now have the problem of deriving the most probable value of the measured quantity on the basis of these results $x_1, x_2, \ldots, x_n$.

Let us suppose that the basic measurements from which these numbers are derived are equally precise (for example, that they were made on the same type of instrument though at different observatories). We denote by $\sigma$ the mean square error of a single measurement. From formula (14.11) of Section 69, for the mean square errors of the numbers $x_1, x_2, \ldots, x_n$, we have the expressions

$$\sigma_k = \frac{\sigma}{\sqrt{m_k}}, \quad k = 1, 2, \ldots, n. \tag{15.1}$$

Since the mean square errors of the given values $x_1, x_2, \ldots, x_n$ are different, these quantities cannot be considered equally precise.

In other cases, the given values $x_1, x_2, \ldots, x_n$ must be considered unequally precise on the basis of information regarding the various conditions under which the measurements are made, the varying accuracy of the instruments used, etc.

The mean square errors $\sigma_1, \sigma_2, \ldots, \sigma_n$ of the measurements that gave these values are not known in all problems of this type. Sometimes, on the basis of general information regarding the conditions under which the measurements are made and the ways in which $x_1, x_2, \ldots, x_n$ are determined, it is known that the measurements are unequally precise, but there are no definite numerical criteria for the degree of inequality of precision.

The formal test of unequal precision of the measurements is the fact that the mean square errors $\sigma_1, \sigma_2, \ldots, \sigma_n$ of the measurements that gave the random values $x_1, x_2, \ldots, x_n$, respectively, are different. Let us assume that $\sigma_1, \ldots, \sigma_n$ are unknown.

In considering unequally precise measurements, it is convenient to use the numbers $p_1, p_2, \ldots, p_n$, known as the weights of the measurements, instead of the quantities $\sigma_1, \sigma_2, \ldots, \sigma_n$. These are defined by the equations

$$p_k = \frac{\sigma_0^2}{\sigma_k^2}, \tag{15.2}$$

where $\sigma_0^2$ is an *arbitrary* positive number. From the definition, it follows

(a) that the weights of unequally precise measurements are inversely proportional to their variances (that is, to the squares of the mean square errors) and

(b) that the weights are relative numbers; that is, all the weights may be multiplied or divided by a single number (this being true because of the arbitrary choice of $\sigma_0^2$).

There is a simple interpretation of the proportionality constant $\sigma_0^2$. If there exists a $k = \bar{k}$ such that $\sigma_{\bar{k}} = \sigma_0$, then $p_{\bar{k}} = 1$. Therefore, we may say that $\sigma_0$ is the mean square error of a measurement of unit weight. Sometimes, we say briefly that $\sigma_0$ is the mean square error per unit weight. Sometimes, $\sigma_0$ is chosen in such a way that the sum of the weights for all the measurements is equal to unity. Then, all the weights will be fractions. In astronomical work, we usually choose $\sigma_0$ in such a way that all the weights are integers.

We should mention one case, referred to above, in which the weights can be determined immediately. Suppose that the numbers $x_1, x_2, \ldots, x_n$ are the arithmetic means obtained from $m_1, m_2, \ldots, m_n$ equally precise observations. It is clear from formulas (15.1) for the $\sigma_k$ that the $\sigma_k^2$ are inversely proportional to the numbers $m_k$. But, according to (15.2), the weights are inversely proportional to the $\sigma_k^2$. Therefore, in the present case, the weights are directly proportional to the number of observations $m_k$. In this case, we take for the weights those numbers of observations from which the means were obtained. This can be stated in another way. Each mean obtained from $m_k$ observations is equivalent to $m_k$ equally precise values. Therefore, $m_k$ is the "weight" of the number $x_k$.

Thus, the method of determining the weights of unequally precise measurements consists in the following:

1. If the $\sigma_k$ are known, we choose $\sigma_0$ arbitrarily. It is advisable to take a value close to the mean of the $\sigma_k$. We calculate the weights from the formula

$$p_k = \frac{\sigma_0^2}{\sigma_k^2}.$$

2. If $x_1, x_2, \ldots, x_n$ are the arithmetic means obtained from sets of $m_1, m_2, \ldots, m_n$ equally precise measurements, we take these numbers for the weights.

3. If neither of the above conditions is satisfied but, for some reason or other, we must consider the observations as unequally precise, the weights are assigned by the investigator somewhat arbitrarily (though in such a way that the most precise observations have the greatest weights).

## 74. THE MOST PROBABLE VALUE OF THE MEASURED QUANTITY

Suppose that values $x_k$ with weights $p_k$ are given. Independent of the method in which the weights are obtained, we can, from the definition of weights (15.2), write

$$p_k = \frac{\sigma_0^2}{\sigma_k^2},$$

where $\sigma_0^2$ is an as yet unknown factor. (It has a definite value, however, because the choice of the given numbers $p_k$ means that a definite value is assigned to the number $\sigma_0^2$.) For the moment, let us assume that $\sigma_0$ is given. From the weights and the value of $\sigma_0$, we determine the mean square errors of the measurements:

$$\sigma_k = \frac{\sqrt{p_k}}{\sigma_0}. \tag{15.3}$$

If the numbers $\sigma_k$ are given instead of the weights, we assign a value to $\sigma_0$ and calculate the weights from the same formula. The normal distribution law of the errors can be written in the form

$$f_k(\delta) = \frac{1}{\sigma_k\sqrt{2\pi}} \exp\left[-\frac{\delta^2}{2\sigma_k^2}\right] = \frac{\sqrt{p_k}}{\sigma_0\sqrt{2\pi}} \exp\left[-\frac{p_k\delta^2}{2\sigma_0^2}\right]$$

for each measurement.

Suppose that some hypothesis is made regarding the unknown quantity $a$. Then, for each measurement, we can determine the error

$$\delta_k = x_k - a$$

and can calculate the probability of obtaining an error close to $\delta_k$. We denote this probability by $P(\delta_k < \delta < \delta_k + \Delta\delta)$ or, more briefly, $P(\delta \approx \delta_k)$.

From the normal law,

$$P(\delta \approx \delta_k \mid a) = \frac{\sqrt{p_k}\,\Delta\delta}{\sigma_0 \sqrt{2\pi}} \exp\left[-\frac{p_k \delta_k^2}{2\sigma_0^2}\right].$$

Assuming, as in the preceding chapter, that the results of the measurements are mutually independent random variables, we use the theorem on multiplying probabilities to obtain the probability of a set of errors close to $\delta_1, \delta_2, \ldots, \delta_n$:

$$P(\delta \approx \delta_1, \delta_2, \ldots, \delta_n \mid a) = \left(\frac{\Delta\delta}{\sigma_0 \sqrt{2\pi}}\right)^n \sqrt{p_1 p_2 \ldots p_n} \exp\left[-\frac{\sum p_k \delta_k^2}{2\sigma_0^2}\right]. \tag{15.4}$$

Under the hypothesis chosen regarding the quantity $a$, the errors $\delta_1, \delta_2, \ldots, \delta_n$ are uniquely determined by the numbers $x_1, x_2, \ldots, x_n$. Therefore,

$$P(\delta \approx \delta_1, \delta_2, \ldots, \delta_n) = P(x \approx x_1, x_2, \ldots, x_n \mid a),$$

that is, the right side of the preceding equation gives the conditional probability that the results of the measurements will be close to those obtained for the given value of $a$. This probability is a function of $a$. Let us assume that prior to the measurements all the hypotheses regarding the quantity $a$ are equally probable in some region. From the corollary to Bayes' formula, the *a posteriori* probabilities of the hypotheses after the event has occurred are proportional to the conditional probabilities of the event under those hypotheses. Here, the set of results of the measurements $(x_1, x_2, \ldots, x_n)$ is a random event. Therefore, we may write

$$P(a \mid x_1, x_2, \ldots, x_n) = C \exp\left[-\frac{\sum_{k=1}^{n} p_k \delta_k^2}{2\sigma_0^2}\right], \tag{15.5}$$

Where $C$ includes the proportionality constant and the factors

$$\left(\frac{\Delta\delta}{\sigma_0 \sqrt{2\pi}}\right)^n \sqrt{p_1 p_2 \ldots p_n}.$$

It follows from the equation above that the most probable hypothesis with regard to $a$ will be the one that gives the quantity

$$S(a)=\sum_{k=1}^{n} p_k\delta_k^2 \tag{15.6}$$

its minimum value. We replace $\delta_k$ with $x_k-a$ and we find the value of $a$ at which $S(a)$ has its minimum value. When we differentiate $S(a)$ and set the derivative equal to 0, we obtain

$$\frac{dS(a)}{da}=-\sum_{k=1}^{n} 2p_k(x_k-a)=0, \quad a\sum_{k=1}^{n} p_k=\sum_{k=1}^{n} p_kx_k. \tag{15.7}$$

For brevity in writing, we define

$$p=\sum_{k=1}^{n} p_k. \tag{15.8}$$

From (15.7), we obtain the expression

$$\overline{x}_p=\frac{\sum_{k=1}^{n} p_kx_k}{p} \tag{15.9}$$

for the most probable value $\overline{x}_p$ of the quantity $a$. This quantity is called the weighted mean of the unequally precise measurements. Thus, when unequally precise measurements are made, we need to take the weighted mean of the results of the measurements as the most probable value of the quantity being measured.

Formula (14.9) is a special case of the formula that we have just written. If the measurements are equally precise, we may take the weight of each measurement as being equal to unity and obtain the simple mean.

It is easy to see that the weighted mean has the following property. The weighted sum of all deviations from the weighted mean is equal to 0. For, on the basis of (15.9), we have

$$\sum_{k=1}^{n} p_k(x_k-\overline{x}_p)=\sum_{k=1}^{n} p_kx_k-\overline{x}_p\sum_{k=1}^{n} p_k=$$
$$=\sum_{k=1}^{n} p_kx_k-\overline{x}_p p=0. \tag{15.10}$$

## 75. THE MEAN SQUARE ERROR OF THE WEIGHTED MEAN

The quantities $x_1, x_2, \ldots, x_n$ are the individual values of the random variables that are the possible results of the measurements $\xi_1, \xi_2, \ldots, \xi_n$. Therefore, the weighted mean $\overline{x}_p$ is one of the values of the random variable

$$\bar{\xi}_p = \frac{\sum_{k=1}^{n} p_k \xi_k}{p}.$$

Since $\bar{\xi}_p$ is a linear function of $\xi_k$, it obeys a normal distribution law (this follows from the basic hypothesis of a normal law for random errors and from the property of a normal law). Therefore, to evaluate the possible spread of the values $\bar{\xi}_p$, it will be sufficient to determine the variance of this quantity. From the theorem on the variance of a linear function of mutually independent random variables, we have

$$\sigma^2_{\bar{\xi}_p} = \frac{1}{p^2} \sum_{k=1}^{n} p_k^2 \sigma_k^2,$$

where the $\sigma_k^2$ are the variances of the random results of the successive measurements. If we use the weights $p_k$ instead of the $\sigma_k^2$ in accordance with formulas (15.2), we obtain

$$\sigma^2_{\bar{\xi}_p} = \frac{\sigma_0^2}{p^2} \sum_{k=1}^{n} p_k = \frac{\sigma_0^2}{p},$$

so that

$$\sigma_{\bar{\xi}_p} = \frac{\sigma_0}{\sqrt{p}}. \qquad (15.11)$$

This formula is exact, but the mean square error per unit weight is unknown except in those exceptional cases in which the quality of the measurements is carefully studied with precision measuring devices. The fact that the denominator is the square root of the sum of the weights is the basis for choosing the weights in such a way that their sum is equal to unity (thus using the fact that the weights are relative). When this condition holds, the mean square error of the weighted mean is equal to the mean square error per unit weight.

Formula (14.11) of Section 70 can be considered a special case of formula (15.11). If the measurements are equally precise, the weight of each of them will be equal to unity.

## 76. THE MOST PROBABLE VALUE OF THE MEAN SQUARE ERROR OF A MEASUREMENT OF UNIT WEIGHT

In Section 74, to find the most probable value of the quantity measured, we used formula (15.4) to determine the conditional probability of the set of measurements under a hypothesis regarding the value of $a$ with the quantity $\sigma_0$ given. To find the most probable value of the mean square error with unit weight, we use the same expression (15.4), but now we treat $\sigma_0$ as unknown and make hypotheses with regard to its value. Therefore, we single out the factors in (15.4) containing $\sigma_0$ and $\frac{1}{\sqrt{2\pi}}$ and denote the remaining factors by $C'$:

$$P(x \approx x_1, x_2, \ldots, x_n \mid a, \sigma_0) =$$

$$= C' \frac{1}{\sigma_0 \sqrt{2\pi}} \sigma_0^{-n+1} \exp\left[-\frac{\sum_{k=1}^{n} p_k \delta_k^2}{2\sigma_0^2}\right].$$

We assume that all the values of $a$ are equally probable and we integrate the above expression from $-\infty$ to $+\infty$ with respect to $a$. Then, on the basis of the generalized formula for the total probability, we find the probability that the results of the measurements will be close to those obtained for all values of $a$ under the hypotheses made regarding the value of $\sigma_0$. Denoting this probability by $P(x \approx x_1, x_2, \ldots, x_n \mid \sigma_0)$, we have

$$P(x \approx x_1, x_2, \ldots, x_n \mid \sigma_0) =$$

$$= C_1 \sigma_0^{-n+1} \int_{-\infty}^{+\infty} \frac{1}{\sigma_0 \sqrt{2\pi}} \exp\left[-\frac{\sum_{k=1}^{n} p_k \delta_k^2}{2\sigma_0^2}\right] da. \tag{15.12}$$

To calculate the integral in (15.12), we rewrite the sum appearing in the argument of the exponential:

$$\sum_{k=1}^{n} p_k \delta_k^2 = \sum_{k=1}^{n} p_k (x_k - a)^2 =$$

$$= \sum_{k=1}^{n} p_k [(x_k - \bar{x}_p) + (\bar{x}_p - a)]^2 =$$

$$= \sum_{k=1}^{n} p_k (x_k - \bar{x}_p)^2 + 2 \sum_{k=1}^{n} p_k (x_k - \bar{x}_p)(\bar{x}_p - a) +$$

$$+ \sum_{k=1}^{n} p_k (\bar{x}_p - a)^2.$$

In the second term, we can take out the factor $(\bar{x}_p - a)$ since it is a constant, although an unknown one (since $a$ is unknown). We can replace the other sum

$$\sum_{k=1}^{n} p_k (x_k - \bar{x}_p)$$

with 0 on the basis of the property referred to above of the weighted mean (cf. (15.10)). In the third term, the constant factor $(\bar{x}_p - a)^2$ can be taken out of the summation and the sum of the weights

$$\sum_{k=1}^{n} p_k$$

can be replaced by $p$. Then,

$$P(x \approx x_1, x_2, \ldots, x_n \mid \sigma_0) =$$

$$= C' \sigma_0^{-n+1} \exp\left[-\frac{\sum_{k=1}^{n} p_k (x_k - \bar{x}_p)}{2\sigma_0^2}\right] \times$$

$$\times \int_{-\infty}^{+\infty} \frac{1}{\sigma_0 \sqrt{2\pi}} \exp\left[-\frac{p(\bar{x}_p - a)^2}{2\sigma_0^2}\right] da. \qquad (15.13)$$

We make one further obvious transformation:

$$P(x \approx x_1, x_2, \ldots, x_n \mid \sigma_0) =$$

$$= \frac{C'}{\sqrt{p}} \sigma_0^{-n+1} \exp\left[-\frac{\sum_{k=1}^{n} p_k (x_k - \bar{x}_p)^2}{2\sigma_0^2}\right] \times$$

$$\times \int_{-\infty}^{+\infty} \frac{1}{\frac{\sigma_0}{\sqrt{p}} \sqrt{2\pi}} \exp\left[-\frac{(a - \bar{x}_p)^2}{2\left(\frac{\sigma_0}{\sqrt{p}}\right)^2}\right] da. \qquad (15.14)$$

The integrand in this equation can be *formally* considered as the probability density of the normally distributed "random" variable $a$ with center of distribution $\bar{x}_p$ and mean square deviation $\frac{\sigma_0}{\sqrt{p}}$. Because of the property of the probability density, its integral over the entire region is equal to unity. Therefore,

$$P(x \approx x_1, x_2, \ldots, x_n \mid \sigma_0) =$$

$$= C'' \sigma_0^{-n+1} \exp\left[-\frac{\sum_{k=1}^{n} p_k (x_k - \bar{x}_p)^2}{2\sigma_0^2}\right], \qquad (15.15)$$

where $C'' = \frac{C'}{\sqrt{p}}$.

We have found the conditional probability of the event $(x_1, x_2, \ldots, x_n)$ under the hypothesis made regarding the value $\sigma_0$. Let us now suppose that the values of $\sigma_0$ are equally probable prior to the measurements in some region, which can here be assumed small. From the corollary to Bayes' formula, the probabilities of the hypotheses after the measurements are proportional to the conditional probabilities of the event (the results of the measurements) under the hypotheses made.

Therefore,

$$P(\sigma_0 \mid \sim x_1, x_2, \ldots, x_n) =$$

$$= KC'' \sigma_0^{-n+1} \exp\left[-\frac{\sum_{k=1}^{n} p_k (x_k - \bar{x}_p)^2}{2\sigma_0^2}\right], \qquad (15.16)$$

where $K$ is a proportionality constant.

We may now seek the most probable value of $\sigma_0$ that can be obtained from the measurements. To do this, it will be sufficient to find that value of $\sigma_0$ at which the right side of (15.16) has its maximum. It is clear from the last formula that $P$ will be greatest if the exponential is minimized. For brevity in writing, we define

$$\overline{S}_p = \sum_{k=p}^{n} p_k (x_k - \overline{x}_p)^2, \qquad f(\sigma_0) = \sigma_0^{-n+1} \exp\left(-\frac{\overline{S}_p}{2\sigma_0^2}\right).$$

Taking the logarithm of the second equation and differentiating, we obtain

$$\ln f(\sigma_0) = (1-n)\ln \sigma_0 - \frac{1}{2}\overline{S}_p \sigma_0^{-2},$$

$$\frac{df(\sigma_0)}{d\sigma_0} = f(\sigma_0)\left[\overline{S}_p \sigma_0^{-3} - (n-1)\sigma_0^{-1}\right],$$

$$\frac{d^2 f(\sigma_0)}{d\sigma_0^2} = f(\sigma_0)\left[\overline{S}_p \sigma_0^{-3} - (n-1)\sigma_0^{-1}\right]^2 +$$

$$+ f(\sigma_0)\left[-3\overline{S}_p \sigma_0^{-4} + (n-1)\sigma_0^{-2}\right].$$

If we set the first derivative equal to 0, we obtain a value of $\sigma_0$ representing an extremum:

$$\sigma_{0,\,\mathrm{e}}^2 = \frac{\overline{S}_p}{n-1}$$

(The e in the subscript indicates an extremum.) The first term in the expression for the second derivative vanishes at $\sigma = \sigma_{0,\,\mathrm{e}}$ and, after some obvious manipulations, the second term gives

$$\left(\frac{d^2 f(\sigma_0)}{d\sigma_0^2}\right)_{\sigma_0 = \sigma_{0,\,\mathrm{e}}} = -2(n-1)\,\sigma_{0,\,\mathrm{e}}^{-(n+1)}\, e^{-\frac{n-1}{2}} < 0. \tag{15.17}$$

It follows from (15.17) that the value found for $\sigma_{0,\mathrm{e}}$ is the most probable one. We shall henceforth denote this most probable value $\sigma_{0,\,\mathrm{e}}$ of the mean square error per unit weight simply by $\sigma$ without subscript. Then,

$$\sigma = \sqrt{\frac{\sum_{k=1}^{n} p_k (x_k - \overline{x}_p)^2}{n-1}}. \tag{15.18}$$

Obviously, formula (14.20) of the preceding chapter is a particular case of (15.18) because in the case of equally precise measurements, the weight of each can be taken equal to unity.

We note the following fact, which is of significance in actual work. If the mean square errors of unequally precise measurements are given, to calculate the weights, we need to introduce a "preliminary" value of the mean square error per unit weight. Let us denote it by $\sigma_0$. After the weights are calculated, the mean square errors of the measurements are discarded, as it were, and only the weights are used. Therefore, the most probable value of a single mean square error $\sigma$ can again be determined from the weights and the results of the measurements. Sometimes, the value of $\sigma$ differs rather sharply from $\sigma_0$. Usually, we take $\sigma$ rather than $\sigma_0$ for the final value (since $\sigma_0$ is a formally chosen constant in no way connected with the measurements that are made). In calculating $\sigma$, we depend on observations, and therefore this number may be considered to reflect to some degree the properties of the measurements. The number $\sigma_0$, on the other hand, is only an auxiliary number used to determine the weights of the measurements.

In formula (15.11) for determining the mean square error of the weighted mean, we must replace $\sigma_0$ with $\sigma$ after calculating the most probable value of the mean square error per unit weight. If there are measurements that are in sharp disagreement with most of the remaining measurements, then these exceptional measurements should be assumed to contain gross errors and must be excluded according to the 3-sigma rule. If the $\sigma_k$ are given, measurements for which

$$|x_k - \bar{x}| > 3\sigma_k.$$

are discarded. If it is the weights and not the $\sigma_k$ that are given, the $\sigma_k$ must be calculated from the value of $\sigma$ and the weights $p$, and the 3-sigma rule must be used. Calculation of the $\sigma_k$ must be made only for those measurements in which $x_k$ differs appreciably from $\bar{x}$. If measurements with gross errors are found when the 3-sigma rule is used (sometimes the 2- or 4-sigma rule is employed instead), these measurements must either be discarded or be verified by some other supplementary means.

## 77. THE PROCEDURE FOR ANALYZING UNEQUALLY PRECISE MEASUREMENTS OF A FIXED QUANTITY. AN EXAMPLE

In calculating the geographical latitude of the Moscow State University Observatory on the Presna, Schweitzer's observations on nine stars were used. Each star was observed several times. Therefore, the mean square errors, shown in the third column of the following table, were used:

| I | II | III | IV | V | VI | VII | VIII | IX | X |
|---|---|---|---|---|---|---|---|---|---|
| No. | $x_k$ | $\sigma_k$ | $\sigma_0 \cdot \sigma_k$ | $p_k$ | $p_k x_k$ | $x_k - \bar{x}$ | $p_k(x_k - \bar{x})$ | $p_k(x_k - \bar{x})^2$ | $p_k x_k^2$ |
| 1 | 1″.29 | 0″.25 | 0.80 | 0.64 | 0″.83 | +0″.52 | +0″.33 | 0.17 | 1.07 |
| 2 | 0.39 | 0.27 | 0.74 | 0.55 | 0.21 | −0.38 | −0.21 | 0.08 | 0.08 |
| 3 | 1.61 | 0.20 | 1.00 | 1.00 | 1.61 | +0.84 | +0.84 | 0.71 | 2.59 |
| 4 | 1.27 | 0.23 | 0.87 | 0.76 | 0.97 | +0.50 | +0.38 | 0.19 | 1.23 |
| 5 | 0.81 | 0.19 | 1.05 | 1.10 | 0.89 | +0.04 | +0.04 | 0.00 | 0.72 |
| 6 | 0.61 | 0.40 | 0.50 | 0.25 | 0.15 | −0.16 | −0.04 | 0.01 | 0.09 |
| 7 | 0.22 | 0.21 | 0.95 | 0.90 | 0.20 | −0.55 | −0.50 | 0.28 | 0.04 |
| 8 | 0.08 | 0.18 | 1.11 | 1.23 | 0.10 | −0.69 | −0.85 | 0.59 | 0.01 |
| 9 | 0″.71 | 0″.28 | 0.71 | 0.50 | 0″.36 | −0″.06 | −0″.03 | 0.00 | 0.26 |
| $\sigma_0 = 0''.20$ | | | | $p = 6.93$ | 5″.32 | | (−0″.04) | 2.03 | 6.09 |

The first column gives the number of observations. Since the latitude is determined from observations of the different stars, in practice this column often gives not the number of observations, but the stars that were used. In the present example, observations were made on five stars from the constellation Draco, one star from Cygnus, and three stars from Ursa Major.

Column II gives the numbers $x_k = \varphi_k - \varphi_0$. Here, $\varphi_0 = 55°45'19''$; that is in practice, just as in the example of Chapter 13, a new origin is chosen in such a way that all the $x_k$ are positive.

Column III gives the mean square errors of the values obtained by the method described in the preceding chapter.

Columns IV and V contain a calculation of the weights from the mean square errors by use of the formula

$$p_k = \frac{\sigma_0^2}{\sigma_k^2},$$

in which a preliminary value of 0.20" was taken for $\sigma_0$. The ratios $\sigma_0/\sigma_k$ are calculated first (column IV). The squares of these numbers are given by column V. Column VI, giving the values $p_k x_k$, is necessary for calculating the weighted mean, that is, for calculating the most probable value of the latitude. Therefore, the sums of the numbers appearing in columns V and VI are written in the last line. The values in columns VII, VIII, and IX are explained by the column headings. We need only remember that the weighted mean is denoted by $\bar{x}$ without subscript for simplification in writing.

Column X is necessary for a check of the weighted sum of the squares of the deviations from the weighted mean. This check can be made by the easily derived formula

$$\sum_{k=1}^{n} p_k (x_k - \bar{x})^2 = \sum_{k=1}^{n} p_k x_k^2 - p\bar{x}^2, \tag{15.19}$$

where $p$ is defined by equation (15.8).

Column VIII is necessary for a check of the calculation of the deviations from the weighted mean and their multiplication by the weights. The check consists in determining the sum of the numbers in column VIII. If the division is precise in the calculation of the weighted mean, the sum will, because of the property of a weighted mean, have to be exactly equal to 0. Of course, such cases happen rarely since the weighted mean is only approximately calculated (usually with rounding off). Therefore, the limiting error of the sum is equal to the product of one half the unit of the last digit in the number $\bar{x}$ and the sum of the weights, provided the sum is obtained on a calculating machine by accumulation. (In this check, the numbers $x_k$ and $p_k$ can be formally considered exact.) If the sum of the numbers in column VIII is less than this limiting error, we may assume that there were no errors in this part of the work. Otherwise, it will be necessary to find the error.

The procedure described above is rather detailed. The person performing an experiment can shorten it somewhat as follows. First, to calculate the weights, he may calculate the numbers $\sigma_k^2$ and then obtain the weights by dividing $\sigma_0^2$ by the numbers obtained. Second, if he does not intend to make the check of the weighted sum of the squares of the deviations from the weighted mean, column VI can be excluded and the sum of the numbers in this column can be obtained on a calculating machine by the method of accumulation. Third, column IX may be omitted and the sum obtained again by the method of accumulation.

A portion of the calculations is performed outside the scheme: determination of the weighted mean:

$$\bar{x} = \frac{5.32''}{6,93} = 0.77'', \quad \bar{\varphi} = 55°45'19'' + 0.77'' = 55°45'19.77'';$$

calculation of the mean square error per unit weight:

$$\sigma^2 = \frac{2.03}{9-1} = 0.25, \quad \sigma = 0.50'';$$

calculation of the mean square error of the weighted mean:

$$\sigma_{\bar{\varphi}} = \frac{0.50''}{\sqrt{6{,}93}} = \frac{0.50''}{2{,}63} = 6.19''.$$

Calculations for checking:

The absolute value of the sum of the numbers in column VIII is equal to 0.4″. To show the admissability of such a deviation from 0, we must calculate the limiting error of this sum, taking into account the way in which it was derived (see Section 6). The limiting error is computed here in a manner somewhat more complicated than that explained above. In addition to the error resulting from the fact that the weighted mean is determined only approximately, we need to consider the error resulting from discarding the digits in the individual terms.

Since the numbers $p_k$ and $x_k$ can be considered as exact, the limiting error of each of the terms added must be taken equal to one half the unit of the last digit, that is, 0.005. Therefore, the total value found for the error of the sum is

$$9 \cdot 0.5 \cdot 10^{-2} + 0.5 \cdot 10^{-2} \cdot 6.93 = 8 \cdot 10^{-2}.$$

The value of the sum is only one half its limiting error. Therefore, there is no reason for supposing that there are errors in the calculations.

A check of the weighted sum of the squares of the deviations from the mean by using the formula given earlier yields

$$\overline{x^2} = 0.59, \qquad p\overline{x^2} = 4.1, \qquad \left(\sum_{k=1}^{n} p_k (x_k - \bar{x})^2\right) = 6.1 - 4.1 = 2.0.$$

The discrepancy between the value of the sum (in the parentheses) obtained in the check and the value found in the original calculations is insignificant. Therefore, we may assume that there are no errors here.

The result may be written

$$\varphi = 55°45'1977'' \pm 0.19'' \text{ (mean square error)}.$$

Since the hundredth parts of a second are not sufficiently reliable, we may write the result as

$$\varphi = 55°45'19.8'' \pm 0.2''.$$

Chapter 16

# DETERMINATION OF SEVERAL UNKNOWNS IN EQUATIONS BY THE METHOD OF LEAST SQUARES

## 78. CONDITIONAL AND NORMAL EQUATIONS. LEGENDRE'S PRINCIPLE

In astronomical work and in a number of other applied disciplines, problems are frequently encountered in which the quantities to be determined are not observed directly. Instead of the quantities themselves, certain other quantities, which are functions of the unknowns, can be determined from observations.*

Example 1. Suppose that observations yield values $x_k$ and $y_k$ for the quantities $x$ and $y$. Let us suppose that these quantities are related as follows:

$$y = a + bx + cx^2,$$

where $a$, $b$, and $c$ are coefficients that are to be determined. Each observation gives an equation with three unknowns

$$y_k = a + bx_k + cx_k^2 \qquad (k = 1, 2, \ldots, n),$$

where $n$ is the number of measurements.

Example 2. In examining certain instruments, the problem arises of determining the errors in the individual components of the instrument in question. Knowledge of the errors in the components makes it possible to calculate the error inherent in the entire instrument under different conditions. Direct measurements of the errors in the components would require taking the instrument apart, and making measurements with each component separately. Such a course is not always convenient and it may not give reliable results because in reassembling the instrument errors in some of the components (for example, the sizes of gaps) may change. For the sake of clarity, let us consider an instrument for measuring angles. Let us proceed as follows. First we measure several angles of different magnitudes with a much more precise instrument than the one that we are testing, so that the result may be considered virtually exact in comparison with the measurements of the instrument that we are testing. Measurements of the angles taken with the instrument that we are testing will yield values different from those treated as exact values. The differences can be considered as exact errors of the instrument for

---

*Thus, direct measurement of the desired quantities is replaced by measurement of other quantities; that is, the unknown quantities are determined by means of other quantities. Therefore, it is sometimes said that indirect or intermediary measurements are made. This terminology, however, is somewhat unfortunate.

the different values of the angle. Knowing the construction of the instrument, we can think of its total error as a function of the errors of the components. Applying this functional relationship for the various values of the angle, we obtain equations of the form

$$\Delta\alpha_k = f_k(\alpha_k, \Delta a, \Delta b, \ldots),$$

where $\Delta\alpha_k$ is the error in the angle, $\Delta a$, $\Delta b$, .. are the errors in the components of the instruments, and $f_k$ is the functional relationship. The subscript $k$ shows that, under certain conditions, the form of the functional relationship may depend on the quantity measured.

Various examples of problems similar to this are encountered in astrometry, celestial mechanics, and other divisions of astronomy.

In its general form, the problem is as follows. If $a, b, c, \ldots$ are the quantities that we wish to find, we first obtain instead the quantities $l_k$, which represent particular functions of the unknowns $a, b, c, \ldots$ . Each observation gives a conditional equation of the form

$$f_k(a, b, c, \ldots) = l_k, \tag{16.1}$$

where $k$ is the number of the particular observation in question. It is assumed that the $f_k$ are differentiable functions of the argument $a, b, c, \ldots$. Generally speaking, these functions also contain parameters, which vary from observation to observation.

If there were no random errors in the observations or if they were so small that we might neglect them, it would, in the general case, be sufficient to make just as many observations as there are unknowns, set up the equations, and solve them. Only with special combinations of values of the $l_k$ could it happen that some of the equations would be consequences of the others, so that the number of equations would have to be increased.

But in problems of the usual type, the numbers $l_k$ contain random errors large enough so that they cannot be neglected. If we set up only as many independent equations as we have unknowns, these errors will show up in full force in the solutions to the system. In order to hope for a partial cancellation of the errors, we need to make considerably more observations and, consequently, set up considerably more equations of the form (16.1) than we have unknowns.* Then, we have a system of equations of the form

$$f_k(a, b, c, \ldots) = l_k \qquad (k = 1, 2, \ldots, n); \tag{16.2}$$

where $n$ is much greater than the number of unknowns—which, from an algebraic point of view, is somewhat peculiar. Equations of such a system are called conditional or initial.**

*The problem of the accumulation of errors in such systems and of their effect on the overall error is very complicated and has not been studied in the case of nonlinear equations.

**We note that there is confusion in the terminology used in this connection. According to a remark of M. I. Idel'son, such equations are said to be conditional "in the astronomical sense." The problem consists in the fact that in geodesy the term "conditional equations" is applied to exact equations giving the connection between the unknowns, for example, equations like the one stating that the sum of the angles of a triangle is 180°. (The sum of the measurements of the angles usually differs from 180° by a small amount.) In geodesy, the equations of which we are speaking in the present section are called initial. However, we shall refer to them as "conditional" equations.

The peculiarity about the system of conditional equations (16.2) consists in the fact that, because of the random errors that appear in them, the system is incompatible, even if the functional relationships are exact (which is not always the case). This means that values $a, b, c, \ldots$ which satisfy all the equations of the system simultaneously do not exist. In other words, for any values $a', b', c', \ldots$ that may be substituted into the system,

$$f_k(a', b', c', \ldots) - l_k = \delta_k \neq 0 \qquad (k = 1, 2, \ldots, n). \tag{16.3}$$

Because of the incompatibility of the system of conditional equations, we must make some agreement as to the method of solution and we must clarify the probabilistic meaning of the method chosen. Obviously, we would naturally choose a convention according to which the absolute values of the discrepancies will be as small as possible, but this cannot always be done. If there are as many equations as there are unknowns, we can make all the discrepancies equal to 0. In the usual case, however, the problem of minimizing the absolute values of the discrepancies is indeterminate. For example, we may pick out as many equations as we have unknowns and solve them. The discrepancies in these equations will be equal to 0, but we will be able to say nothing about the discrepancies in the remaining equations, which may be quite large. Obviously, we may speak only of certain over-all conditions to be imposed on the discrepancies. We mention two such conditions.

It would be quite natural to require that the sum of the absolute values of the discrepancies be minimized. This condition was proposed by Edgeworth. However, solution of conditional equations by Edgeworth's method has not attained widespread use.

Another convention had already been proposed by Legendre and published by him. After the publication of Legendre's work, Gauss stated that he had used such a convention over a period of several years; however, it is naturally referred to as Legendre's principle.

Legendre's principle. *If a system of equally precise conditional equations is given, let us agree to seek unknowns such that the sum of the squares of the discrepancies will be minimized.*

This condition was soon accepted for completely understandable reasons. Although it is impossible to ensure that the individual discrepancies will be small, minimization of the sum of the squares does ensure that the individual errors are bounded. The sum of the squares of the discrepancies is an analytic function of the unknowns, provided, of course, the functions appearing in the conditional equations are analytic. Therefore, it is always possible to set up equations for determining the values of the unknowns that correspond to a minimum. Furthermore, as will be shown in the following section, Legendre's principle has a simple probabilistic interpretation.

Following Legendre's principle, let us form the sum of the squares of the discrepancies

$$S = \sum_{k=1}^{n} [f_k(a, b, c, \ldots) - l_k]^2 \qquad (16.4)$$

for the case of equally precise measurements, and let us write the necessary conditions for a minimum of this sum:

$$\frac{\partial S}{\partial a} = \frac{\partial S}{\partial b} = \frac{\partial S}{\partial c} = \ldots = 0. \qquad (16.5)$$

These equations for $a, b, c, \ldots$ are called *normal equations*. We can always obtain a system of equations containing as many equations as there are unknowns to be determined. Therefore, the problem is well defined in the general case.

If the conditional equations are nonlinear, they may have several systems of values of the unknowns, and it is then necessary to choose a system that will give the "minimum minimorum" to the sum of the squares of the discrepancies. The existence of such a minimum is ensured by the fact that $S$ is a positive-definite function of the unknowns that can vanish only when all the discrepancies are equal to 0. This is impossible if there are random errors in the numbers $l_k$. Therefore, $S(a, b, c, \ldots)$ must have a minimum.

## 79. THE PROBABILISTIC MEANING OF LEGENDRE'S PRINCIPLE

Let us suppose that random errors are contained only in the results of the measurements $l_k$. The functions $f_k$ may also contain the results of measurements in the form of parameters, but we shall assume that they do not contain random errors. This is legitimate if the errors in the parameters are small in comparison with the errors in the values for the $l_k$. Let us assume also, as in the preceding chapters, that the measurements of the $l_k$ are mutually independent and that the errors in the numbers $l_k$ obey a normal law of distribution. Under these conditions, the discrepancies

$$\delta_k = f_k(a, b, c, \ldots) - l_k \qquad (16.6)$$

represent exact errors, which obey the same normal law, by virtue of the condition of equal precision. The variances in the successive measurements are the same and the expectations of the errors are equal to 0.

Let us assume for the moment that $a, b, c, \ldots$ are known and that the errors $\delta_k$ have been calculated. The probability of obtaining errors that are close in magnitude to the errors made when the measurements were taken is given by

$$P_k(\delta_k < \delta < \delta_k + \Delta\delta) = \frac{1}{\sigma\sqrt{2\pi}} e^{-\frac{\delta_k^2}{2\sigma^2}} \Delta\delta, \qquad (16.7)$$

where $\Delta\delta$ is a small positive number (see Chapter 11). Let us agree to write the left side of this equation briefly as $P_k(\sim \delta_k)$. Since $a, b, c, \ldots$ are unknown, we cannot obtain the numbers $\delta_k$. We can only make various hypotheses concerning the quantities $a, b, c, \ldots$, find the corresponding values of $\delta_k$, and calculate the probabilities. To bring out the dependence of $\delta_k$ and $P_k$ on $a, b, c, \ldots$, let us write equation (16.7) in the form

$$P_k(\sim \delta_k \mid a, b, c, \ldots) = \frac{\Delta\delta}{\sigma\sqrt{2\pi}} e^{-\frac{\delta_k^2}{2\sigma^2}}. \tag{16.8}$$

This probability can also be treated as the probability of obtaining the numbers $l_k$ when the measurements are made, since $\delta_k$ is expressed in terms of $l_k$ and the nonrandom variables $-f_k(a, b, c, \ldots)$. Therefore, the expression for the probability is finally written in the form

$$P_k(\sim l_k \mid a, b, c, \ldots) = \frac{\Delta}{\sigma\sqrt{2\pi}} e^{-\frac{\delta_k^2}{2\sigma^2}}, \tag{16.9}$$

where $\sigma$ is treated as a known quantity and $\delta_k$ is defined by equation (16.6).

The probability of obtaining a set of results of measurements close to that obtained is a function of $a, b, c, \ldots$ and is therefore obtained from the theorem on multiplying probabilities of mutually independent events (we are considering the measurements independent):

$$P(\sim l_1, l_2, \ldots, l_n \mid a, b, c, \ldots) = \left(\frac{\Delta}{\sigma\sqrt{2\pi}}\right)^n \exp\left[-\frac{\sum_{k=1}^{n} \delta_k^2}{2\sigma^2}\right]. \tag{16.10}$$

If we make various hypotheses on the magnitudes of the numbers $a, b, c, \ldots$, we shall obtain various probabilities of the actual results of the measurements.

Let us suppose that all the hypotheses regarding the quantities $(a, b, c, \ldots)$ are equally probable in some region (which can be made arbitrarily small) in the neighborhood of the unknown exact values. Then, we may use the corollary to Bayes' formula according to which the *a posteriori* probabilities of the hypotheses after the event has occurred are proportional to the conditional probabilities of the events under the corresponding hypotheses. According to this corollary,

$$P(a, b, c, \ldots \mid l_1, l_2, \ldots, l_n) = K \exp\left(-\frac{\sum_{k=1}^{n} \delta_k^2}{2\sigma^2}\right), \tag{16.11}$$

where $K$ is the product of a proportionality constant and a factor that does not depend on $a, b, c, \ldots$. Thus, the probability of the hypotheses concerning the values $a, b, c, \ldots$ is a function of these values. Therefore, the question arises determining those values $a, b, c, \ldots$ at which the probability has a maximum. Since $a, b, c, \ldots$ appear only in the exponential, the hypothesis regarding $a, b, c, \ldots$ will be most probable at those values at which $\sum_{k=1}^{n} \delta_k^2$ is smallest. This is simply Legendre's principle. Thus, we come to the following conclusion:

*If a system of equally precise conditional equations is given, the most probable values of the unknowns are obtained when the sum of the squares of the discrepancies is smallest.*

## 80. GENERALIZATION OF LEGENDRE'S PRINCIPLE TO UNEQUALLY PRECISE CONDITIONAL EQUATIONS. REDUCTION OF UNEQUALLY PRECISE TO EQUALLY PRECISE EQUATIONS

Suppose that for some reason the results of one's measurements cannot be considered equally precise. Let us suppose that the mean square errors $\sigma_1, \sigma_2, \ldots, \sigma_n$ are known for these measurements, and that the weights $p_1, p_2, \ldots, p_n$ are known. We can again calculate the probability of obtaining approximately the number $l_k$ on taking the $k$th measurement, under a definite hypothesis regarding the values $a, b, c, \ldots$:

$$P_k(\delta_k < \delta < \delta_k + \Delta\delta) = \frac{1}{\sigma_k \sqrt{2\pi}} e^{-\frac{\delta_k}{2\sigma_k^2}} \Delta\delta, \tag{16.12}$$

where, according to (16.6),

$$\delta_k = f_k(a, b, c, \ldots) - l_k.$$

We introduce the weights

$$p_k = \frac{\sigma_0^2}{\sigma_k^2},$$

where $\sigma_0$ is the mean square error per unit weight. In the parenthesized expression in (16.12) we write $l_k$ instead of $\delta_k$ since $\delta_k$ is a function of $l_k$ for given values of $a, b, c, \ldots$. Using the abbreviated notation for the inequalities in the parenthesized expression in (16.12), we obtain

$$P(\sim l_k \mid a, b, c, \ldots) = \frac{\sqrt{p_k}}{\sigma_0 \sqrt{2\pi}} \exp\left(-\frac{p_k \delta_k^2}{2\sigma_0^2}\right) \Delta\delta.$$

R

As in the preceding section, we may write the probability of the set of results of the measurements as a function

$$P(\sim l_1, l_2, \ldots, l_n \mid a, b, c, \ldots) = \left(\frac{\Delta\delta}{\sigma_0 \sqrt{2\pi}}\right)^n \left(\prod_{k=1}^{n} \sqrt{p_k}\right) \exp\left[-\frac{\sum_{k=1}^{n} p_k \delta_k^2}{2\sigma_0^2}\right].$$

If we again apply the corollary to Bayes' formula under the assumption of equal probability of the possible sets $(a, b, c)$, we obtain

$$P(a, b, c \mid l_1, l_2, \ldots, l_n) = M \exp\left[-\frac{\sum_{k=1}^{n} p_k \delta_k^2}{2\sigma_0^2}\right], \tag{16.13}$$

where $M$ represents all of the factors not depending on $a, b, c$, that appear in the preceding equation, and also the proportionality constant in the corollary to Bayes' formula.

It follows from this that the most probable set of values of $a, b, c$, are obtained if we require that the sum

$$S_p = \sum_{k=1}^{n} p_k \delta_k^2$$

be minimized. Thus, we come to a generalization of Legendre's principle, which we can formulate as follows:

*If the conditional equations are unequally precise, we should find values of the unknowns that will minimize the sum of the products of the squares of the discrepancies and the weights (the weighted sum of the squares of the discrepancies).*

If the equations are equally precise, all the weights can be considered equal to unity, and we have Legendre's principle in its simple form.

From the generalization of Legendre's principle, it is easy to obtain a rule for reducing non-equally-precise conditional equations to equally precise ones. We write the weighted sum of the squares of the discrepancies as follows:

$$S_p = \sum_{k=1}^{n} (\delta_k \sqrt{p_k})^2.$$

We use the notation $\varepsilon_k = \delta_k \sqrt{p_k}$. Then,

$$S_p = \sum_{k=1}^{n} \varepsilon_k^2.$$

This means that the weighted sum of the squares of the discrepancies can be considered the sum of the squares of the discrepancies for a set of equally precise conditional equations that have discrepancies $\varepsilon_k$. The given equations for the discrepancies

$$\delta_k = f_k(a, b, c) - l_k$$

can easily be converted into equations with discrepancies $\varepsilon_k$ if we consider the relationship between $\delta_k$ and $\varepsilon_k$. Thus, we have the following rule:

*To reduce unequally precise conditional equations to equally precise ones, we should multiply each conditional equation by the square root of its weight.*

The normal equations in the case of nonequally precise conditional equations are obtained by minimizing the function of several arguments:

$$\frac{\partial S_p}{\partial a} = \frac{\partial S_p}{\partial b} = \frac{\partial S_p}{\partial c} = \ldots = 0.$$

## 81. THE REDUCTION OF NONLINEAR CONDITIONAL EQUATIONS TO LINEAR FORM

It is possible to set up normal equations no matter what the form of the conditional equations, that is, for arbitrary functions $f_k(a, b, c)$. The solution of normal equations in the case of nonlinear conditional equations, on the other hand, can present great difficulties. What is still more important is the fact that here the roots of the normal equations will not be linear functions of the random numbers $l_k$. The significance of this fact is due to the following considerations. The most probable values of the roots of the normal equations are obviously functions of the random variables $l_k$ and, consequently, are themselves random. To determine the possible oscillations of the most probable values of the unknowns, we need to know at least the variances of the unknowns. Note that in speaking of the variances of the unknowns, we must consider not only the chosen set of numbers $l_k$ obtained in the series of conditional equations in question but also all possible series of values of $l_k$ that can be obtained due to other combinations of reasons that cause random errors. To each such series will correspond a set of most probable values $\bar{a}, \bar{b}, \bar{c}, \ldots$. This family of sets constitutes the region of possible values of $\bar{a}, \bar{b}, \bar{c}, \ldots$. We may set $E(\bar{a}) = a$, $E(\bar{b}) = b$, $E(\bar{c}) = c, \ldots$ and determine the variances of the random variables $\bar{a}, \bar{b}, \bar{c}, \ldots$; this will give an idea of the reliability of the calculated values of $\bar{a}, \bar{b}, \bar{c}, \ldots$ obtained from the set of measurements.

It is this necessity of determining the variances of $\bar{a}, \bar{b}, \bar{c}, \ldots$ that compel us to consider the matter of the linearity of the conditional equations. In this case, not only is the solution of the normal equations simplified, but so is the problem of determining the variances of the unknowns. This is true because linear conditional equations give linear normal equations. Their roots will be linear functions of the numbers $l_k$, in other words, linear functions of the random errors. If we may consider these errors mutually independent, we have a simple problem of determining the variance of a linear function of the independent variables. This is why the method of least squares is developed only for linear conditional equations.

In the case in which we are given nonlinear conditional equations (for example, in the setting up of an empirical formula that is nonlinear with respect to the parameters), they must be reduced to linear form.* We can show two methods of reducing the equations to linear form.

The first method, which is quite simple, consists in making a change of variables that, after suitable manipulations, will render the conditional equations linear with respect to the new unknowns.

**Example 1.** Suppose that the conditional equations are of the form

$$\alpha_k \sin(a+b) + \beta_k \sin(a-b) + \gamma_k e^{-2c} = l_k, \qquad k = 1, 2, \ldots, n,$$

where $\alpha_k$, $\beta_k$, $\gamma_k$, and $l_k$ are given numbers and $a$, $b$, and $c$ are unknowns. Then, by making the substitution

$$\sin(a+b) = x, \qquad \sin(a-b) = y, \qquad e^{-2c} = z$$

we obtain the linear equations

$$\alpha_k x + \beta_k y + \gamma_k z - l_k = 0.$$

After solving this system, we obtain the most probable values of the unknowns $\bar{x}$, $\bar{y}$, and $\bar{z}$. These random values are linear functions of the random variables $l_k$ and, because of the postulate regarding a normal law for the random errors, we may assert that $\bar{x}$, $\bar{y}$, and $\bar{z}$ are also normally distributed. It follows from the formulas relating $a$, $b$, and $c$ to $x$, $y$, and $z$ that

$$\bar{a} = \frac{1}{2}(\arcsin \bar{x} + \arcsin \bar{y}),$$

$$\bar{b} = \frac{1}{2}(\arcsin \bar{x} - \arcsin \bar{y}),$$

$$\bar{c} = -\frac{1}{2}\ln \bar{z}.$$

Since the distribution laws of $\bar{x}$, $\bar{y}$, and $\bar{z}$ are known (normal), we may find the distribution laws of $\bar{a}$, $\bar{b}$, and $\bar{c}$. Consequently, we may also find their variances, which completely solves the problem in the probabilistic sense.

However, this method is by no means always applicable.

A general method, which is suitable for all conditional equations, rests on the assumption that the discrepancies in the conditional equations are small, for which we need to assume that the coefficients of the conditional equations are exact and that the random errors in the numbers $l_k$ are small (in absolute value). In other words, the incompatibility of the system of conditional equations is "weak."

Let us now find preliminary approximate values of the unknowns by some method and let us denote them by $a_0$, $b_0$, and $c_0$. We can

*This operation is sometimes called *linearization* of the equations.

demonstrate two methods that can be used for choosing the original approximation. The first consists in choosing from the given system as many conditional equations as there are unknowns, taking care to see that the equations chosen are approximately evenly distributed over the system. The solution of the chosen equations yields the numbers $a_0$, $b_0$, and $c_0$. The second method is applicable to those problems whose solutions are obtained gradually as the amount of observational data increases. In astronomical work, such a problem is the determination of the fundamental constants (the parallax of the sun, the precessional constant, etc.). Initial research of this type gives values of the unknowns that can be taken as the original values when new research is done.

Let us set

$$a = a_0 + x_1, \quad b = b_0 + y_1 \quad c = c_0 + z_1, \dots \tag{16.14}$$

We now substitute these expressions into the conditional equations, expand the functions $f_k$ in series of powers of $x_1, y_1, z_1, \dots$, and keep only the first order terms of these corrections.

We then obtain linear conditional equations of the form

$$f_k(a_0, b_0, c_0, \dots) - l_k + \left(\frac{\partial f_k}{\partial a}\right)_0 x_1 + \left(\frac{\partial f_k}{\partial b}\right)_0 y_1 + \left(\frac{\partial f_k}{\partial c}\right)_0 z_1 + \dots = 0, \tag{16.15}$$

where the subscript zero by the partial derivatives indicates that, after the differentiation, we should take $a = a_0$, etc. Solution of the system of linear conditional equations by a method to be shown below yields the probable values $\bar{x}_1$, $\bar{y}_1$, and $\bar{z}_1$ and the mean square errors $\sigma_{\bar{x}_1}$, $\sigma_{\bar{y}_1}$, $\sigma_{\bar{z}_1}$. We then make the approximation

$$a_1 = a_0 + \bar{x}_1, \quad b_1 = b_0 + \bar{y}_1, \quad c_1 = c_0 + \bar{z}_1, \dots$$

with the above mean square errors, since $a_0, b_0, c_0, \dots$ are fixed (nonrandom) numbers. We proceed with this approximation just as with the original one; that is, we set up a linear system of the form

$$f_k(a_1, b_1, c_1) - l_k + \left(\frac{\partial f}{\partial a}\right)_1 x_2 + \left(\frac{\partial f}{\partial b}\right)_1 y_2 + \left(\frac{\partial f}{\partial c}\right)_1 z_2 + \dots = 0,$$

where the subscript 1 by the partial derivative indicates that after the differentiation we set $a = a_1$, etc. Solution of the system yields values $\bar{x}_2, \bar{y}_2, \bar{z}_2, \dots$ and mean square errors $\sigma_{\bar{x}_2}$, $\sigma_{\bar{y}_2}$, $\sigma_{\bar{z}_2}$, .... Then,

$$a_2 = a_1 + x_2, \quad b_2 = b_1 + y_2, \quad c_2 = c_1 + z_2, \dots$$

or

$$a_2 = a_0 + x_1 + x_2, \quad b_2 = b_1 + y_1 + y_2, \quad c_2 = c_1 + z_1 + z_2, \dots$$

In this case, the mean square errors are found from the theorem on the variance of a sum:

$$\sigma_{a_2} = \sqrt{\sigma^2_{\bar{x}_1} + \sigma^2_{\bar{x}_2}}$$

(and similar formulas for $b_2, c_2, \dots$).

For every given system, the question arises as to the convergence of this process of successive approximations. Since formal investigation of the convergence is rather complicated, what one usually does is see whether the approximations are in fact converging. All the calculations are made with a finite number of digits after the decimal point (or with a finite number of significant figures). If the same value is found for two approximations in a row (with the degree of accuracy that is being used), it is assumed that the process of successive approximations is concluded and the values $a$, $b$, $c$ that are obtained are considered final.

This method of linearization is rather tedious. Therefore, it is used only rarely, e.g., only in very important problems. If the method of substitution cannot be applied in a problem, investigators usually prefer to replace the approximately conditional equations with others to which the first method is applicable.

Example 2. Suppose that the table on the right gives the values of an approximately periodic function. Determine the parameters $a$, $b$, $c$, and $P$ of the law of harmonic oscillation approximating it:

$$w = a \sin\left(\frac{2\pi t}{P} + b\right) + c,$$

assuming that there are random errors in the values given for $w$ and that the measurements are equally precise.

| $t$ | $w$ |
|---|---|
| 0.00 | 2.02 |
| 0.52 | 1.86 |
| 1.04 | 1.49 |
| 1.56 | 1.02 |
| 2.08 | 0.51 |
| 2.60 | +0.14 |
| 3.12 | −0.03 |
| 3.64 | +0.15 |
| 4.16 | 0.53 |
| 4.68 | 0.97 |
| 5.20 | 1.46 |
| 5.72 | 1.90 |
| 6.24 | 1.98 |
| | 14.00 |

If we substitute the values given for $t_k$ and $w_k$ into the above equation, we obtain a system of 13 nonlinear conditional equations:

$$a \sin\left(\frac{2\pi t_k}{P} + b\right) + c = w_k, \qquad k = 0, 1, 2, \ldots, 12.$$

From the table and the graph constructed on the basis of it, we may take the following initial approximate values for the unknowns:

$P_0 = 6{,}30$ (since, for $t = 6{,}24$, the initial value of (2.02) has not yet been re-attained);

$c_0 = 1{,}08$ and $a_0 = 0{,}90$ (since the maximum value is close to 2 and among the values there is one close to 0, so that $a$ and $c$ are of the same order; for the value of $c_0$, we take the arithmetic mean of all the $w$);

$b_0 = 1{,}50$, which may be obtained by a crude comparison of the graph with a sine curve and a determination of the displacement.

Let us set

$$a = a_0 + x_1, \qquad b = b_0 + y_1, \qquad c = c_0 + z_1, \qquad P = P_0 + u_1.$$

By linearization, we obtain the following system of linear conditional equations:

$$\sin \tau_k x_1 + a_0 \cos \tau_k y_1 - a_0 \cos \tau_k \frac{2\pi t_k}{P_0^2} u_1 +$$
$$+ z_1 + (a_0 \sin \tau_k + c_0 - w_k) = 0 \qquad (k = 0, 1, 2, \ldots, 12),$$

where

$$\tau_k = \frac{2\pi t_k}{P_0} + b_0.$$

We rewrite this system in the form

$$a_k x_1 + b_k y_1 + c_k z_1 + d_k u_1 + l_k = 0 \qquad (k = 1, 2, \ldots, 12),$$

where

$$a_k = \sin \tau_k, \qquad b_k = a_0 \cos \tau_k,$$

$$c_k = 1, \qquad d_k = -a_0 \cos \tau_k \frac{2\pi t_k}{P_0^2},$$

$$l_k = a_0 \sin \tau_k + c_0 - w_k.$$

In the following sections, a method (based on Legendre's principle) will be examined for solving such a system of conditional equations, and the values of $x_1$, $y_1$, $z_1$, and $u_1$ in this example will be determined. Here, we only note the results of the determination of the first approximation:

$$x_1 = +0.0973; \quad y_1 = +0.0875; \quad z_1 = -0.0749; \quad u_1 = -0.0354.$$

The initial values of the unknowns and the result of the first approximation are shown in the first two columns of the table:

| | | |
|---|---|---|
| $a_0 = 0.90$ | $a_1 = 0.9973$ | $(a) = 1$ |
| $b_0 = 1.50$ | $b_1 = 1.5875$ | $(b) = \frac{\pi}{2} = 1.5708$ |
| $c_0 = 1.08$ | $c_1 = 1.0051$ | $(c) = 1$ |
| $P_0 = 6.30$ | $P_1 = 6.2646$ | $(P) = 6.2832 = 2\pi$ |

We note that an artificial device was used for constructing this example. The exact values of $w$ were calculated for the values of $t$ with step $\frac{\pi}{6}$ to get the value of the parameters $(a)$, $(b)$, $(c)$, and $(P)$ appearing in the third column of this table. These values were increased or decreased in a random manner by 1, 2, or 3 hundredths. The values of $t$ are given in radians with accuracy up to one half of a hundredth. Values of the tabulated function $w = w(t)$, were obtained; the approximative function was constructed for these values. The results of the calculations show that the first approximation already gives values of the parameters close to the original values.

## 82. LINEAR CONDITIONAL AND NORMAL EQUATIONS

Suppose that we have the system of linear conditional equations*

$$a_k x + b_k y + c_k z + d_k u + l_k = 0 \qquad (k = 1, 2, \ldots, n), \tag{16.16}$$

where $x$, $y$, $z$, and $u$ are unknowns and $a_k$, $b_k$, $c_k$, $d_k$, and $l_k$ are numbers that vary from equation to equation, and where $n$ is the number of conditional equations. It should be remembered that we are assuming that only the numbers $l_k$ contain random errors. The numbers $a_k$, $b_k$, $c_k$, and $d_k$ may be approximate, but, by hypothesis, they do not contain random errors. We shall call the numbers $l_k$ the free terms and we shall call $a_k$, $b_k$, $c_k$, and $d_k$ the coefficients.

The discrepancies $\delta_k$ of the equations are found from the relations

$$\delta_k = a_k x + b_k y + c_k z + d_k u + l_k \qquad (k = 1, 2, \ldots, n), \tag{16.17}$$

*For brevity in writing, we shall confine ourselves to the case of four unknowns in all future calculations in this chapter.

in which $x$, $y$, $z$, and $u$ refer to as yet arbitrary numbers. There is a sort of contradiction between the systems of equations (16.16) and (16.17). In connection with this, we should remember that the system of given conditional equations is incompatible and therefore the system (16.16) has only a formal meaning. The sum of the squares of the discrepancies (16.17) is of the form

$$S=\sum_{k=1}^{n}\delta_k^2=\sum_{k=1}^{n}(a_kx+b_ky+c_kz+d_ku+l_k)^2. \tag{16.18}$$

Assuming the conditional equations equally precise, we use Legendre's principle to write the necessary conditions for a minimum:

$$\left.\begin{aligned}\frac{\partial S}{\partial x}&=2\sum_{k=1}^{n}(a_kx+b_ky+c_kz+d_ku+l_k)\,a_k=0,\\ \frac{\partial S}{\partial y}&=2\sum_{k=1}^{n}(a_kx+b_ky+c_kz+d_ku+l_k)\,b_k=0,\\ \frac{\partial S}{\partial z}&=2\sum_{k=1}^{n}(a_kx+b_ky+c_kz+d_ku+l_k)\,c_k=0,\\ \frac{\partial S}{\partial u}&=2\sum_{k=1}^{n}(a_kx+b_ky+c_kz+d_ku+l_k)\,d_k=0.\end{aligned}\right\} \tag{16.19}$$

These conditions lead to the normal equations:

$$\left.\begin{aligned}x\sum a_k^2+y\sum a_kb_k+z\sum a_kc_k+u\sum a_k\,d_k+\sum a_kl_k&=0,\\ x\sum b_ka_k+y\sum b_k^2+z\sum b_kc_k+u\sum b_kd_k+\sum b_kl_k&=0,\\ x\sum c_ka_k+y\sum c_kb_k+z\sum c_k^2+u\sum c_kd_k+\sum c_kl_k&=0,\\ x\sum d_ka_k+y\sum d_kb_k+z\sum d_kc_k+u\sum d_k^2+\sum d_kl_k&=0\end{aligned}\right\} \tag{16.20}$$

(the summations being taken from $k=1$ to $k=n$).

The normal equations are set up analogously for an arbitrary number of unknowns.

The question of the *sufficiency* of these conditions for a minimum of a function of several arguments can be investigated by the familiar means of analysis, but there is no need to do this. The sum of the squares of the discrepancies $S$ is a quadratic form in the arguments $x$, $y$, $z$, and $u$. Therefore, it can have only one extremum. This form is positive-definite. Therefore, it must have a minimum and the roots of the normal equations determine that minimum.

In astronomy and geodesy, Gauss' notation is almost always used in writing the normal equations:

$$\sum_{k=1}^{n}a_k^2=[aa],\quad \sum_{k=1}^{n}a_kb_k=[ab],\ \ldots,\quad \sum_{k=1}^{n}a_kl_k=[al] \tag{16.21}$$

and so forth. In this notation, the system of normal equations with four unknowns becomes

$$\left.\begin{aligned}
[aa]\,x + [ab]\,y + [ac]\,z + [ad]\,u + [al] = 0,\\
[ba]\,x + [bb]\,y + [bc]\,z + [bd]\,u + [bl] = 0,\\
[ca]\,x + [cb]\,y + [cc]\,z + [cd]\,u + [cl] = 0,\\
[da]\,x + [db]\,y + [dc]\,z + [dd]\,u + [dl] = 0.
\end{aligned}\right\} \quad (16.22)$$

We then have the obvious equations

$$[ba] = [ab], \qquad [ca] = [ac] \quad \text{etc.}$$

If unequally precise conditional linear equations and their weights $p_k$. are given, we must apply the general rule for reducing unequally precise equations to equally precise ones. Each conditional equation should be multiplied by the square root of its weight. The transformed system of conditional equations will take the form

$$a_k \sqrt{p_k} x + b_k \sqrt{p_k} y + c_k \sqrt{p_k} z + d_k \sqrt{p_k} u + l_k \sqrt{p_k} = 0.$$

If we apply Legendre's principle to this system and set up the normal equations, we obtain

$$\left.\begin{aligned}
[paa]\,x + [pab]\,y + [pac]\,z + [pad]\,u + [pal] = 0,\\
[pba]\,x + [pbb]\,y + [pbc]\,z + [pbd]\,u + [pbl] = 0,\\
[pca]\,x + [pcb]\,y + [pcc]\,z + [pcd]\,u + [pcl] = 0,\\
[pda]\,x + [pdb]\,y + [pdc]\,z + [pdd]\,u + [pdl] = 0,
\end{aligned}\right\} \quad (16.23)$$

where

$$[paa] = \sum_{k=1}^{n} p_k a_k^2; \quad [pab] = \sum_{k=1}^{n} p_k a_k b_k \quad \text{etc.} \qquad (16.24)$$

The coefficient matrix for the unknowns of the system of normal equations possesses the following two properties: (1) It is symmetric about the principal diagonal; (2) all the elements of the principal diagonal are positive numbers. The second property is a result of the fact that all the elements are the sums of the squares of the coefficients of successive unknowns in the conditional equations (or the sums of the products formed when the squares of the coefficients are multiplied by the weights, which are positive numbers). Such a sum can vanish only if each addend is equal to 0. But this would mean that the conditional equations would contain no terms at all with the corresponding unknowns. Therefore, we do not need to consider this case.

If we switch terms or even equations in the set of normal equations, we shall only get permutations, which conserve these two matric properties.

We shall not examine the question of the existence of a solution to the system of normal equations for the general case. We note only that solutions may fail to exist in exceptional cases. To show this, let us consider the system of conditional equations with two unknowns:

$$a_k x + b_k y + l_k = 0.$$

The determinant of the system of normal equations can be transformed by use of Lagrange's identity:

$$\sum_{k=1}^{n} a_k^2 \sum_{k=1}^{n} b_k^2 - \left(\sum_{k=1}^{n} a_k b_k\right)^2 = \sum_{k=1}^{n} \sum_{m=1}^{n} (a_k b_m - a_m b_k)^2.$$

From this it is clear that the determinant will vanish if $\frac{a_k}{b_k} = \frac{a_m}{b_m}$ for all $k$ and $m$, that is if the ratio of the coefficients is constant. If $\frac{a_k}{l_k}$ are equal to the same constant, the problem is indeterminate. If the numbers $l_k$ are arbitrary, Legendre's condition cannot be satisfied by finite values of the unknowns, since we have a system of equations with two unknowns in which the terms containing the unknowns are the same, while the free terms are different.

In the general case of an arbitrary number of unknowns, the relationships between the coefficients of the unknowns that will result in the vanishing of the determinant of the system of normal equations are more complicated. In problems of the usual type, in which these coefficients are arbitrary, the determinant does not vanish and the problem has a unique solution.

We note without proof that a necessary and sufficient condition for the determinant of the system of normal equations not to vanish is the maximality of the rank of the matrix of the system of conditional equations (that is, equality of this rank with the number of unknowns). Also, we note that, in practice, it is easier to evaluate the determinant of the normal system than it is to see whether this condition is satisfied or not.

Setting up the linear system of normal equations is a tedious process. If the number of conditional equations is $n$ and the number of unknowns is $m$, we need to perform $\frac{nm(m+3)}{2}$ multiplications with two factors appearing in each and $\frac{m(m+3)}{2}$ additions with $n$ addends in each. For example, if $m=4$ and $n=10$, we would need to perform 140 multiplications and 14 additions. Although this work is elementary, the tediousness of it could dull the attention of the person making the calculations so that he would tend to make errors. If $n$ is great, it would be sensible to use a mechanical computer. The simplest mechanization would be calculation of the coefficients in the normal equations on a calculating machine by the method of accumulation. (The first product of two factors is left on the register of the calculating machine, to it is added the following product, etc.).

## 83. A CHECK ON THE SETTING UP OF THE NORMAL EQUATIONS

In both mechanical and pencil-and-paper calculations, it is necessary to check whether the normal equations are set up properly. This check is ordinarily made in the following simple manner. In each conditional equation, we form the sum $s_k$ of the coefficients of all the unknowns and of the free term. In other words, $s_k$ is the sum of the elements of the $k$th row of the augmented matrix of the system of equations. The values found for the numbers $s_k$ must be checked. To do this, we calculate by columns the sums of all the elements in the augmented matrix; that is, we find the sums of the coefficients of all the unknowns and the sums of the free terms. At the same time, we calculate the sum of all the numbers $s_k$. Using Gauss' notation, we denote the last sum by $[s]$ and the column sums of the elements by $[a]$, $[b]$, $[c]$, $[d]$, $[l]$.

We have the obvious checking equation

$$([s]) = [a] + [b] + [c] + [d] + [l],$$

where the parentheses denote the checking number. If the additions referred to are performed formally exactly, the control equation must be exactly satisfied. It is easy to make such a check on a tabulator if the number of cônditional equations is great. After calculating and checking the numbers $s_k$, we form the control sum of the products

$$[as],\ [bs],\ [cs],\ [ds].$$

The number of these products is equal to the number of unknowns. It is easy to see that we get a check of the normal equations from the following equations (in a problem with four unknowns):

$$\left.\begin{aligned} [aa] + [ab] + [ac] + [ad] + [al] &= [as], \\ [ba] + [bb] + [bc] + [bd] + [bl] &= [bs], \\ [ca] + [cb] + [cc] + [cd] + [cl] &= [cs], \\ [da] + [db] + [dc] + [dd] + [dl] &= [ds]. \end{aligned}\right\} \qquad (16.25)$$

The left sides of these equations represent the sums of the coefficients of the unknowns and the free terms of the consecutive normal equations.

Let us agree to number the unknowns in the order in which they are written in the conditional equations and to use the same numbering for the consecutive normal equations. Then, the checking rule can be stated as follows.

To check the $m$th conditional equation, we must take the sum of the products of the numbers $s_k$ and the coefficients with subscript $k$ of the $m$th unknown. This sum should be equal to the sum of the coefficients of the unknowns and the free terms of the conditional equation that is being checked.

To ensure a reliable check, it is convenient, when performing the multiplications, to ignore at first the fact that the coefficients are approximate numbers and to take the coefficients of the normal equations with all digits that are formally obtained. Then, the control equations must be exactly satisfied. It is expedient to make the check in the same way for all the normal equations. This makes it easier to find the errors in case there is a discrepancy in the check. For example, if, in the case of four unknowns, there is a discrepancy in the check only in the third normal equation, it will be necessary to check in turn the coefficients $[cc]$, $[cl]$, and the control sum. The reason is obvious: the remaining coefficients in this equation appear in other equations in which the control does not indicate an error and which may therefore be considered reliable.

For the check, we need in total: $n$ additions with $m+1$ addends (the numbers $s_k$) in each, $m+2$ additions with $n$ addends in each (for checking the $s_k$), $nm$ multiplications with two factors in each, $m$ additions with $n$ addends in each, and $n$ additions with $m+1$ addends in each. If $m=4$ and $n=10$, we have the following total amount of computation:

10 additions of 5 addends,
6 additions of 10 addends,
40 multiplications of 2 factors,
4 additions of these products,
10 additions of 5 addends for
checking the normal equations.

Example. In example 2 of Section 81, a system of 13 linear conditional equations with four unknowns $x_1$, $y_1$, $z_1$, and $u_1$ was obtained in literal form by means of linearization. If we substitute the values taken for the quantities $a_0$, $b_0$, $c_0$, $P_0$, $t_1$, $t_2$, ..., $t_{12}$ for the coefficients $a_k$, $b_k$, $c_k$, $d_k$, and $l_k$, we can write this system in the following schematic form:

| $x$ | $y$ | $z$ | $u$ | $L$ | $S$ |
|---|---|---|---|---|---|
| 0.998 | 0.061 | 1 | 0.000 | −0.042 | 2.017 |
| 0.897 | −0.398 | 1 | 0.033 | 0.027 | 1.559 |
| 0.566 | −0.742 | 1 | 0.122 | 0.099 | 1.045 |
| 0.081 | −0.897 | 1 | 0.222 | 0.133 | 0.539 |
| −0.416 | −0.819 | 1 | 0.269 | 0.196 | 0.230 |
| −0.812 | −0.525 | 1 | 0.216 | 0.209 | 0.088 |
| −0.995 | −0.093 | 1 | 0.046 | 0.215 | 0.173 |
| −0.915 | 0.365 | 1 | −0.210 | 0.107 | 0.347 |
| −0.591 | 0.725 | 1 | −0.478 | 0.018 | 0.674 |
| −0.113 | 0.895 | 1 | −0.663 | 0.008 | 1.127 |
| 0.386 | 0.831 | 1 | −0.683 | −0.033 | 1.501 |
| 0.793 | 0.547 | 1 | −0.495 | −0.106 | 1.739 |
| 0.991 | 0.120 | 1 | −0.118 | −0.008 | 1.985 |
| 0.870 | +0.070 | +13 | −1.739 | +0.823 | 13.024 |
| | | | | | (13.024) |

The column headings indicate those unknowns whose coefficients are given in the columns. The free terms are given in the column labeled $L$. The column labeled $S$, giving the control sums, is obtained by adding the numbers in the different columns (in the same row). They are checked by means of the last row, which gives the sums of the coefficients of the numbers appearing in each column. The number in parentheses in the last column is the control sum 13.024, which is obtained by adding the sums of the first five columns. Since it is exactly equal to $[s]$, we may assume that there are no errors in the column $S$ (provided that no errors were made in this column that canceled each other out when the addition was made).

The sums of the products of the coefficients of the unknowns and the free terms in the conditional equations (which yield the coefficients of the normal equations) are easily calculated mechanically without writing down the individual products. This considerably reduces the amount of computational labor in comparison with the old methods, whereby each product was calculated using a table of logarithms. The control sums for all the normal equations are calculated at the same time as the coefficients of the normal equations. For a complete check, all the digits that are formally obtained when the multiplications are performed are written down. The results are written in the form of a matrix with column heads denoting the unknowns, the free terms $l$, and the control sums.

| $x_1$ | $y_1$ | $z_1$ | $u_1$ | $L$ | $S$ |
|---|---|---|---|---|---|
| 6.909156 | 0.080654 | 0.870000 | −0.439975 | −0.630230 | 6.789605 |
| 0.080654 | 4.936378 | 0.070000 | −2.509864 | −0.523411 | 2.053757 |
| 0.870000 | 0.070000 | 13.000000 | −1.739000 | +0.823000 | 13.024000 |
| −0.439975 | −2.509864 | −1.739000 | 1.623981 | +0.189828 | −2.875030 |

The last column is a check. It enables one to check the coefficients of the normal equations by comparing the number of the last column with the sum of the other numbers in the same row. Since the multiplications are formally computed exactly, each $s_j$ (for $j = 1, 2, 3, 4$) must be exactly equal to the next sum. If this turns out not to be the case, there must be an error either in the coefficients in the normal equations or in the control sum. It should be noted that errors of the latter kind are frequently encountered. This is explained by the tediousness of the calculations in making the check at the end of the entire process and by a drop in attentiveness on the part of the person making the calculations.

In almost all problems, the coefficients and free terms in the conditional equations are approximate numbers in which only the digits written down are correct (and even these are not always correct). Frequently, the last digit is unreliable in the sense that it may differ by several units from the one that would be obtained in a more exact calculation. Therefore, by no means all the digits that are written in the last matrix are correct. As we know from Part I, the number of certain digits in the product of two numbers cannot be greater than the smaller number of certain digits in the original factors. When the products of the pairs are added, the limiting absolute errors of the addends are added, and it is now not the number of reliable digits but rather the number of digits after the decimal point in the addends that has an effect on the error in the result. Therefore, the question of evaluating the error in the coefficients of the normal equations is somewhat tedious to solve. On the other hand, we know that the errors incurred in rounding off (which is what we should deal with in the present case) can be either positive or negative and, in the majority of operations, they may partially offset each other. Therefore, estimates of the errors based on the maximum possible error are almost always exaggerated, and it is advisable to leave more digits in the coefficients of the normal equations than would be done if we were trying to find the maximum error.

In the example that we have been examining, the elements of the matrix of the conditional equations are given with three digits to the right of the decimal point. Any system can be reduced to a similar form by an obvious substitution of the unknowns. For example, if in the system

$$a_k x + b_k y + l_k = 0, \qquad k = 1, 2, \ldots, n$$

the numbers $a_k$ are given with three digits to the right of the decimal and the $b_k$ are given with two, we only need to introduce a new unknown $\eta = 10y$ in order to have the coefficients of $\eta$ have three digits to the right of the decimal also. In such cases, we often assume that the coefficients of the normal equations cannot have a greater number of certain digits to the right of the decimal than have the original numbers. Accordingly, the coefficients obtained for the normal equations are rounded off.

In the present example, after the numbers that we have obtained are rounded off to three digits to the right of the decimal, we have the following diagrammatically written system of normal equations:

| $x_1$ | $y_1$ | $z_1$ | $u_1$ | $L$ | $S$ |
|---|---|---|---|---|---|
| 6.909 | 0.081 | 0.870 | −0.440 | −0.630 | 6.790 |
| 0.081 | 4.936 | 0.070 | −2.510 | −0.523 | 2.054 |
| 0.870 | 0.070 | 13.000 | −1.7939 | 0.823 | 13.024 |
| −0.440 | −2.510 | −1.739 | 1.124 | 0.190 | −2.875 |

The column $S$ is included because these numbers will afterwards be used to check the solution of the system of normal equations. The result of rounding the number $S$ off can differ from the sum of the rounded coefficients of the normal equations by one or two units of the last digit. This is true because the absolute value of the error in $S$ that results from rounding off does not exceed one half the unit of the third digit to the right of the decimal in this example. This is true for each coefficient. Since we have five of them, the limiting error of the sum of the coefficients is equal to $2.5 \cdot 10^{-3}$, the limiting error of $S$ is equal to $0.5 \cdot 10^{-3}$, and the limiting error of the difference is equal to $3 \cdot 10^{-3}$. This calculation emphasizes the possibility that we mentioned earlier of there being a discrepancy between $S$ and the sum of the coefficients. The use of $S$ to check the solution of the normal equations is possible only if $S$ and the sum of the coefficients are exactly equal. Therefore, we must ensure this equality by changing either a number in the column $S$ or the coefficients in the normal equations. The latter procedure is more accurate since the error in $S$ is less, as can be seen from the calculations that we have just performed. However, this course of action is more indefinite because we do not know which coefficient or coefficients should be changed. Therefore, it is $S$ that is usually changed.

## 84. THE SOLUTION OF A SYSTEM OF LINEAR NORMAL EQUATIONS

If we need to find *only the values of the unknowns*, we may solve the system of normal equations by any of the familiar methods of solving systems of linear equations. In particular, we may use the method of iteration if the number of unknowns is great.

However, it was noted in Section 78 that we need to apply the method of least squares in natural-science problems for the reason that the numbers $l_k$ contain random errors. The roots of the normal equations, which we shall consider as approximate values of the unknowns, are functions of the random variables $l_k$ and hence are themselves random. To determine their possible variance, we need to find the mean square errors of the unknowns. When we are confronted with such a problem, we usually use only two methods: (1) The method of determinants and (2) the method of successive elimination of unknowns, usually called Gauss' method.*

The method of solving systems of linear equations by determinants is generally known and, therefore, we shall not stop to explain it. We only note that direct evaluation of determinants of order higher than four is an extremely laborious process. Therefore, systems of higher order than four are usually not solved by means of determinants.

The method of successive elimination of the unknowns is often used even with systems containing three or four unknowns and is always used when the number is greater than four.

This method is quite simple. We rewrite the first normal equation so as to express the first unknown in terms of the remaining unknowns and we call the equation in this form the first elimination equation.** In the case of a system containing four unknowns, it will be of the form

$$x = -\frac{[ab]}{[aa]}y - \frac{[ac]}{[aa]}z - \frac{[ad]}{[aa]}u - \frac{[al]}{[aa]}. \qquad (16.26)$$

This equation is schematically written as follows: In the column labeled $y$ in the system of normal equations, we write the number $-\frac{[ab]}{[aa]}$; in the following column, we write the number $-\frac{[ac]}{[aa]}$, and so on to the end. We note (for the moment without explanation) that we must perform the same operations with the numbers in the column $S$ as with the numbers in the column $L$. In the present case, we must write the number $-\frac{[as]}{[aa]}$ in the column $S$. Here, $[as]$ is the highest number in the column $S$. If we substitute this expression for $x$ in all the other equations, we obtain an intermediary system with one fewer unknown. We write the coefficients of the intermediary system in the form of the following matrix:

*This name is somewhat ill-chosen. The essentials of this method of solving systems of linear equations was apparently known to the Arabs. The part that Gauss played was not in discovering the method but in showing that in using it one could, at the same time, determine the weights of the unknowns.

**It is often advisable to arrange the equations and the unknowns in such a way that the coefficient of the first unknown is the greatest of the diagonal elements.

| y | z | u | L | S |
|---|---|---|---|---|
| $[bb1]$ | $[bc1]$ | $[bd1]$ | $[bl1]$ | $[bs1]$ |
| $[cb1]$ | $[cc1]$ | $[cd1]$ | $[cl1]$ | $[cs1]$ |
| $[db1]$ | $[dc1]$ | $[dd1]$ | $[dl1]$ | $[ds1]$ |

If we actually make the substitution of the first elimination equation, we obtain, after combining the coefficients of like unknowns, the following expressions for the coefficients:

$$\left.\begin{aligned}
[bb1] &= [bb] + \left\{-\frac{[ab]}{[aa]}[ba]\right\},\\
[bc1] &= [bc] + \left\{-\frac{[ac]}{[aa]}[ba]\right\},\\
[bd1] &= [bd] + \left\{-\frac{[ad]}{[aa]}[ba]\right\},\\
[bl1] &= [bl] + \left\{-\frac{[al]}{[aa]}[ba]\right\},\\
[cb1] &= [cb] + \left\{-\frac{[ab]}{[aa]}[ca]\right\}
\end{aligned}\right\} \tag{16.27}$$

etc.

There is a mnemonic for checking all these formulas. The first term on the right contains the same letters as the term on the left without the 1. The second term on the right must be such that after we perform a (formal!) cancellation we get the same term again (with a minus sign). After all formal cancellations and collection of "like" terms, the right side must be equal to 0.

Let us represent the coefficient matrix of the normal equations with the control column $S$ by dots. We write the elimination row under this matrix and denote its elements by hollow circles:

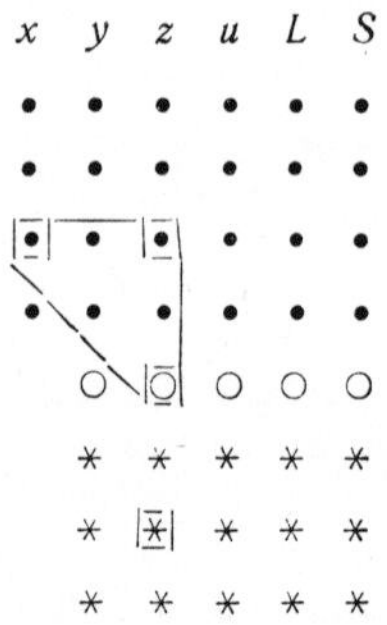


The matrix of the intermediary system with three unknowns is denoted by asterisks. We can give a simple diagrammatic rule for forming the numbers represented by the asterisks. The first row of the original matrix is discarded: it has been used for obtaining the row with the hollow circles (the elimination row). To obtain the $m$th row in the asterisk matrix, we must add to each number (other than the first) of the $m$th shortened row the product of the number in the elimination row appearing in the same column and the first number of the point row taken. In the diagram, the original numbers and those obtained from them are shown in a square box. Such an operation must be performed in all columns (except the first in the original matrix) and in all rows (except the first in the original matrix). This rule is sometimes called the right-triangle rule, which can be explained by the drawing in our conventional diagram. The number at the right angle of the triangle must be added to the product of the numbers at the ends of the hypotenuse.

The system obtained by eliminating the first unknown possesses the two properties of a normal system referred to above: the matrix of the coefficients of the unknown is symmetric about the principal diagonal and the numbers along the principal diagonal are all positive. However, it is advisable to calculate the mutually symmetric elements ($[bc1]$ and $[cb1]$, etc.). Since they are not obtained by exactly the same operations, a discrepancy between them indicates the presence of an error only if the difference is greater than two or three units of the last digit. When the numbers are rounded off, a difference of one or two units in the last digit is possible. In such a case, we have to change one or both of them in such a way that there will be exact equality.

The accuracy in setting up the elimination row is checked in the column $S$ if we perform the same operations in it as in the other columns. The number in the column $S$ must be equal to the sum of all the other numbers of this same elimination row minus 1. If, because of variation in rounding off the numbers, there is a difference of one or two units in the last digits (or sometimes even more than this if there are many unknowns), we need to change the number in the column $S$ of the elimination row in such a way that there will be exact equality in the check. This ensures reliability of the check in subsequent calculations.

The first intermediary system obtained after elimination of the first unknown can also be checked by the numbers in the column $S$. It is easy to show that each of the numbers in this column should be equal to the sum of the remaining numbers in the same row. Again, a discrepancy in the units of the last digit is possible and must be removed by changing the number in the column $S$.

After the first unknown is eliminated, we have a system of normal equations with one fewer unknown than in the original system. The second unknown is eliminated in the same manner as the first unknown was eliminated from the first system, and the checks are made in the same manner. The elimination equation is of the form*

*Before eliminating the second unknown, it is sometimes advisable to change the order of the equations and the unknowns in such a way that the coefficient of the first unknown in the intermediary system will be the greatest number in the principal diagonal.

$$y = -\frac{[bc1]}{[bb1]} z - \frac{[bd1]}{[bb1]} u - \frac{[bl1]}{[bb1]}. \tag{16.28}$$

Only the coefficients are written in the diagram in their respective positions. The substitution of this expression for $y$ into all the equations in the first intermediary system (other than the first equation of this system) will give a system with two fewer unknowns than the original system. From a system with four unknowns, we obtain a system of the form

| $z$ | $u$ | $L$ | $S$ |
|---|---|---|---|
| $[cc2]$ | $[cd2]$ | $[cl2]$ | $[cs2]$ |
| $[dc2]$ | $[dd2]$ | $[dl2]$ | $[ds2]$. |

The coefficients are calculated from formulas similar to formulas (16.27) for a system with three unknowns:

$$\left.\begin{aligned}
[cc2] &= [cc1] + \left\{-\frac{[bc1]}{[bb1]}[cb1]\right\},\\
[cd2] &= [cd1] + \left\{-\frac{[bd1]}{[bb1]}[cb1]\right\},\\
[cl2] &= [cl1] + \left\{-\frac{[bl1]}{[bb1]}[cb1]\right\},\\
[dc2] &= [dc1] + \left\{-\frac{[bc1]}{[bb1]}[db1]\right\}
\end{aligned}\right\} \tag{16.29}$$

etc. Here again, the calculations are made according to the right-triangle rule. We must calculate $[cs2]$ and $[ds2]$ to check the new intermediary system. We also must check the elimination row (immediately after it is formed) by the formula

$$-\frac{[bs1]}{[bb1]} = -1 + \left(-\frac{[bc1]}{[bb1]}\right) + \left(-\frac{[bd1]}{[bb1]}\right) + \left(-\frac{[bl1]}{[bb1]}\right), \tag{16.30}$$

that is, the sum of the numbers in the elimination row (other than $S$) must be 1 less than the number obtained in the elimination row in the column $S$.

The equations of the second intermediary system are checked in exactly the same manner as the equations of the first intermediary system, and the equations of the original system are checked by means of the numbers in the column $S$.

We then get from the first equation of the second intermediary system the following elimination equation:

$$z = -\frac{[cd2]}{[cc2]} u - \frac{[cl2]}{[cc2]}. \tag{16.31}$$

In the column "$u$," we write the coefficients of $u$. In the column $L$, we write the free term. In the column $S$, we write the number $-\frac{[cs2]}{[cc2]}$. When the expression for $z$ is substituted into the next equation, we obtain an equation of the form

$$[dd3]\,u + [dl3] = 0 \qquad (16.32)$$

with one unknown, namely $u$. Diagrammatically, it is written in the $u$ and $L$ columns as follows:

| $u$ | $L$ |
|---|---|
| $[dd3]$ | $[dl3]$; |

The control number $[ds3]$ is written in the column $S$. The coefficients are calculated from the formulas

$$\left.\begin{aligned} [dd3] &= [dd2] + \left\{-\frac{[cd2]}{[cc2]}[dc2]\right\}, \\ [dl3] &= [dl2] + \left\{-\frac{[cl2]}{[cc2]}[dc2]\right\}, \\ [ds3] &= [ds2] + \left\{-\frac{[cs2]}{[cc2]}[dc2]\right\}. \end{aligned}\right\} \qquad (16.33)$$

The check of equation (16.32) is made from the formula

$$[dd3] + [dl3] = [ds3].$$

From equation (16.32) for $u$, we obtain the last elimination equation

$$\bar{u} = -\frac{[dl3]}{[dd3]}. \qquad (16.34)$$

Here, $\bar{u}$ denotes the root of the system of normal equations, that is, the most probable value of the unknown $u$. Substituting the value that we have found for $\bar{u}$ into the elimination equation (16.31), we obtain

$$\bar{z} = -\frac{[cd2]}{[cc2]}\bar{u} - \frac{[cl2]}{[cc2]}. \qquad (16.35)$$

Substitution of $\bar{u}$ and $\bar{z}$ into the elimination equation (16.28) yields

$$\bar{y} = -\frac{[bc1]}{[bb1]}\bar{z} - \frac{[bd1]}{[bb1]}\bar{u} - \frac{[bl1]}{[bb1]}. \qquad (16.36)$$

Finally, the first elimination equation (16.26) yields

$$\bar{x} = -\frac{[ab]}{[aa]}\bar{y} - \frac{[ac]}{[aa]}\bar{z} - \frac{[ad]}{[aa]}\bar{u} - \frac{[al]}{[aa]}. \qquad (16.37)$$

The values of the unknowns are checked on the basis of the following simple consideration. Suppose that we make the following change of variables in the normal equations:

$$\begin{aligned} x &= \xi + 1, \\ y &= \eta + 1, \\ z &= \zeta + 1, \\ u &= \nu + 1. \end{aligned}$$

The first normal equation will be of the form

$$[aa]\xi + [ab]\eta + [ac]\zeta + [ad]\nu + \\ + \{[aa] + [ab] + [ac] + [ad] + [al]\} = 0.$$

In the transformed equation, the term without an unknown is equal to $[as]$, in agreement with the control formula for the first normal equation. The other equations are transformed analogously. From this, it follows that if the column $L$ is replaced with $S$ in the normal equations, we obtain a system of equations for determining $\xi$, $\eta$, $\zeta$, and $\nu$ that is, the unknowns that are exactly 1 less than the unknowns $x$, $y$, $z$, and $u$. When the same operations are carried out in the column $S$ as in the column $L$, the system with the unknowns $\xi$, $\eta$, $\zeta$, and $\nu$ is in effect solved. Therefore, in solving the system of normal equations, the same operations are performed simultaneously with the column $S$ and with the column $L$, which gives $x$, $y$, $z$, and $u$. The column $S$ yields the values $\bar{\xi}$, $\bar{\eta}$, $\bar{\zeta}$, and $\nu$, which are used as a check. If there are no errors, they must be exactly 1 less than $x$, $y$, $z$, and $u$. Ordinarily, the presence of errors in rounding off will make $\bar{x}$ and $\bar{\xi}$, etc. differ by slightly more or slightly less than 1. The amount by which this difference may deviate from 1 increases with the number of unknowns.

We note the following fact, which is important for calculating the mean errors of the unknowns. In solving a system of normal equations by Gauss' method, one should perform only those arithmetic operations that are necessary for that purpose. One should not multiply or divide the original or the intermediary equations by any numbers.

Methods for solving a system of normal equations by the method of successive elimination of the unknowns other than the one that we have been examining are used. For example, the so called Gauss-Doolittle method is widely used in geodesy. Here, the amount of writing is considerably less than in the above method. Only the elimination rows and one (the first) column in each intermediary system are written out (see, for example, Romanovskii, *Matematicheskaya statistika*). A convenient procedure for arranging the work in this case has been given by P. T. Reznikovskii. S. G. Makover developed a matrix method of solving systems of normal equations that leads to a computational procedure analogous to the Gauss-Doolittle procedure.

Still other methods, besides those of successive elimination and determinants, are applicable to a system of normal equations. A detailed exposition can be found in the book by V. N. Faddeeva. However, not all of these methods are applicable if we are required to find not only the values of the unknowns but also their weights.

## 85. CALCULATION OF THE WEIGHTS OF THE UNKNOWNS

As was mentioned in Section 81, the most probable values of the unknowns, which we can obtain from a system of linear normal equations, are linear functions of the random variables $l_1, l_2, \ldots, l_n$. To obtain these functions, we write the solution of the system of normal equations in terms of the determinants of the augmented and coefficient matrices (in the case of a system of four unknowns):

$$\bar{x} = \frac{D_x}{D}, \quad \bar{y} = \frac{D_y}{D}; \quad \bar{z} = \frac{D_z}{D}, \quad \bar{u} = \frac{D_u}{D}. \tag{16.38}$$

where $D$ is the determinant of the system

$$D=\begin{vmatrix} [aa] & [ab] & [ac] & [ad] \\ [ba] & [bb] & [bc] & [bd] \\ [ca] & [cb] & [cc] & [cd] \\ [da] & [db] & [dc] & [dd] \end{vmatrix}, \tag{16.39}$$

and $D_x$ is a determinant of the form

$$D_x=-\begin{vmatrix} [al] & [ab] & [ac] & [ad] \\ [bl] & [bb] & [bc] & [bd] \\ [cl] & [cb] & [cc] & [cd] \\ [dl] & [db] & [dc] & [dd] \end{vmatrix}, \tag{16.40}$$

$D_y$, $D_z$, and $D_u$ have analogous expressions except that the column of free terms in the normal equations is, successively, in the second, third, and fourth position.

If we expand the terms in the first column of the determinant $D_x$, we obtain

$$D_x=-\sum_{k=1}^{n} l_k \begin{vmatrix} a_k & [ab] & [ac] & [ad] \\ b_k & [bb] & [bc] & [bd] \\ c_k & [cb] & [cc] & [cd] \\ d_k & [db] & [dc] & [dd] \end{vmatrix}. \tag{16.41}$$

From (16.38) and (16.41), we obtain the desired linear expression for $\bar{x}$ in terms of the numbers $l_k$:

$$\bar{x}=-\sum_{k=1}^{n} \frac{\Delta_k}{D} l_k, \tag{16.42}$$

where

$$\Delta_k=\begin{vmatrix} a_k & [ab] & [ac] & [ad] \\ b_k & [bb] & [bc] & [bd] \\ c_k & [cb] & [cc] & [cd] \\ d_k & [db] & [dc] & [dd] \end{vmatrix}. \tag{16.43}$$

Let us now find the variance of the unknown quantity $\bar{x}$, treating the numbers $l_k$ as random. From the theorem on the variance of a linear function of mutually independent random variables $l_k$, we obtain

$$\sigma_{\bar{x}}^2=\sum_{k=1}^{n} \frac{\Delta_k^2}{D^2} \sigma_k^2, \tag{16.44}$$

where $\sigma_k^2$ are the variances of the successive conditional equations. We shall assume the conditional equations to be equally precise (or reducible to equally precise equations). Therefore,

$$\sigma_k^2 = \sigma_0^2, \quad k = 1, 2, \ldots, n, \tag{16.45}$$

where $\sigma_0$ is the mean square error of an equation of unit weight. Thus, for equally precise conditional equations,

$$\sigma_{\bar{x}}^2 = \frac{\sigma_0^2}{D^2}\Delta, \tag{16.46}$$

where $\Delta = \sum_{k=1}^{n} \Delta_k^2$, and $\Delta_k$ is determined from formula (16.43). To get an expression for $\sigma_{\bar{x}}$, we must find the quantity $\Delta$. We use (16.43) to rewrite $\Delta$ in the form

$$\Delta = \sum_{k=1}^{n} \Delta_k\Delta_k = \sum_{k=1}^{n} \Delta_k \begin{vmatrix} a_k & [ab] & [ac] & [ad] \\ b_k & [bb] & [bc] & [bd] \\ c_k & [cb] & [cc] & [cd] \\ d_k & [db] & [dc] & [dd] \end{vmatrix}.$$

Using the rule for multiplying a determinant by a real number and the rule for adding determinants, we obtain

$$\Delta = \begin{vmatrix} \sum_{k=1}^{n} a_k\Delta_k & [ab] & [ac] & [ad] \\ \sum_{k=1}^{n} b_k\Delta_k & [bb] & [bc] & [bd] \\ \sum_{k=1}^{n} c_k\Delta_k & [cb] & [cc] & [cd] \\ \sum_{k=1}^{n} d_k\Delta_k & [db] & [db] & [dd] \end{vmatrix}. \tag{16.47}$$

We know from algebra that a determinant with two identical columns is equal to zero. Therefore,

$$\sum_{k=1}^{n} b_k\Delta_k = \begin{vmatrix} \sum_{k=1}^{n} b_k a_k & [ab] & [ac] & [ad] \\ \sum_{k=1}^{n} b_k^2 & [bb] & [bc] & [bd] \\ \sum_{k=1}^{n} b_k c_k & [cb] & [cc] & [cd] \\ \sum_{k=1}^{n} b_k d_k & [db] & [dc] & [dd] \end{vmatrix} = 0$$

and analogously,

$$\sum_{k=1}^{n} c_k \Delta_k = 0,$$

$$\sum_{k=1}^{n} d_k \Delta_k = 0.$$

Furthermore, we have

$$\sum_{k=1}^{n} a_k \Delta_k = \begin{vmatrix} \sum_{k=1}^{n} a_k^2 & [ab] & [ab] & [ad] \\ \sum_{k=1}^{n} a_k b_k & [bb] & [bc] & [bd] \\ \sum_{k=1}^{n} a_k c_k & [cb] & [cc] & [cd] \\ \sum_{k=1}^{n} a_k d_k & [db] & [dc] & [dd] \end{vmatrix} = D.$$

If we substitute the sums that we have found into the determinant $\Delta$, and expand it in elements of its first column, we obtain

$$\Delta = D \cdot D_{11}, \tag{16.48}$$

where $D_{11}$ is the cofactor of the first element in the diagonal of the determinant $D$ of the system of normal equations.

If we substitute (16.48) into the formula (16.46), we finally obtain

$$\sigma_{\bar{x}}^2 = \frac{D_{11}}{D} \sigma_0^2. \tag{16.49}$$

From the definition of weights, we have

$$p_{\bar{x}} = \frac{\sigma_0^2}{\sigma_{\bar{x}}^2} = \frac{D}{D_{11}};$$

and analogously, (16.50)

$$p_{\bar{y}} = \frac{D}{D_{22}}; \qquad p_{\bar{z}} = \frac{D}{D_{33}}; \qquad p_{\bar{u}} = \frac{D}{D_{44}},$$

where $D_{22}$, $D_{33}$, and $D_{44}$ are the cofactors of successive elements in the principal diagonal of the determinant of the system of normal equations.

Thus, we may formulate the following rule for finding the weights by means of determinants.

*The weight of each unknown is equal to the determinant of the system of normal equations divided by the cofactor of that element of the diagonal that is the coefficient of the unknown in question.*

This is a good rule to use if the system of normal equations itself is solved by means of determinants, which, as we stated earlier, is expedient only for systems with two or three unknowns.

Suppose now that the system of normal equations is solved by Gauss' method. We shall show that in this case the rule given for calculating the weights is applicable not only to the original normal system, but also to any of the intermediary systems.*

On the determinant $D$ of the system of normal equations, we perform transformations analogous to those that we made in setting up the first intermediary system. We divide the first row of this determinant by $[aa]$, and we then subtract this row from rows II, III, and IV, multiplying it respectively by $[ba]$, $[ca]$, and $[da]$. We then obtain

$$D = [aa] \begin{vmatrix} 1; & \frac{[ab]}{[aa]}; & \frac{[ac]}{[aa]}; & \frac{[ad]}{[aa]} \\ 0; & [bb1] & [bc1] & [bd1] \\ 0; & [cb1] & [cc1] & [cd1] \\ 0; & [db1] & [dc1] & [dd1] \end{vmatrix}, \tag{16.51}$$

that is,

$$D = [aa] \cdot D^{(1)}, \tag{16.52}$$

where $D^{(1)}$ denotes the determinant of the first intermediary system.

Analogous transformations of the cofactors of the diagonal elements of the determinant $D$ yield

$$D_{22} = [aa]\, D_{22}^{(1)}, \quad D_{33} = [aa]\, D_{33}^{(1)}, \quad D_{44} = [aa]\, D_{44}^{(1)},$$

where $D_{22}^{(1)}$, $D_{33}^{(1)}$, and $D_{44}^{(1)}$ are the cofactors of the elements $[bb1]$, $[cc1]$, and $[dd1]$ of the determinant $D^{(1)}$. From these formulas and (16.50), we find

$$p_{\bar{y}} = \frac{D^{(1)}}{D_{22}^{(1)}}, \quad p_{\bar{z}} = \frac{D^{(1)}}{D_{33}^{(1)}}, \quad p_{\bar{u}} = \frac{D^{(1)}}{D_{44}^{(1)}}. \tag{16.53}$$

Thus, the assertion made is proven for the first intermediary system. In just the same manner, it is proven for the remaining intermediary systems. We now use this fact to prove the following theorem of Gauss:

*In solving a system of normal equations by the Gauss method, the coefficient of the last unknown in the last intermediary equation (which contains no other unknown) is equal to its weight, provided only those operations that are necessary for this method have been performed.*

---

*Proof of this fact and the proof to be given below of Gauss' theorem are due to P. T. Reznikovskii.

*Proof:* Let us use the rule that we have formulated to obtain the weights of the next-to-the-last and the last unknowns that appear in the next-to-the-last intermediary system:

$$p_{\bar{z}} = \frac{\begin{vmatrix} [cc2] & [cd2] \\ [dc2] & [dd2] \end{vmatrix}}{[dd2]}, \quad p_{\bar{u}} = \frac{\begin{vmatrix} [cc2] & [cd2] \\ [dc2] & [dd2] \end{vmatrix}}{[cc2]}.$$

From the formula given in the preceding section for the coefficient $[dd3]$ of the last intermediary equation, it follows that

$$\begin{vmatrix} [cc2] & [cd2] \\ [dc2] & [dd2] \end{vmatrix} = [dd3]\,[cc2].$$

Therefore,

$$\left.\begin{aligned} p_{\bar{z}} &= \frac{[dd3]\,[cc2]}{[dd2]}, \\ p_{\bar{u}} &= [dd3]. \end{aligned}\right\} \qquad (16.54)$$

This proves Gauss' theorem.

Thus, in solving a system of normal equations by Gauss' method, the weight of the last unknown is obtained more or less automatically: it is equal to the coefficient, which must still be calculated.

The weight of the next-to-the-last unknown is easily obtained from the first of formulas (16.54). It is equal to the product of the weight of the last unknown and the ratio of the elements of the principal diagonal in the next-to-the-last Gauss system consisting of the last two equations (with two unknowns). As a rule, the weights of the last and the next-to-the-last unknowns are determined, and then the order of the unknowns in the equations is changed in such a way that the next two unknowns, counting from the end, are last. Here, the equations must be rearranged so that the matrix of the coefficients of the unknowns will be symmetric, with positive elements on the principal diagonal. In other words, the unknowns and equations should be rearranged in such a way that the system has the properties of a system of normal equations.

Solution of the transformed system yields the weights of two more unknowns. This gives us another check of the solution, since we may obtain all the unknowns a second time. If we are sure of the results of the first solution, we may confine ourselves to setting up the intermediary systems, since this is enough for calculating the weights. When we have three or four unknowns, we must solve the system twice, when we have five or six unknowns, we must solve it three times, etc.

We can show that the weight of the third-to-the-last unknown is given by the formula*

---

*We might write analogous formulas for the weights of the fourth, fifth, etc. unknowns from the end, but these formulas contain, respectively, third-, fourth-, etc. order determinants, and therefore, they are not suitable.

$$p_{\bar{y}} = [dd3]\,[cc2]\frac{[bb_1]}{\begin{vmatrix}[cc1] & [cd_1] \\ [dc1] & [dd1]\end{vmatrix}}. \qquad (16.55)$$

If, in addition to formulas (16.54), we apply this formula, we must solve a system of normal equations with three unknowns once, a system of four, five, or six unknowns twice, etc.

The method that we have been expounding for determining the weights rests heavily on the Gauss procedure for solving systems of normal equations (wherein we write out all the intermediary systems). In geodesic literature, this method is called Enke's method. If the number of unknowns in the system of normal equations is greater than six, to determine the weights by Enke's method, we must solve the system of normal equations no fewer than three times (four times, in fact, if we use only formulas (16.54)). Therefore, for systems with many unknowns, we need to resort to other methods of calculating the weights.

In a method developed by N. I. Idel'son, in addition to the given system of normal equations with $m$ unknowns, we solve (simultaneously) $m$ more systems with the same determinant and the following sequences of free terms (1, 0, 0, ...), (0, -1, 0, ...), (0, 0, -1, ...), ... . It is easy to show that in each of these systems, one of the unknowns is equal to the reciprocal of one of the weights of the unknowns in the system of normal equations. The amount of extra calculation necessary to determine the weights by this method is approximately equal to the amount used in the basic calculations involved in solving a system of normal equations by the method of successive elimination of the unknowns. Therefore, this method is definitely more suitable than Enke's method if the number of unknowns is greater than six.

It follows from (16.53) that the reciprocals of the weights are equal to the diagonal elements of the matrix inverse to the matrix of the system of normal equations. Therefore, if we apply to the normal equations any of the methods of solution of a system of linear algebraic equations that are based on finding the inverse matrix, we shall obtain not only the values of the unknowns, but also their weights. The matrix exposition of Idel'son's method given by Makover is based on this fact.

## 86. THE APPROXIMATE VALUE OF THE MEAN SQUARE ERROR PER UNIT WEIGHT. THE MEAN SQUARE ERROR OF THE UNKNOWNS

After solving the normal equations, we obtain the most probable values of the unknowns $\bar{x}$, $\bar{y}$, $\bar{z}$, and $\bar{u}$. If we substitute these values into the conditional equations, we obtain discrepancies satisfying the condition that the sum of the squares be minimized. These discrepancies are often called residual errors, reserving the more general name discrepancies for the results obtained when arbitrary numbers $x$, $y$, $z$, and $u$ are substituted. To show that the numbers found for $\bar{x}$, $\bar{y}$, $\bar{z}$, and $\bar{u}$ satisfy the conditional equations, we must calculate the residual error of each conditional equation. Such a calculation presents no difficulties when one is using a calculating machine, since we need to find the sum of products, which can be done without writing down the individual addends. We denote the residual errors* by $\varepsilon_k$ (for $k = 1, 2, \ldots, n$) and we shall refer to them

*Knowledge of all the $\varepsilon_k$ is essential because sometimes there are gross errors in the conditional equations. Such equations must be discarded and the calculations made again. Conditional equations with gross errors are detected by excessively high residual errors in comparison with the great majority of the $\varepsilon_k$. Usually, the three-sigma rule is used.

as the remainders. Let us now determine the sum of the squares of the remainders, that is, the minimum of the sum of the squares of the discrepancies. We denote this minimum value by $\bar{s}$. In the case of four unknowns,

$$\bar{s}=\sum_{k=1}^{n}\varepsilon_k^2=\sum_{k=1}^{n}(a_k\bar{x}+b_k\bar{y}+c_k\bar{z}+d_k\bar{u}+l_k)^2. \tag{16.56}$$

The quantity $\bar{s}$ can easily be calculated directly from the $\varepsilon_k$ since the individual $\varepsilon_k$ must be calculated anyway. A rather simple formula exists for calculating $\bar{s}$. A simple calculation yields

$$\begin{aligned}\bar{s}=\sum_{k=1}^{n}\bar{x}\left(a_k^2\bar{x}+a_kb_k\bar{y}+a_kc_k\bar{z}+a_kd_k\bar{u}+a_kl_k\right)+\\ +\sum_{k=1}^{n}\bar{y}\left(b_ka_k\bar{x}+b_k^2\bar{y}+b_kc_k\bar{z}+b_kd_k\bar{u}+b_kl_k\right)+\\ +\sum_{k=1}^{n}\bar{z}\left(c_ka_k\bar{x}+c_kb_k\bar{y}+c_k^2\bar{z}+c_kd_k\bar{u}+c_kl_k\right)+\\ +\sum_{k=1}^{n}\bar{u}\left(d_ka_k\bar{x}+d_kb_k\bar{y}+d_kc_k\bar{z}+d_k^2\bar{u}+d_kl_k\right)+\\ +\sum_{k=1}^{n}l_k^2+\bar{x}\sum_{k=1}^{n}a_kl_k+\bar{y}\sum_{k=1}^{n}b_kl_k+\bar{z}\sum_{k=1}^{n}c_kl_k+\bar{u}\sum_{k=1}^{n}d_kl_k.\end{aligned}$$

Each term is squared, all the terms with doubled products are written in different rows in the form of the sum of two identical addends, and the terms are factored. In Gauss' notation, the equation obtained can be written as

$$\begin{aligned}\bar{s}=\bar{x}([aa]\,\bar{x}+[ab]\,\bar{y}+[ac]\,\bar{z}+[ad]\,\bar{u}+[al])+\\ +\bar{y}([ba]\,\bar{x}+[bb]\,\bar{y}+[bc]\,\bar{z}+[bd]\,\bar{u}+[bl])+\\ +\bar{z}([ca]\,\bar{x}+[cb]\,\bar{y}+[cc]\,\bar{z}+[cd]\,\bar{u}+[cl])+\\ +\bar{u}([da]\,\bar{x}+[db]\,\bar{y}+[dc]\,\bar{z}+[dd]\,\bar{u}+[dl])+\\ +[ll]+\bar{x}\,[al]+\bar{y}\,[bl]+\bar{z}\,[cl]+\bar{u}\,[dl].\end{aligned}$$

Since $\bar{x}$, $\bar{y}$, $\bar{z}$, and $\bar{u}$ are the roots of the normal equations, all the sums in the parentheses are equal to 0 and we are left with the simple expression

$$\bar{s}=\bar{x}\,[al]+\bar{y}\,[bl]+\bar{z}\,[cl]+\bar{u}\,[dl]+[ll], \tag{16.57}$$

for which we need to perform only the extra calculation of the sum of the squares of the numbers $l_k$.

When we use this formula to calculate $\bar{s}$, the errors resulting from rounding off will be considerably less than by direct calculation of the sum of the squares of the remainders. Therefore, it should be considered the basic formula and a direct calculation of the sum of the squares of the errors should be considered as a check. There may be a considerable discrepancy between these two values of $\bar{s}$ if $n$ is great. For comparison, one should estimate the limiting error of the direct sum of the squares of the residual errors. Suppose, for example, that all the remainders are given with three reliable digits to the right of the decimal and that the number of conditional equations is 10. If the remainders are of the order of 0.05, the limiting error of the square of a single remainder is equal to

$$2 \cdot 0.05 \cdot 0{,}5 \cdot 10^{-3} = 0{,}5 \cdot 10^{-4}.$$

Since there are 10 of them, the limiting error of the direct sum of the squares of the discrepancies is equal to $0{,}5 \cdot 10^{-3}$. If we add to this the limiting error of the sum given by formula (16.57), we obtain an upper bound on the absolute value of the difference between the two values of $\bar{s}$. An excess over this value definitely indicates an error in one number or the other (sometimes both).

After we have calculated the sum of the squares of the remainders, we can calculate the most probable value of the mean square error per unit weight $\sigma_0$ by using the formula

$$\sigma_0^2 = \frac{\bar{s}}{n-m}, \tag{16.58}$$

where $m$ is the number of unknowns.

We give this formula without proof, since the proof is rather tedious. It is similar to the proof given for the analogous problem for equally precise and unequally precise measurements of a single quantity. These problems can be considered a special case of the problem discussed in the present chapter.

After $\sigma_0$ is calculated, the mean square errors of the unknowns are determined from the familiar formulas, since the weights of the unknowns have already been found:

$$\sigma_{\bar{x}} = \frac{\sigma_0}{\sqrt{p_{\bar{x}}}}, \quad \sigma_{\bar{y}} = \frac{\sigma_0}{\sqrt{p_{\bar{y}}}} \quad \text{etc.} \tag{16.59}$$

It is convenient to put the result in the following form:

$$x = \bar{x} \pm \sigma_{\bar{x}}, \quad y = \bar{y} \pm \sigma_{\bar{y}} \quad \text{etc.}$$

If we assume a normal distribution of the random errors for the numbers $l_k$, then $\bar{x}, \bar{y}, \ldots$, being linear functions of $l_k$, are also normally distributed. Therefore, we may calculate probabilities of the form

$$P(|x-\bar{x}| < \sigma_{\bar{x}}) = 0.68, \quad P(|x-\bar{x}| < 3\sigma_{\bar{x}}) = 0.9973$$

(and analogously for the other unknowns); that is, we may find bounds between which the true value lies with a given probability, or we may solve the inverse problem. If we cannot use a normal law, analogous probabilities can be found from Chebyshev's inequalities.

The bounds obtained in this manner are correct if the number of observations is great (approximately twenty or more). If the number of observations is small, the results should be evaluated by using Student's distribution (see V. I. Romanovskii's book *Osnovnye zadachi teorii oshibok* (Basic Problems in the Theory of Errors)).

## 87. AN EXAMPLE ILLUSTRATING THE PROCEDURE FOR SOLVING SYSTEMS OF LINEAR CONDITIONAL EQUATIONS

Suppose that we have the following system of thirteen conditional equations with four unknowns:

| $x$ | $y$ | $z$ | $u$ | $l$ | $s$ | $\varepsilon$ | $\varepsilon^2$ |
|---|---|---|---|---|---|---|---|
| + 0.998 | + 0.061 | + 1.000 | + 0.000 | − 0.042 | + 2.017 | − 0.015 | 0.000225 |
| + 0.897 | − 0.398 | + 1 | + 0.033 | + 0.027 | + 1.559 | + 0.003 | 9 |
| + 0.566 | − 0.742 | + 1 | + 0.122 | + 0.099 | + 1.045 | + 0.010 | 100 |
| + 0.081 | − 0.897 | + 1 | + 0.222 | + 0.133 | + 0.539 | − 0.020 | 400 |
| − 0.416 | − 0.819 | + 1 | + 0.269 | + 0.196 | + 0.230 | + 0.000 | 0 |
| − 0.812 | − 0.525 | + 1 | + 0.216 | + 0.209 | + 0.088 | + 0.001 | 1 |
| − 0.995 | − 0.093 | + 1 | + 0.046 | + 0.215 | + 0.173 | + 0.033 | 1089 |
| − 0.915 | + 0.365 | + 1 | − 0.210 | + 0.107 | + 0.347 | − 0.018 | 324 |
| − 0.591 | + 0.725 | + 1 | − 0.478 | + 0.018 | + 0.674 | − 0.034 | 1156 |
| − 0.113 | + 0.895 | + 1 | − 0.663 | + 0.008 | + 1.127 | + 0.024 | 576 |
| + 0.386 | + 0.831 | + 1 | − 0.683 | − 0.033 | + 1.501 | + 0.027 | 729 |
| + 0.793 | + 0.547 | + 1 | − 0.495 | − 0.106 | + 1.739 | − 0.038 | 1444 |
| + 0.991 | + 0.120 | + 1.000 | − 0.118 | − 0.008 | + 1.985 | + 0.028 | 0.000784 |
| Sums | | | | | | | |
| + 0.870 | + 0.070 | + 13.000 | − 1.739 | + 0.823 | + 13.024 | − 0.001 | 0.006837 |

We set up the normal equations, calculating their coefficients by the method of accumulation, and we write them down in the same type of tabular form as the conditional equations:

| $x$ | $y$ | $z$ | $u$ | $L$ | $S$ |
|---|---|---|---|---|---|
| + 6.909156 | + 0.080654 | + 0.870000 | − 0.439975 | − 0.630230 | + 6.789605 |
| + 0.080654 | + 4.936378 | + 0.070000 | − 2.509864 | − 0.523411 | + 2.053757 |
| + 0.870000 | + 0.070000 | + 13.000000 | − 1.739000 | + 0.823000 | + 13.024000 |
| − 0.439975 | − 2.509864 | − 1.739000 | + 1.623981 | + 0.189828 | − 2.875030 |

If the control equations are exactly satisfied when we keep all the digits that we formally obtain, we can assume that no errors were made in setting up the normal equations.

Now, we discard those digits in the normal equations that are not completely reliable and keep only three digits to the right of the decimal in each number. It should be noted that, according to the rules for estimating errors by means of limiting errors, the third digit to the right of the decimal may be uncertain. However, we retain it because there are quite a few operations performed, and we may assume that with a probability close to unity that the actual errors in the coefficients will be considerably less than the limiting errors.

Let us rewrite the system of normal equations, retaining three digits to the right of the decimal and let us write the entire schema for the solution:

| $x$ | $y$ | $z$ | $u$ | $L$ | $S$ | |
|---|---|---|---|---|---|---|
| 6.909 | 0.081 | 0.870 | −0,440 | −0,630 | 6,790 | |
| 0.081 | 4,936 | 0,070 | −2,510 | −0,523 | 2,054 | |
| [0.870] | 0,070 | 13,000 | [−1,739] | 0,823 | 13,024 | |
| −0.440 | −2,510 | −1,739 | 1,621 | 0,190 | −2,875 | |
| $x = +0.0973$ | −0.0117 | −0.1259 | [+0,0637] | +0,0912 | −0,9827 | (1) |
| ($\xi = -0,9027$) | | | | | | |
| | 4,935 | 0,060 | −2,505 | −0,516 | 1,974 | I |
| | 0,060 | 12,890 | [−1,684] | 0,902 | 12,168 | I |
| | −2,505 | −1,684 | 1,596 | 0,150 | −2,443 | I |
| | $y = +0,0875$ ($\eta = -0,9125$) | −0,0122 | +0,5076 | +0.1046 | −0,4000 | (2) |
| | | 12,889 | −1,654 | 0,908 | 12,143 | II |
| | | −1,654 | 0,325 | −0,112 | −1,441 | II |
| | | $z = -0,0749$ ($\zeta = -1,0749$) | 0,1283 | −0,0704 | −0,9421 | (3) |
| | | | *0.113* | 0,004 | 0.117 | III |
| | | | $u = -0,0354$ ($\nu = -1.0354$) | | | (4) |

*Exposition of the calcalating procedure:* (1) denotes the elimination row of the unknown $x$. Written in full, it would be

$$x = -0,0117y \quad -0.1259z \quad +0.637u \quad +0.0912.$$

The coefficients are obtained by dividing the coefficients of the first normal equation by 6.909 and changing the sign.

I denotes the system of three equations with unknowns $y$, $z$, and $u$. The coefficients of this system are obtained from the coefficients of the given system by the right-triangle rule. For example, to obtain the number -1.684, we must add the product of the numbers 0.870 and 0.0637 at the ends of the hypotenuse to the number -1.739 at the right angle. (The numbers forming the triangle are shown in boxes in the diagram.) In every row, the left end of the hypotenuse is constant, namely, the first number of the row.

(2) denotes the elimination row of the unknown $y$ in system I.

II denotes the system with unknowns $z$ and $u$. It is obtained from I and (2) by the right-triangle rule.

(3) denotes the elimination row of the unknown $z$ in system II.

III denotes the equation with only one unknown, namely, $u$. It is obtained from II and (3) by the same procedure.

The first number in each elimination row is the value of the unknown in question. These numbers are obtained by the reverse process by means of the elimination rows. The numbers in parentheses under them are checks. They are obtained by the same reverse procedure, if we take numbers from the column $S$ instead of the column $L$. in the elimination rows. In two places in the column $S$, the last digit is decreased by unity. This was done for the sake of agreement with the check (the removal of an admissible difference).

The last number in the column labeled $u$, printed in italics, is the weight of the last unknown, derived by use of Gauss' theorem

$$p_{\overline{u}} = 0,113.$$

We obtain the weight $\overline{z}$ if we multiply the weight $\overline{u}$ by the ratio of the elements of the principal diagonal in system II:

$$p_{\overline{z}} = 0,113 \cdot \frac{12,889}{0,325} = 4,480.$$

To obtain the weights of the remaining unknowns we again solve the system of normal equations reversing the orders of the unknowns and the equations:

| $u$ | $z$ | $y$ | $x$ | $L$ | $S$ | |
|---|---|---|---|---|---|---|
| 1.624 | −1.739 | −2.510 | −0.440 | 0.190 | −2.875 | (0) |
| −1.739 | 13.000 | 0.070 | 0.870 | 0.823 | 13.024 | (1) |
| −2.510 | 0.070 | 4.936 | 0.081 | −0.523 | 2.054 | (0) |
| −0.440 | 0.870 | 0.081 | 6.909 | −0.630 | 6.790 | (0) |
| $(\bar{u}) = -0.0424$ | +1.0708 | +1.5456 | +0.2709 | −0.1170 | +1.7703 | |
| | 11.138 | −2.618 | 0.399 | 1.026 | 9.945 | |
| | −2.618 | 1.057 | −0.599 | −0.229 | −2.339 | |
| | 0.399 | −0.599 | 6.790 | −0.579 | 6.011 | |
| | $(\bar{z}) = -0.0759$ | +0.2351 | −0.0358 | −0.0921 | −0.8928 | |
| | | −0.442 | −0.505 | +0.012 | −0.051 | |
| | | −0.505 | 6.776 | −0.616 | 5.655 | |
| | | $(\bar{y}) = +0.0838$ | +1.1425 | −0.0271 | +0.1154 | |
| | | | *6.199* | −0.602 | 5.597 | |
| | | | $(\bar{x}) = +0.0971$ | | | |

The calculations are carried out as before. As a check, we again calculate the values of the unknowns, although this is not absolutely necessary. Since all the roots are small, even noticeable differences in the roots in the second calculation should be considered admissible. For final values, we take the averages of the two calculations. A check of the first and second sets of roots in the normal equations shows that the two sets are equally acceptable, since the roots of both satisfy the normal equations with sufficient accuracy (the maximum deviation being 0.0005).

We find the weights of the "last" two unknowns:

$$p_{\bar{x}} = 6.199, \quad p_{\bar{y}} = \frac{0.442}{6.776} \cdot 6.199 = 0.404.$$

We recall also that

$$p_{\bar{z}} = 4.480, \qquad p_{\bar{u}} = 0.113.$$

The values that we take for the unknowns (the averages of the two solutions) are

$$\bar{x} = +0.0972; \quad \bar{y} = +0.0856; \quad \bar{z} = -0.0754; \quad \bar{u} = -0.0390$$

We substitute these values in all the conditional equations to obtain the residual errors. The results should be written in a column labelled $\varepsilon$ along with the matrix of the conditional equations. We then obtain directly

$$\bar{s} = \sum_{k=1}^{n} \varepsilon_k^2 = 0.006837.$$

Calculating the sum of the squares of the residual errors according to formula (16.57) derived in the preceding section, we obtain

$$\bar{s}' = 0.007081.$$

Here $[ll] = 0.182531$. If we consider the accumulation of errors resulting from rounding off when the calculations are made directly and also when they are made by means of formula (16.57), we may consider the difference between $\bar{s}$ and $\bar{s}'$ as admissible. The four significant figures that are written above are obtained formally, but they are not accurate. Therefore, we take

$$\bar{s} = 0.0070,$$

that is, we take a number close to $\bar{s}'$ on the basis of the observation with regard to the greater accuracy of $\bar{s}'$ as compared with that of $\bar{s}$. According to formula (16.58), the most probable value of the mean square error per unit weight is given by

$$\sigma_0^2 = \frac{0.0070}{13-4} = 0.000778,$$

$$\sigma_0 = 0.028.$$

Since the conditional equations are equally precise, this number is the mean square error of one conditional equation. According to formulas (16.59), we find the variances of the unknowns to be

$$\sigma_{\bar{x}}^2 = \frac{0.00078}{6.2} = 0.00013; \qquad \sigma_{\bar{y}}^2 = \frac{0.00078}{0,40} = 0.0020;$$

$$\sigma_{\bar{z}}^2 = \frac{0.00078}{4.5} = 0.00017; \qquad \sigma_{\bar{u}}^2 = \frac{0.00078}{0.113} = 0.0069.$$

Therefore,

$$\sigma_{\bar{x}} = 0.011, \quad \sigma_{\bar{y}} = 0.045, \quad \sigma_{\bar{z}} = 0.013, \quad \sigma_{\bar{u}} = 0,083.$$

We write the results in the form

$$x = 0.097 \pm 0,011, \qquad y = 0,086 \pm 0.045,$$

$$z = -0.075 \pm 0.013, \qquad u = -0.039 \pm 0.083.$$

These results show that the given system of conditional equations makes it possible to determine only the unknowns $\bar{x}$ and $\bar{z}$, with sufficient sureness. The value of $\bar{y}$ that we find is doubtful and the value found for $\bar{u}$ is completely unreliable. For, if we take into account the normal law of distribution, we may use the three-sigma rule to write

$$P(-0.122 < u < +0,044) = 0.68.$$

Consequently, even the sign of $u$ is doubtful because we may expect with a probability of only 0.68 that $u$ will be positive.

Chapter 17

# EMPIRICAL FORMULAS

## 88. STATEMENT OF THE PROBLEM

The most important problem in astronomy and in science in general is that of finding the principles governing natural phenomena. This is done by accumulating observational material and deducing from it information as to the laws that the phenomenon in question obeys. The solution of such a problem is exceedingly important, since if we know the laws governing phenomena, we can predict the pattern that the phenomena will follow in the future. For illustration, we need only cite one example from astronomy. The discovery of the laws governing the motions of heavenly bodies (the laws of Kepler and Newton) enables us to predict solar and lunar eclipses with an accuracy that is quite sufficient for practical purposes. In ancient times, when eclipses were considered catastrophic events, priests of various cults who had learned empirically to predict eclipses used this ability to enhance their power.

In what follows, we shall speak of numerical and functional regularities of behavior.

Let us consider the following (relatively) simple problem. In connection with some phenomenon, we observe the values of two quantities $t$ and $x$; that is, from $n$ observations we obtain the $t_k$ and $x_k$ (for $k=1, 2, \ldots, n$). Let us assume that $x$ is some unknown function of $t$. We wish to find a function that approximately represents the relationship between $t$ and $x$.

In a sense, the recording of the observations in this problem amounts to defining a tabular function, which we need to approximate by some function.

One important remark should be made in connection with this. In nature, there are no such simple relationships between only two quantities. Ordinarily every quantity depends on quite a number of other quantities. A problem of finding a relationship between two quantities can arise either when we assume that the influence on the quantity $x$ of the remaining arguments can be neglected, or when we assume that all these other arguments have at least approximately constant values during the entire period of observation.

The first assumption means that, taking into consideration the accuracy with which the observations were made, the errors resulting from disregarding the remaining arguments have only a slight effect on the value of the function. In the second case, the other arguments appear in the functional relationship as constant parameters.

In addition to the basic problem of finding the principles governing the phenomena, we also must, in analyzing the results of observations, deal with a more modest problem. Observations cannot give the values of a function for *arbitrary* values of the argument. Therefore, if we wish to have the values of a function for values of the argument that are not given in the table, we must resort to a mathematical apparatus for calculating approximate values of the function at values of the argument not included in the table. This is the problem of interpolation (or sometimes, of extrapolation), which we encountered in Part II. One of the methods of solving interpolational problems was shown then.

In such cases, what we sometimes do is simply connect the points of the graph with a smooth curve giving the values of the function for arbitrary values of the argument. If only a very crude approximation of the values is required, this method is quite satisfactory since it does not require any calculations. Its obvious disadvantage is its excessive dependence on the observer because he draws the "smooth" curve by eye and to some extent subjectively, inasmuch as different observers have different concepts of smoothness and their eyes are not just alike. Therefore, it is difficult to compare the results of different investigators or to consolidate them, which often has to be done in astronomy.

Any function approximating a tabulated function obtained from observations is called an empirical function or formula.

The problem of constructing an empirical function requires the introduction of two conditions without which this problem, like the general problem of approximating a function, is indeterminate.

1. An analytical expression for the function must be chosen that will approximate the tabulated empirical function.

2. The empirical formula must be as consistent as possible with the observed results.

## 89. CHOICE OF THE TYPE OF FORMULA

Choice of the type of formula is the most indefinite and difficult part of the work. Sometimes, it needs to be done more than once. First a graph of the empirical table is constructed. In many cases, a comparison of this point graph with various curves with whose equations we are familiar gives an indication as to the possible type of formula. For example, if the points of the graph are distributed as shown in Figure 9, that is, if they occur at only slight distances from a straight line, we should look for a formula of the form

$$x = a + bt,$$

where $a$ and $b$ are coefficients to be determined from the observational data.

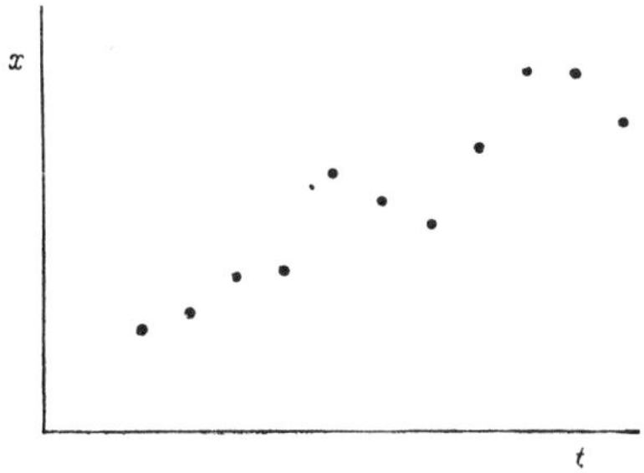

Fig. 9. An example of an empirical distribution close to direct proportionality.

Sometimes very general properties of the relationship between the variables are known. For example, one variable may be approximately inversely proportional to the other, or one variable may be a periodic function of the other, with the approximate value of the period known, etc. Figure 10 illustrates a distribution of points more or less along one branch of a hyperbola with asymptotes parallel to the coordinate axis. In such a case, we may try the general equation for an equilateral hyperbola,

$$x = \frac{a + bt}{c + dt},$$

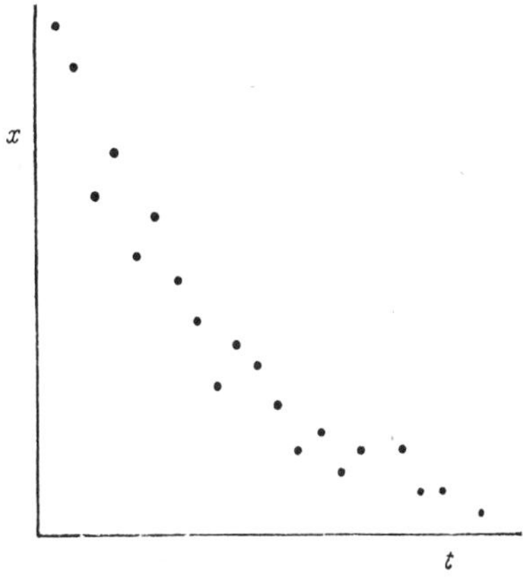

Fig. 10. An example of an empirical distribution close to inverse proportionality.

that is, we may seek a rational function of $t$. (One of these coefficients can be set equal to unity.) We can choose such a function when we know that the variables are approximately inversely proportional to each other.

In the case of periodicity, we may seek a formula of the form

$$x = a \sin\left(\frac{2\pi b}{P} t + c\right)$$

or a trigonometric polynomial of order higher than first.

Finally, there may be cases in which we can construct a crude theory concerning the phenomenon. Then, the function determined by this theory can indicate the possible form of an empirical formula.

Example 1. A law can be constructed relating the mass and radiation of stars. From general considerations, we may roughly assume that the radiation of stars of a particular spectral class is proportional to the surface area of the star. Assuming the star to be spherical, we see that the radiation is proportional to the square of the radius. According to the same simplifying assumption, the mass is proportional to the cube of the radius (when the mass is assumed proportional to the volume). We can then eliminate the radius and obtain the following formula:

$$L = am^{\frac{2}{3}},$$

where $L$ is the radiation, $m$ is the mass, and $a$ is a proportionality constant. In this form, the formula is, of course, unsatisfactory because the simplifications made were too great. Therefore, we should take a formula of the form

$$L = am^b + c,$$

where $a$, $b$, $c$ are constants to be determined from observational data.

Example 2. Construct an empirical law for the solubility of a particular substance in a particular liquid. We need a formula expressing the amount of substance dissolved as a function of time. As a basis, we may take a simple differential law. The amount of the substance that will be dissolved in a small interval of time is proportional to that interval and to the amount of the substance that has not been dissolved. We denote by $M$ the original amount of the substance and by $x$ the amount that has dissolved at the instant $t$. Then, according to the law that we stated,

$$dx = k(M - x)\,dt,$$

where $k$ is a positive proportionality constant. The variables in this differential equation are separable and its solution is

$$x = M - be^{-kt},$$

where $b$ is an arbitrary constant. Since $x = 0$ when $t = 0$, we have $b = M$, and hence,

$$x = M - Me^{-kt}.$$

Starting with this approximate relationship, we may seek a formula of the form

$$x = M - ae^{-bt},$$

where $a$ and $b$ are parameters.

Whatever the form of the empirical formula, it will have one feature that is common to all the formulas, namely, the presence of literal parameters that must be determined according to some criterion of closeness of the formula to the table. The presence of several parameters makes the formula more flexible.

Usually, we try to satisfy one further condition. It is desirable to have a formula that is linear with respect to the parameters or that can be reduced to linear form by simple substitutions. For this reason, we often use algebraic or trigonometric polynomials.

## 90. THE USE OF LEGENDRE'S PRINCIPLE FOR DETERMINING THE VALUES OF THE PARAMETERS

The method of calculating the parameters in the empirical formulas of course depends on the criterion agreed upon for the closeness of the values given by the formula to those of the table. In the problem of exact interpolation (see Part II), we chose an algebraic (or a trigonometric) polynomial that would coincide exactly with the tabulated values of the function at the basic points. As we recall, this convention is meaningful if the table is exact, that is, if we can rely on *all* the digits of the numbers given in the table. In our present problem, where both the values of the function and the values of the argument are obtained from observations, we cannot consider them exact in all formally obtained digits. For example, if measurements of an angle are made with an accuracy of $0.1''$, the random errors and the systematic errors that are not taken into account may together amount to $1$-$2'$ or even more (for example, when observations are made of a comet). Therefore, there is no point in requiring that an empirical formula *exactly* represent the tabular function.*

Let us illustrate this graphically (see Fig. 11).

It is assumed that we know the limiting errors of the observations or their mean square errors. Let us suppose that we know the limiting errors of $t_k$ and $x_k$. We denote these by $\tau_k$ and $\xi_k$. We denote by $P_k$ the point on the graph with coordinates $(t_k, x_k)$.

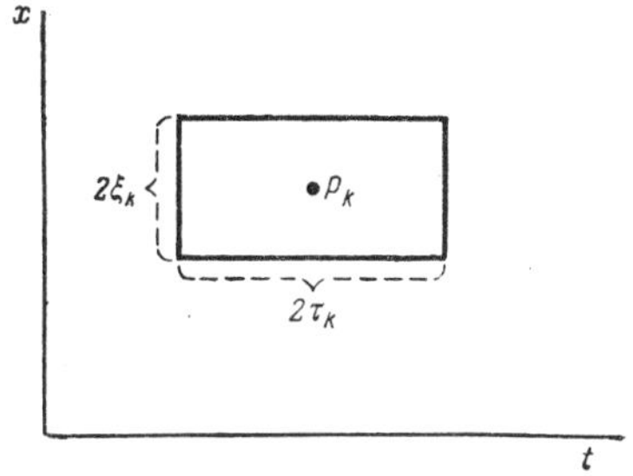


Fig. 11. A "rectangle of possible deviations" of a point in an empirical distribution.

---

*This would be difficult even from a purely technical point of view because we would need to make more observations and we would then have to use polynomials of higher orders. (In the method of point interpolation, the degree of the polynomial is 1 less than the number of basic points.)

Observations yield a sequence of points $P(t_k, x_k)$. If the errors in $t$ and $x$ can be assumed independent, the abscissa $t$ could yield an arbitrary value from $t_k-\tau_k$ to $t_k+\tau_k$, depending on how the factors that produce errors are combined. Analogously, instead of $x_k$, we could obtain an arbitrary number from $x_k-\xi_k$ to $x_k+\xi_k$. Thus, because of the errors, the point $P_k$ can fall at an arbitrary point of a rectangle whose sides are $2\tau_k$ and $2\xi_k$ and whose center is at the point $(t_k, x_k)$. Such rectangles should be constructed around every point obtained from observations. It would be essentially sufficient for the graph of the empirical formula to pass through all these rectangles.

If, instead of the limiting errors, the quadratic means $\sigma_{t,k}$ and $\sigma_{x,k}$ are given, they can be reduced to the limiting errors with a probability close to unity ($2\sigma$ with probability 0.95 or $3\sigma$ with probability 0.9973).

However, the problem of constructing empirical formulas was not discussed in such a formulation because it would have been too complicated. Therefore, another method has been chosen in practice, namely, the use of Legendre's principle, with which we are already familiar:

*The parameters of the chosen empirical formula are determined in such a way that the sum of the squares of the deviations from the tabulated values of the function are minimized.*

This condition of approximating an empirical tabulated function is simply a convention to which we cannot give a probabilistic explanation. We can only note that the choice of this convention is motivated by the following considerations. In most problems, the number of values of an empirical function is not very small. Therefore, it is not possible to make the deviations of the individual points small. We can only introduce some general condition applying to the entire set of points. There is no sense in stipulating that the deviations, with signs considered, be minimized, since ordinarily there are both positive and negative deviations. Such deviations, even if they are large in absolute value, can cancel each other out. The condition that the sum of the absolute values of the deviations be small is a quite natural one. However, it would lead to more tedious calculations. Finally, we might require that the sum of the fourth- or sixth- or even higher-order powers be minimized, but this would be a formal exercise in generalizations. Therefore, at the present time, it is customary to determine the parameters by the method of least squares, which leads to rather simple computations.

Determination of the parameters of an empirical formula on the basis of Legendre's principle is done in the following manner. Successive substitution of all the tabulated values of the argument and the function into the chosen formula with literal parameters leads to a system of conditional equations for determining the numerical values of the parameters from observations. In the general case, these equations are incompatible, which is explained not only by the random errors in the measurements, but also by the facts that the chosen function is only an approximation of the unknown exact formula and that we are neglecting the dependence of the function on other arguments. The normal equations are set up from the conditional equations and are solved by one of the methods explained above.

Since it is convenient to have linear conditional equations for carrying out the calculations, the formulas should be chosen in such a way that they are linear with respect to the parameters or can easily be reduced to linear equations by suitable substitutions.

Here, the calculation of the mean square errors of the unknowns loses its probabilistic meaning. It would be more correct to call them the "mean square deviations." However, these quantities still need to be calculated, since they give a representation of the reliability of the values calculated for the parameters. In particular, they show how many digits can be kept in the figures for the parameters.

## 91. CHECKING OF EMPIRICAL FORMULAS

Since, in contrast with point interpolation, an empirical formula does not represent *exactly* the tabular values of the function, the natural method of making a first check consists in calculating the values of the function at the tabulated values of the argument by the derived formula and comparing the results with the observed values. In other words, we calculate the residual errors of the conditional equations. A similar table can serve for checking the suitability of the empirical formula.

If none of the remainders exceed the limiting errors of the measurements of the function in absolute value, we may consider the deduced empirical formula as satisfactory. If all the errors appreciably exceed the limiting errors in absolute value, the formula is obviously unsatisfactory. In most cases, what we have is an intermediary case—both large and small remainders. Then, we can use the signs of the remainders. If the signs alternate, the formula can be accepted. However, if the positive and negative remainders come in groups, the validity of the formula should be questioned, since there are systematic deviations.

Finally, to evaluate the suitability of a formula, we may use the mean square error of a simple equation. If this quantity is of the order of approximately one half the limiting error of the measurements of the function, the formula may be accepted. If it exceeds the limiting error, the formula is unsatisfactory.

If, upon investigation, the formula is found to be completely unusable or if it raises doubts, the investigator is advised to repeat the work with some modification of the formula. After several formulas have been set up, the one whose mean square error per unit weight is least should be considered the best. It is convenient to begin the choice of formulas by constructing a graph of the empirical formula and comparing it with the graph of the tabulated values.

In evaluating the suitability of a formula, we can sometimes use physical information regarding the fixed function. For example, if an empirical formula gives a maximum at some value of the argument and if we know that the fixed function is monotonic in a neighborhood of this value of the argument, the empirical formula found cannot be considered satisfactory.

## 92. AN ILLUSTRATION OF THE DERIVATION OF AN EMPIRICAL FORMULA

Suppose that observations yield the following tabulated function:

| | | | | | | |
|---|---|---|---|---|---|---|
| $t$ | 0.0 | 0.1 | 0.2 | 0.3 | 0.4 | 0.5 |
| $x$ | 1.3 | 1.0 | 0.8 | 0.6 | 0.4 | 0.1 |

Construction of a small-scale graph gives approximately a straight line. Therefore, let us construct a linear formula of the form

$$x = a + bt,$$

where $a$ and $b$ are unknown coefficients.

Let us set up the conditional equations according to the scheme in which the control numbers $s$. are included, that is, the sums of the coefficients and the free terms are transferred to the left. This scheme also includes the columns of residual errors $\varepsilon$ and their squares. (Of course, these two columns are filled in after solution of the system of normal equations.) The last column can not be filled in if $\bar{s} = \sum_{k=1}^{6} \varepsilon_k^2$ is calculated on a calculating machine by the method of accumulation.

| $a$ | $b$ | $-x$ | $s$ | $\varepsilon$ | $\varepsilon^2 \cdot 10^4$ |
|---|---|---|---|---|---|
| 1 | 0.0 | −1.3 | −0.3 | −0.03 | 9 |
| 1 | 0.1 | −1.0 | +0.1 | +0.04 | 16 |
| 1 | 0.2 | −0.8 | +0.4 | +0.01 | 1 |
| 1 | 0.3 | −0.6 | +0.7 | −0.02 | 4 |
| 1 | 0.4 | −0.4 | +1.0 | −0.05 | 25 |
| 1 | 0.5 | −0.1 | +1.4 | +0.03 | 9 |
| 6 | 1.5 | −4.2 | +3.3 | −0.02 | 0.0064 |

The normal equations are of the form

| $a$ | $b$ | $L$ | $S$ |
|---|---|---|---|
| 6.0 | 1.5 | −4.2 | 3.3 |
| 1.5 | 0.55 | −0.65 | 1.4 |
| 7.5 | 2.05 | −4.85 | 4.7 |

We can check the normal equations by using the number $S$, which is obtained in the first equation by adding all the numbers $s$ (since the coefficients of $a$ are all equal to unity). In the second equation, $S$ is the sum of the products of the numbers $s$ and the coefficients $b$ in the conditional equations. Furthermore, a supplementary control may be obtained by adding the coefficients and the free terms in the normal equations, and comparing this sum with the sum of all the numbers $S$. This check appears in the third row.

Let us solve the system of normal equations by means of determinants. In order to avoid an accumulation of errors resulting from the approximate calculations, we perform the calculations as if the coefficients of the normal equations were the exact numbers. In the present problem, this presents no difficulties because all the coefficients have only a small number of digits. We evaluate the determinants:

$$D=\begin{vmatrix} 6 & 1.5 \\ 1.5 & 0.55 \end{vmatrix}, \quad D_a=\begin{vmatrix} 4.2 & 1.5 \\ 0.65 & 0.55 \end{vmatrix}, \quad D_\alpha=\begin{vmatrix} -3.3 & 1.5 \\ -1.4 & 0.55 \end{vmatrix},$$

$$D_b=\begin{vmatrix} 6 & 4.2 \\ 1.5 & 0.65 \end{vmatrix}, \quad D_\beta=\begin{vmatrix} 6 & -3.3 \\ 1.5 & -1.4 \end{vmatrix}.$$

The determinants $D_\alpha$ and $D_\beta$ are obtained by replacing the column $L$ with the column $S$ (in order to check the solution to the normal equations obtained by solving the system of normal equations). The unknowns $\alpha$ and $\beta$ must be one less than $a$ and $b$, respectively. Evaluation of the determinants yields

$$D=1.05, \quad D_a=1.335, \quad D_b=-2.4, \quad D_\alpha=0.285, \quad D_\beta=-3.45.$$

We now calculate the original and the control unknowns:

$$a=\frac{1.335}{1.05}=1.271, \quad b=-\frac{2.4}{1.05}=-2.286,$$

$$\alpha=\frac{0.285}{1.05}=0.271, \quad \beta=-\frac{3.45}{1.05}=-3.286.$$

We calculate the mean square error of a single conditional equation by substituting into the conditional equations the values found for the coefficients; we then calculate the remainders, denoted in the diagram of the conditional equations by the letter $\varepsilon$:

$$\sigma_0^2=\frac{0.0064}{6-2}=0.0016, \qquad \sigma_0=0.04.$$

We determine the weights of the unknowns by means of the determinants:

$$p_a=\frac{1.05}{0.55}=1.91, \qquad p_b=\frac{1.05}{0.18}=0.18.$$

We determine the mean square errors (or, more precisely, the mean square deviations) of the unknowns:

$$\sigma_a^2=\frac{0.0016}{1.91}=0.00084, \qquad \sigma_b^2=\frac{0.0016}{0.18}=0.0089,$$

$$\sigma_a=0.029, \qquad \sigma_b=0.094.$$

The result obtained when we determine the coefficients can be written as

$$a=1.271\pm 0.029, \quad b=-2.286\pm 0.094.$$

When we calculate the values of the mean square errors, we write the result in the form

$$a=1.27\pm 0.03, \quad b=-2.29\pm 0.09.$$

The empirical formula is then

$$x=1.27-2.29\,t.$$

Examination of the residual errors shows that the formula represents the observations quite satisfactorily, provided we assume that the values of $x$ are given with a limiting error of 0.05. The absolute value of only one of the remainders is equal to 0.05 and the absolute values of the other remainders are less than this.

# Part V

# ANALYSIS OF STATISTICAL MATERIAL

Chapter 18

# ANALYSIS OF A ONE-DIMENSIONAL STATISTICAL SET

## 93. STATISTICAL SETS

One of the problems encountered in the natural sciences consists in studying objects or phenomena that have certain common characteristics. (The individual objects in such a set may differ one from the other in certain other characteristics.) In astronomy and in other disciplines, such problems are encountered quite often. The stars in a catalogue, the catalogue of elements of the orbits of the minor planets, etc., are such sets. For example, in the catalogue of elements of the orbits of the minor planets, known asteroids are included in a single catalogue, because these heavenly bodies are small in mass and dimensions and their motion is determined in large measure by solar attraction. We may say that the objects of the catalogue are grouped together in a set according to some *qualitative* criterion.

But every object in the set has its own individual characteristics (in our example, there are characteristics which vary from one minor planet to another). If we single out those characteristics of the minor planets that determine their motion (that is, the elements of the osculating ellipses of some epoch), we obtain a statistical set in which each member has numerical values for the six orbital elements describing the motion. If we choose a single orbital element, for example, the declination, we obtain a one-dimensional statistical set.

We shall limit ourselves to consideration of one- and two-dimensional sets, although we sometimes must deal with sets of greater dimension. In such cases, one should consult more complete texts, for example, the book by V. I. Romanovskii.

The first problem in the study of statistical sets consists in finding an approximate expression for the distribution function or the probability density from empirical material and in developing a method of obtaining a few well chosen numerical characteristics (in order to gain an overall picture of the entire statistical set).

This problem is closely related to another, namely, that of finding the probability that a randomly chosen object in the set has a value within given bounds.

We could confine ourselves to these problems if the empirical set contained *all* objects of the type investigated. Such complete sets are called *general* sets. The simplest example of a general set is census material giving information about all countries. In the sets studied in astronomy (the set of minor planets, the set of variable stars of a definite type, etc.), the general set is almost always unknown because every year new members of each such set are discovered. We might consider as an exception the set of stars of visible magnitude attainable by ordinary instruments. *All* such stars are known, but the set consisting only of stars of visible magnitude is not of great interest to science.

In most problems, we know a set which can be considered a *sample* of an existent general set only a part of which has been discovered by observations. If some objects of the general set fall *purely by chance* into the observed material and other objects do not, we have a random sample of the general set. However, in a large number of problems, the reason that not all objects of the general set appear in the statistical material does not lie in random causes, but is due to the fact that certain of the objects cannot be discovered by present-day methods of observation. In other cases, it is impossible, for various reasons, to ascertain that criterion according to which the set is chosen. If either of the above two situations occur, we say that the set is the result of selection.

Examples of the first type of selection (due to the limitations of observational methods) are obvious: with present-day instruments, it is impossible to discover stars with a visible magnitude of less than $+24^m$. Very small asteroids can be seen only when they get close to the earth, and so on. Somewhat less obvious are the cases of selection that are the results of properties of the heavenly bodies. We mention two examples: (1) It is possible to see an eclipsed double star only when the observer is in a certain restricted region of space formed by the cone tangent to the surfaces of both stars. (2) Because of the limited resolving power of spectroscopic devices, we cannot detect the radial velocities of stars unless they exceed a definite value. If the first two problems are completely solved for the sample set, the third problem then arises, that of finding out to what extent the numerical parameters obtained for the sample set describe the general set.

In this part of the book, we shall consider primarily the first two problems. We confine ourselves to the basic problem mentioned above, namely, that of developing means of obtaining certain numbers that might be considered as satisfactorily describing the given statistical set. To solve such a problem, we shall consider the value of that numerical element (or of those numerical elements) being studied as random. If it is possible to find an approximate law of distribution of this random variable, its parameters may be considered sufficiently characteristic of the entire set, since it is possible to calculate from these parameters the probability that the value of the variable in question will lie between arbitrary given bounds. Knowledge of this probability makes it possible to determine (with the same probability as above) the number of objects corresponding to each interval of values of the variable (by multiplying the total number of objects by the value of the probability).

The method of finding the law of distribution from empirical material is the same as the method of constructing empirical formulas (see the preceding chapter). The difference consists in the fact that the number of known theoretical laws of distribution is finite. Quite frequently, we first check the suitability of the normal distribution law.

The chosen theoretical law must be checked against the observational material.

## 94. A DISCRETE EMPIRICAL DISTRIBUTION AND ITS NUMERICAL CHARACTERISTICS

On rare occasions, it happens (in astronomical studies) that one is dealing with a discrete empirical distribution (for example, the set of multiple stars). Another reason for considering discrete distributions is that the procedure for analyzing a continuous empirical distribution is almost the same as for a discrete one.

The material obtained from observations constitutes a catalogue in which the value of a discrete random variable $X$ is shown for every object of the set (for every observation). Suppose that the variable $X$ can assume the values

$$x_1, x_2, \dots, x_s,$$

written in order of magnitude. The numbers of observations that give each of the possible values $x_1, x_2, \dots, x_s$ of the variable $X$ are called the multiplicities and are denoted by $n_1, n_2, \dots, n_s$. The ratio of the multiplicity $n_k$ to the overall volume (number of elements) $n$ of the set is called the *empirical probability* that the variable $X$ will take the value $x_k$.

The initial processing of the material containing the $n$ objects is begun by calculating the multiplicities and is put in the form of the following table.

| | | |
|---|---|---|
| $x_1, x_2, \dots, x_{s-1}, x_s$ | $(x_{s+1} > x_s)$ | |
| $n_1, n_2, \dots, n_{s-1}, n_s$ | $(0)$ | $\sum_{k=1}^{s} n_k = n,$ |
| $p_1, p_2, \dots, p_{s-1}, p_s$ | $(0)$ | $\sum_{k=1}^{s} p_k = 1,\ p_k = \frac{n_k}{n},$ |
| $0 = N_1, N_2, \dots, N_{s-1}, N_s$ | $N_{s+1} = n$ | $N_k = \sum_{l=1}^{k-1} n_l,$ |
| $0 = P_1, P_2, \dots, P_{s-1}, P_s$ | $P_{s+1} = 1$ | $P_k = \frac{N_k}{n}.$ |

In this table, the numbers $n_1, n_2, \dots, n_s$ represent the multiplicities of the respective values of the variable. The first two rows are called the *empirical distribution table* of the random variable. Instead of the numbers $n_k$, we introduce the empirical probabilities $p_k = n_k / n$ appearing in the third row. However, in performing the calculations, it is more convenient to deal with whole numbers and to leave the division by $n$ (in order to convert to probabilities) until the end of the calculations. Therefore, the numbers $p_k$ are rarely included in the table. The fourth row gives the numbers $N_k$ of objects for which the values of the random variable are less than $x_k$. Obviously, we have

$$N_1 = 0, \qquad N_2 = n_1,$$
$$N_3 = n_1 + n_2, \ \ldots, \ N_s = n_1 + n_2 + \ldots + n_{s-1} = n - n_s.$$

In the first row, let us add one more value $x_{s+1}$ arbitrarily close to $x_s$ but somewhat greater than it. Since observations do not yield such a value, $n_{s+1} = 0$. Then, by the definition of the number $N_k$, it follows that $N_{s+1} = n$. If we divide all the numbers $N_k$ (for $k = 1, 2, \ldots, s, s+1$) by the total number of observations, we obtain the numbers $P_k$ appearing in the fifth row. They may be considered empirical values of the distribution function of the discrete random variable $X$. In the case of a discrete variable, the distribution function has a discontinuity at each of the values of $x_k$.

The basic problem of determining the probability that the random variable will take a value between the given limits $\alpha$ and $\beta$ is easily solved with the help of the table that we have constructed. If we rule out the possibility of $X$ assuming one of these bounds, we will always have

$$P(\alpha < X < \beta) = \sum_{x > \alpha}^{x < \beta} p_k.$$

The summation is taken over all $k$ satisfying the inequality following the probability symbol.

The method of finding the probability

$$P(\alpha \leqslant X \leqslant \beta),$$

depends on the coincidence or non-coincidence of one or both of the bounds with the tabular values. For example, if $\beta = x_r$, where $r \leqslant s$, and $\alpha$ is not equal to any of the numbers $x_k$, we have

$$P(\alpha \leqslant X \leqslant \beta) = \sum_{x > \alpha}^{k = r} p_k.$$

The summation begins with the term corresponding to the smallest value of $X$ that exceeds $\alpha$.

If a table such as we have been considering can be constructed and is not too large, it will give complete information regarding a discrete random variable. Such a table can be used for describing the set and for solving the basic problem when it is a question of a single set of a definite type. If we need to compare different sets of a single type (for example, sets of multiple stars in various regions of the galaxy), comparison of the complete tables is by no means always easy to perform. It is convenient to have a small number of definite and distinctive numerical characteristics of the set (in order to compare these characteristics instead of comparing the complete tables). Let us consider a few such characteristics.

## 1. The Average Value of a Set.

The simplest overall numerical characteristic of a set is probably the average value of the random variable defined as the expectation of the discrete variable by the formula

$$\bar{x} = \sum_{k=1}^{s} x_k p_k. \tag{18.1}$$

However, in contrast with the definition of expectation, the $p_k$ are empirical probabilities.

Like the expectations, the average value is a number with dimensions. Therefore, in comparing sets of a single type, it is necessary that $X$ be measured in the same units. If we measure sets of different types, we cannot compare average values because these are different kinds of quantities. If $\bar{x}$ is not equal to *any* of the possible values of the variable, we may consider $\bar{x}$ a formal characteristic and take as an approximation the closest possible value.

## 2. The Median.

Like the median of the theoretical distribution of a continuous random variable, the median $\bar{x}_m$ of an empirical distribution of a discrete variable is defined by the following condition: the empirical probability of obtaining a value less than the median must be equal to 1/2. (We sometimes say that the median "divides the set in two.") The median of a discrete variable is most conveniently determined from the table of values $N_k$. As was shown above, the numbers in this table increase monotonically (though in the case of individual pairs of points, they may be repeated). If among the numbers $N_k$ there is an $N_m$ exactly equal to one half the total number of observations, we may take any number between $x_{m-1}$ and $x_m$ as the median $\bar{x}_m$ because, by definition,

$$N_m = \sum_{k=1}^{m-1} n_k = nP(x \leqslant x_{m-1}), \qquad P(x \leqslant x_{m-1}) = \frac{1}{2}. \tag{18.2}$$

U

If there is no number $N_k$ exactly equal to $n/2$, we find a number $N_r < n/2$ such that $N_{r+1} > n/2$. The corresponding values of the variable $X$ will be $x_r$ and $x_{r+1}$. In this case, we could say that the median $\bar{x}_m$ lies between the numbers $x_r$ and $x_{r+1}$. For $\bar{x}_m$ we may take either $x_r$ (if $n/2 - N_r < N_{r+1} - n/2$) or $x_{r+1}$ (if the direction of the inequality is reversed). Since we are considering a discrete variable having no values between $x_r$ and $x_{r+1}$, the answer can be given only approximately in the form indicated, that is, either $x_r$ or $x_{r+1}$.

We can also determine the median $\bar{x}_m$ by linear interpolation from the values $N_r$, $N_{r+1}$, $x_r$, and $x_{r+1}$ and treat it as a formal characteristic of the set.

## 3. *The Mean Square Deviation.*

By definition, the mean square deviation is the square root of the variance. If, in the definition of the variance of a discrete random variable, we replace the probabilities with empirical probabilities, we obtain the formula for determining the empirical mean square deviation:

$$\sigma_x^2 = \sum_{k=1}^{s} p_k (x_k - \bar{x})^2. \tag{18.3}$$

In many problems, the numbers $x_k$ are rather simple—in the sense that they do not have many digits. For example, if we consider the set of multiple stars, the numbers $x_k$ have the values 1, 2, 3, 4, . . . (the end of the table cannot as yet be considered definite). In the general case, however, the number $\bar{x}$ is not simple in this sense; that is, it has several significant figures and calculation from the formula given can be complicated. Therefore, it is better to use the formula for calculating the variance (see Section 44 of Part III):

$$\sigma_x^2 = \sum_{k=1}^{s} p_k x_k^2 - \bar{x}^2. \tag{18.4}$$

The number $\sigma_x$ has the same dimension as do the numbers $x_k$. Therefore, the value $\sigma_x$ depends on the choice of units in which the measurements are made. In comparing sets of the same kind, that is, sets of the same quantities selected according to different criteria, it is necessary that the values $x$ of the elements of the different sets be measured in the same units.

If we must compare different sets, it is convenient to introduce dimensionless numerical characteristics. To obtain a dimensionless characteristic of variance, we may take the quantity

$$V_x = \frac{\sigma_x}{\bar{x}}, \tag{18.5}$$

known as the coefficient of variability. It is not a convenient characteristic if $\bar{x}$ is close to 0.

These two numerical characteristics ($\bar{x}$ and $\sigma_x$) are sufficient for us to evaluate the probability that $X$ will assume a value between the given bounds, using Chebyshev's inequality:

$$P(|X-\bar{x}| < t\sigma_x) > 1 - \frac{1}{t^2}.$$

However, the bounds cannot be chosen completely arbitrarily: they must be symmetric about the mean value $\bar{x}$.

The estimate given by Chebyshev's inequality is rather crude. Use of the complete table, if this is possible, will give the exact probability.

## 4. Moments of Distribution.

The moments of distribution have been defined in Part III for continuous random variables as the expectations of the powers of a random variable (the initial moments) and the expectations of the powers of the deviation of a random variable from the center of distribution (the central moments).

Let us use this same definition for a discrete random variable, replacing the theoretical probabilities with empirical ones in the expectations. Then, for the initial moments of order $r$, we obtain the formula

$$\nu_r = \sum_{k=1}^{s} p_k x_k^r, \tag{18.6}$$

where the $r$ are positive integers.

Since the initial moments depend on the chosen zero value, the central moments, defined by the formulas

$$\mu_r = \sum_{k=1}^{s} p_k (x_k - \bar{x})^r; \tag{18.7}$$

are more indicative of the distribution. They do not depend on the zero value since, when a displacement of the zero value is made, $\bar{x}$ is displaced the same amount.

For the most part, it is convenient, in making calculations, to find the initial moments first and then compute the central moments from formulas that are easily obtained from the binomial expansion and the reduction of the last two terms:

$$\mu_r = \nu_r - r\bar{x}\nu_{r-1} + \frac{r(r-1)}{2!}\bar{x}^2\nu_{r-2} + \dots$$
$$\dots + (-1)^r \frac{r(r-1)}{2}\bar{x}^{r-2}\nu_2 + (-1)^{r+1}(r-1)\bar{x}^r.$$

For example,

$$\left.\begin{aligned} \mu_2 = \nu_2 - \bar{x}^2, \quad \mu_3 = \nu_3 - 3\bar{x}\nu_2 + 2\bar{x}^3, \\ \mu_4 = \nu_4 - 4\bar{x}\nu_3 + 6\bar{x}^2\nu_2 - 3\bar{x}^4. \end{aligned}\right\} \tag{18.8}$$

For dimensionless numerical characteristics, we may take the numbers

$$M_r = \frac{\mu_r}{\sigma^r}$$

or

$$m_r = \frac{\sqrt[r]{\mu_r}}{\sigma} \qquad (r = 1, 2, \ldots). \tag{18.9}$$

By using these dimensionless characteristics, we can compare not only the different distributions of a single variable, but also the distributions of different variables.

## 95. CONTINUOUS EMPIRICAL DISTRIBUTIONS

In almost all problems of statistical analysis of material, we must deal with continuous variables.

The observational material is found in different catalogues or in specially performed observations. The "raw" material is a list of the elements of a set with an indication of the numerical values of the variable that are obtained from observations. If the set contains few objects (for example, ten or twenty), the observational material is analyzed directly. If there is a great amount of this material, direct analysis of it would be tedious and the labor involved would not be justified by better results, since the material is almost always of a selective nature.

The raw material is subjected to a preliminary analysis consisting of the following operations:

By consulting a catalogue, we find the smallest and largest values of the variable. The first we either decrease or leave unchanged; the second we either increase or leave unchanged. If a change is made, it is so that the bounds of the region taken for the value of $X$ will have fewer significant figures. Some broadening of the tabulated region of values of $X$ is ordinarily admissible, since the material is almost always of a selective nature and the actual region of values of $X$ may be greater than the region obtained from observations. We divide the region that we now have into $s$ equal parts (intervals), being careful (for purposes of simplifying the calculations) to see that the end points of the intervals are numbers with few significant figures. The question of the number of intervals does not yet have a theoretical basis and is solved by trial and error. It is usually convenient to take somewhere between ten and twenty intervals, but these figures are only guides.

Having decided on some number of intervals, we denote the end points of the intervals by $x^{(0)}, x^{(1)}, x^{(2)}, \ldots, x^{(s)}$. We now count the number of elements of the set for which the values of $X$ fall in each of the intervals. It may happen that the individual values of $X$ that are obtained from observations are equal to the values of the end points of some of the intervals. In such cases, an agreement must be made as to which of the intervals such elements of the set should be assigned to, that is, to the interval on the left or the one on the right. What is frequently done is to assign to each of adjacent intervals half of such cases. In order not to deal with fractions, in such a case we multiply the total number of elements by two. This introduces no error because the total number of observations is multiplied by two; consequently, the empirical probability of falling in each of the intervals remains unchanged. The counting must be made for each of the intervals separately. Then, as a check, the sum is taken for all the intervals. It must be equal to the total number of observations.

If there are many observations (more than a hundred), it will become quite tiresome to make a count for each interval separately, because it will be necessary to look through the catalogue (or list) as many times as there are intervals chosen. The counting can be simplified in the following simple manner. A rectangle of arbitrary dimensions drawn on graph paper is subdivided into identical sub-rectangles by parallel lines. The number of these rectangles is equal to the number of intervals chosen. The values $x^{(k)}$ corresponding to the end points of the intervals are written on the dividing lines bounding the rectangles. We read the catalogue (once) and place a point in the small rectangles corresponding to the value $x$ of each element of the set. When the entire catalogue has been read, there will be a number of points in each of the small rectangles. These still need to be counted. If any of the catalogued values is equal to an end point of one of the intervals, it is advisable to put a cross rather than a point on the dividing line.

After the number of elements in each interval has been counted, we obtain a table like that shown below. The first column shows the end points of the intervals; the second shows the values of $X$ corresponding to the midpoints of the intervals; the fourth shows the number of observations in each interval.

| End points of the intervals | Midpoints of the intervals | Conventional units | Number of observations |
|---|---|---|---|
| $x^{(0)}$ | | | |
| $x^{(1)}$ | $x_1$ | $-(r-1)$ | $n_1$ |
| $x^{(2)}$ | $x_2$ | $-(r-2)$ | $n_2$ |
| ... | ... | ... | ... |
| ... | $x_r$ | $0$ | $n_r$ |
| $x^{(s-1)}$ | ... | ... | ... |
| $x^{(s)}$ | $x_s$ | $s-r$ | $n_s$ |

After the values $n_1, n_2, \ldots, n_s$ have been taken from the table, we may consider them the multiplicities of the values of a discrete variable taking the values $x_1, x_2, \ldots x_s$ with empirical probabilities

$$\frac{n_1}{n}, \frac{n_2}{n}, \ldots, \frac{n_s}{n}.$$

Calculation of the basic characteristics of the distribution (the average value, the mean square deviation, the moments) can be carried out in the same way as for a discrete variable, from the formulas of Section 94.

To make the calculations easier, it is helpful to calculate, from the table of multiplicities, in what interval the average value must fall. Usually it will be the interval in which $n_k$ is greatest. If we consider the $n_k$ as mass points placed in the interiors of the intervals, the average value $\bar{x}$ will correspond to the center of mass. We can use this criterion to determine what interval may contain the average value, if the distribution is very asymmetric.*

Suppose that $x_r$ is the midpoint of the interval in which the average value lies. Let us assign the number zero to that interval. We number the intervals following the zero interval in order, beginning with 1 and going up to $s-r$. We number the intervals preceding the zero interval with the negative numbers from $-1$ to $-(r-1)$. These conventional numbers or units are shown in the third column of the above table.

Instead of $x$, we now introduce a new argument $t$ of the set, whose values are equal to these conventional units. The variables $x$ and $t$ are related by the obvious linear relationship $x_{r+t} = x_r + ht$, where $h$ is the step in the table of values of $x$.

Introduction of the argument $t$ instead of $x$ considerably simplifies the calculations because all the parameters are calculated first for the argument $t$. The average value and the mean square deviations are then expressed in units of the same dimension as those in which the variable being studied is measured. This is done by means of the formulas

$$\bar{x} = x_r + h\bar{t}, \qquad \sigma_x = h\sigma_t. \tag{18.10}$$

If the distribution is not a normal one, the parameters $\bar{x}$ and $\sigma_x$ (or $\bar{t}$ and $\sigma_t$) are not sufficient for describing the set or calculating the probabilities. In such cases, we need to calculate also the asymmetry and excess by the formulas

$$A = \frac{\mu_3(t)}{\sigma_t^3}, \qquad E = \frac{\mu_4(t)}{\sigma_t^4} - 3, \tag{18.11}$$

where $\mu_3(t)$ and $\mu_4(t)$ are the third- and fourth-order central moments for the argument $t$. These two parameters are necessary if

*We note, however, that calculation of the position of the average value has no theoretical value. If we obtain the wrong interval, this only means that the calculations will be made somewhat more complicated.

we wish to approximate the empirical distribution that we are investigating by a Charlier function or, as we say, to compare the empirical distribution with the corresponding Charlier curve.

Let us now clarify the meaning of the asymmetry and the excess.

If the distribution is symmetric about the center of distribution, the central moments of odd order vanish and the asymmetry is equal to 0. The less symmetric the distribution, the greater will $A$ differ from 0. Consequently, $A$ increases with increase in the asymmetry of the distribution.

If the relative maximum of the distribution lies to the right of the center of distribution, $\mu_3$ will be positive, since the distribution will then contain more cases with positive deviations from the center than negative ones. The quantity $\sigma$ is positive by definition. Therefore, we obtain from the formula a positive asymmetry. On the other hand, if the maximum is located to the left of the center of distribution, the asymmetry will be negative. Thus, the sign of the asymmetry indicates the direction of the asymmetry of the distribution curve.

The significance of the excess $E$ is clarified if we remember that, for a normal distribution, we have $\mu_4 = 3\sigma^4$. Therefore, according to (18.11), the excess of a normal distribution is equal to 0.

For simplicity, we assume that the empirical distribution is symmetric. We also assume that the normal distribution corresponding to the empirical one (that is, having the same center and variance as the empirical one) has been constructed.

If the vertex of the graph of the empirical distribution is higher than the vertex of the normal one, $E$ will be positive. If the vertex of the empirical distribution is lower than the vertex of the normal one, $E$ will be negative. Thus, a positive excess indicates that the empirical distribution curve is higher at the center than the normal one (and therefore must be lower than the normal one at some distance from the center, since the area bounded by each curve is equal to unity). If the excess is negative, then the curve will be lower at the center than the normal one (and at some distance from the center, higher than the normal one).

If the distribution is asymmetric, the median and the mode are also calculated.

As we have noted before, the median is a value of the variable that exceeds one half the values in the empirical distribution. It can be determined with the aid of the numbers $x_r$ and $x_{r+1}$ (which are found in the same manner as for a discrete distribution). In this case, however, we cannot confine ourselves to determining the discrete value closest to the median, since the variable is continuous. Therefore, we proceed as follows. After finding the two values $x_r$ and $x_{r+1}$ of the midpoints of the intervals between which the median lies, we evaluate the median by linear interpolation from the numbers $x_r$ and $x_{r+1}$ and the corresponding numbers $N_r$ and $N_{r+1}$, by using the obvious formula

$$\overline{x}_m = x_r + \frac{x_{r+1} - x_r}{N_{r+1} - N_r}\left(\frac{n}{2} - N_r\right). \qquad (18.12)$$

The mode of a theoretical distribution is the value of the variable at which the probability density has a relative maximum. In an empirical distribution, we may assume that the mode is equal to the value of the midpoint of the interval for which the multiplicity is greatest. If greater precision is desired, we choose a theoretical density that satisfies the approximate empirical distribution sufficiently well and we take for the mode the value of the variable corresponding to the maximum of the assumed distribution law.

Sometimes, as a result of mixing of data of various kinds, the table on page 293 will have more than one relative maximum. If the relative maxima are stable, that is, if they do not disappear when the intervals are varied, the problem of dividing the data and determining the parameters of the constituent distributions may arise. Such a problem can be solved for two constituent normal distributions.

The following example illustrates the procedure for calculating the moments up to the fourth order inclusive and the column of values of $N_k$ of an empirical distribution function (see Table A; Table B will be examined in the following section).

Table A

Example. Analysis of the distribution of the absolute magnitudes of stars of the spectral classes B5-B9. Calculation of the moments.

| I | II | III | IV | V | VI | VII | VIII |
|---|---|---|---|---|---|---|---|
| $M$ | $n_k$ (0) | $t$ | $n_k t_k$ | $n_k t_k^2$ | $n_k t_k^3$ | $n_k t_k^4$ | $N_k$ |
| - 2.0 | | | | | | | 0 |
| | 1 | - 4 | - 4 | 16 | - 64 | 256 | |
| - 1.5 | | | | | | | 1 |
| | 3 | - 3 | - 9 | 27 | - 81 | 243 | |
| - 1.0 | | | | | | | 4 |
| | 22 | - 2 | - 44 | 88 | - 176 | 352 | |
| - 0.5 | | | | | | | 26 |
| | 60 | - 1 | - 60 | 60 | - 60 | 60 | |
| 0.0 | | | | | | | 86 |
| | 78 | 0 | 0 | 0 | 0 | 0 | |
| + 0.5 | | | | | | | 164 |
| | 20 | + 1 | + 20 | 20 | + 20 | 20 | |
| + 1.0 | | | | | | | 184 |
| | 3 | + 2 | + 6 | 12 | + 24 | 48 | |
| + 1.5 | | | | | | | 187 |
| | 2 | + 3 | + 6 | 18 | + 54 | 162 | |
| + 2.0 | | | | | | | 189 |
| Total | 189 | | - 85 | 241 | - 283 | 1141 | |

Explanation of Table A

Column I shows the end points of the intervals of the absolute magnitude $M$. The values of $M$ corresponding to the midpoints of the intervals, which we denote by $M_k$, might have been put in this column, but only one of them is used in practice and it is easily determined by inspection. Therefore, there is no need of writing it.

Column II contains the multiplicities in all the intervals indicated in column I. The 0 in the parentheses indicates that the multiplicities $n_k$ are taken from observation.

Column III gives the absolute magnitudes in conventional units (as measured from the zero point corresponding to the mean value). These numbers are denoted by $t_k$. The zero point is taken at the midpoint of that interval corresponding to the largest multiplicity (in the present case 78).

The numbers in column IV are obtained by multiplying the numbers in columns II and III. The sum of the numbers in column IV gives the first-order initial moment after division by $n$, that is, the average value in units of $t$.

The numbers in column V are obtained by multiplying the numbers in columns IV and III. The sum of the numbers divided by $n$ gives the second-order initial moment.

Analogously, columns VI and VII are obtained by multiplying the preceding column by the numbers $t_k$. When we add these numbers and divide the sum by $n$, we obtain the third- and fourth-order initial moment.

Column VIII gives the (net) empirical distribution of the variable in question. The numbers $N_k$ apply to the end points of the intervals. The statistical meaning of these numbers is the following: not one of the values is less than - 2.0; one value is less than - 1.5; in four cases, the value is less than - 1.0, and so on.

## Table B

### Comparison of the empirical and the normal distributions

| IX | X | XI | XII | XIII | XIV | XV | XVI | XVII | XVIII |
|---|---|---|---|---|---|---|---|---|---|
| $t^{(k)}$ | $t^{(k)}-\bar{t}$ | $(t^{(k)}-\bar{t}):\sigma_t$ | $\Phi$ (XI) | $p_k^{(c)}$ | $n_k(c)$ | $(0-c)$ | $(0-c)^2$ | $\frac{(0-c)^2}{c}$ | $N_k^{(c)}$ |
| - 4.5 | - 4.050 | - 3.909 | - 0.4999 | | | | | | 0.0 |
| | | | | 0.0016 | 0.3 | | | | |
| - 3.5 | - 3.050 | - 2.944 | - 0.4983 | | | - 0.5 | 0.25 | 0.06 | 0.3 |
| | | | | 0.0222 | 4.2 | | | | |
| - 2.5 | - 2.050 | - 1.979 | - 0.4761 | | | | | | 4.5 |
| | | | | 0.1322 | 25.0 | - 3.0 | 9.00 | 0.36 | |
| - 1.5 | - 1.050 | - 1.014 | - 0.3439 | | | | | | 29.5 |
| | | | | 0.3248 | 61.4 | - 1.4 | 1.96 | 0.03 | |
| - 0.5 | - 0.050 | - 0.048 | - 0.0191 | | | | | | 90.9 |
| | | | | 0.3395 | 64.2 | + 13.8 | 190.44 | 2.97 | |
| + 0.5 | + 0.950 | + 0.917 | + 0.3204 | | | | | | 155.1 |
| | | | | 0.1496 | 28.3 | - 8.3 | 68.89 | 2.43 | |
| + 1.5 | + 1.950 | + 1.882 | + 0.4700 | | | | | | 183.4 |
| | | | | 0.0278 | 5.3 | | | | |
| + 2.5 | + 2.950 | + 2.847 | + 0.4978 | | | - 0.7 | 0.49 | 0.09 | 188.7 |
| | | | | 0.0021 | 0.4 | | | | |
| + 3.5 | + 3.950 | + 3.813 | + 0.4999 | | | | | | 189.1 |
| Total | — | — | — | 0.9998 | 189.1 | - 0.1 | | 5.94 | |

Calculations Outside the Diagram

(a) The initial moments in conventional units:

$$\bar{t} = \nu_1 = -85 : 189 = -0.450 \qquad \nu_1^2 = +0.202$$
$$\nu_2 = +241 : 189 = +1.275 \qquad \nu_1^3 = -0.0911$$
$$\nu_3 = -283 : 189 = -1.497 \qquad \nu_1^4 = +0.0410$$
$$\nu_4 = +1141 : 189 = +6.037$$

(b) The central moments in conventional units:

$$\mu_2 = +1.275 - 0.202 = 1.073, \quad \sigma_t = \sqrt{1.073} = 1.036$$
$$\mu_3 = -1.497 - 3 \cdot 1.275\,(-0.450) + 2 \cdot (-0.0911) = +0.042$$
$$\sigma_t^3 = 1.112$$
$$\mu_4 = 6.037 - 4 \cdot (-1.497) \cdot (-0.450) + 6 \cdot (1.275) \cdot 0.202 - 3 \cdot 0.410 = 4.765$$
$$\sigma_t^4 = 1.151.$$

The Parameters (numerical characteristics) of an Empirical Distribution

*The average value.* Here, the average value must be calculated in the original unit, that is, in the same units as are given the catalogued data. The zero point agreed upon was taken at the midpoint of the interval between 0.0 and 0.5; that is, the value $M = 0.25$ corresponds to the zero point. The step in actual units is equal to 0.5. Therefore,

$$\overline{M} = 0.25 + (-0.450) \cdot 0.5 = +0.025.$$

*The median.* In the table giving the numbers $N_k$ (column VIII), we have the following: $N_k = 86$ when $M = 0.0$ and $N_k = 164$ when $M = 0.5$. We must find by linear interpolation the value of $M$ at which $N_k = 94.5$ (half the total number of observations). From formula (18.12), we obtain

$$\overline{M}_m = 0.0 + \frac{94.5 - 86}{164 - 86} \cdot 0.5 = 0.054.$$

The mean square deviation:

$$\sigma_M = 1.036 \cdot 0.5 = 0.513.$$

The asymmetry and the excess (according to formulas (18.11)):

$$A = \frac{+0.042}{1.112} = +0.038, \qquad E = \frac{4.765}{1.151} - 3 = +1.14.$$

*The mode.* As was stated above, for the value of the mode of an empirical distribution we may take the value at the midpoint of that interval with the greatest multiplicity. This gives us a value of 0.25 (in the original units, that is, star magnitudes).

The mode can be determined with greater reliability if we can find, in analytical form, a distribution law satisfactorily representing the empirical distribution. If we assume that our material is satisfactorily represented by a normal law of distribution with parameter $\overline{M} = 0.025$, we may take the mode equal to 0.025. The computed parameters of an empirical distribution give a description of the set with the aid of certain numbers. From these, we may obtain certain general facts regarding the random variable in question, without making comparisons with the theoretical distribution.

The value of the mean square deviation shows that the spread (variance) of the values of $M$ is not great. The interval from $\overline{M} - \sigma_M$ to $\overline{M} + \sigma_M$ contains more than 70 per cent of all the observational material. A slight difference between the average value and the median shows that the distribution is approximately symmetric about the center of distribution. This is supported by the small value of the asymmetry. The sign of the asymmetry shows that the mode must be somewhat greater than the average value. The value of the excess cannot be assumed small. This means that near the center there is a preponderance of observations in comparison with what would be the case if the distribution were normal. This is in agreement with the remark about the percentage of the observations in an interval of length $2\sigma_M$ about the center of distribution.

## 96. COMPARISON OF THE EMPIRICAL AND THE THEORETICAL DISTRIBUTIONS

A theoretical distribution function (or probability density) must contain literal parameters, in the general case. Comparison of the distribution obtained from observations with some theoretical distribution consists first in calculating the parameters of the theoretical distribution from observational data and then constructing a theoretical distribution with the numerical values found for the parameters and comparing this distribution with the empirical one.

The parameters of the theoretical distribution must be calculated so that it will represent observations in the best possible manner from some standpoint or other. Pearson suggested the method of moments for this.

With this method, we need to calculate the second- and higher-order central moments and the first-order noncentral moments of the theoretical distribution and equate them to the corresponding moments of the empirical distribution. The moments of the theoretical distribution are functions of the literal parameters of the distribution. The moments of the observed distribution are numbers obtained by processing the statistical material. When we equate these numbers to the functions of the parameters referred to (that is, the moments of the theoretical distribution), we obtain a system of equations for determining the parameters.

For example, if the expression for the probability density contains three parameters, the theoretical moments up to the third order inclusively are equated and we obtain three equations with three unknowns. We note that the moments of zeroth order must also be equal, but this condition will be automatically satisfied if the probability density is normalized (that is, if its integral is equal to unity). Equality of the first-order central moments indicates that the theoretical average and the empirical average must be equal to each other. Equality of the second-order central moments indicates equality of the variances or the mean square deviations.

Quite frequently, the empirical distribution is compared with the normal distribution. The probability density of a normal law contains two parameters. Therefore, to compare the observed distribution with the normal distribution, we only need to equate the first- and second-order moments. This gives us

$$\bar{t} = \bar{\nu}_1, \quad \mu_2 = \sigma^2 = \bar{\mu}_2,$$

where $\bar{t}$ and $\sigma$ denote the parameters of a normal law and $\bar{\nu}_1$ and $\bar{\mu}_2$ are the computed moments of the empirical distribution (in the conventional units).

After we obtain the parameters for a theoretical (e.g., normal) law, we must construct the theoretical distribution and then compare it with the empirical. Here, we may use various criteria regarding the closeness of the theoretical to the empirical distribution (agreement criteria). We give two such criteria here.

### 1. *Kolmogorov's Criterion.*

The parameters of the theoretical distribution are used to calculate the probabilities that the random variable will take values less than the end points of the intervals of the argument of the distribution.

If we multiply these probabilities by the total number of observations $n$, we obtain numbers $N_k^{(c)}$, which are the values of the theoretical distribution function. The superscript $(c)$ indicates that these numbers pertain to the theoretical distribution.

Let us find the maximum absolute value of the difference between the numbers $N_k^{(c)}$ and the values of the function of the empirical distribution $N_k$. If we denote this quantity by $D$

$$D = \max |N_k^{(c)} - N_k|, \tag{18.13}$$

we obtain the argument $\lambda$ of Kolmogorov's criterion:

$$\lambda = \frac{D}{\sqrt{n}}. \tag{18.14}$$

From the argument $\lambda$, we can use the table below to find the value of $P(\lambda)$, which is the probability that the difference $D$ will exceed the value obtained:

| $\lambda$ | 0.3 | 0.4 | 0.5 | 0.6 | 0.7 | 0.8 | 0.9 | 1.0 |
|---|---|---|---|---|---|---|---|---|
| $P(\lambda)$ | 1.000 | 0.997 | 0.964 | 0.864 | 0.711 | 0.544 | 0.393 | 0.270 |

The closer $P(\lambda)$ is to unity, the better the chosen theoretical distribution represents the empirical distribution. If $P(\lambda)$ is small, the theoretical distribution will not represent the observational material satisfactorily.

## 2. The Precision Coefficient.

Using the theoretical law, we calculate the probabilities that the random variable studied will assume values contained within the intervals of the given empirical distribution. If we multiply the probabilities obtained by the total number of observations, we obtain the theoretical multiplicity $c$. Comparison of these numbers with the multiplicities 0 obtained from observations may show how close the observed distribution is to the theoretical distribution.

Using the theoretical distribution, two or three of the boundary intervals are combined into one (see the example). The precision coefficient $H$ is calculated from the formula

$$H = \frac{1}{s' - 1} \sum_{k=1}^{s'} \left[ \frac{(0 - c)^2}{c} \right]_k, \tag{18.15}$$

where $s'$ denotes the final number of intervals of the empirical distribution in contrast with the initial number of intervals. It may be shown that the expectation of $H$ is equal to unity. Therefore, the theoretical distribution constructed is close to the empirical one if $H$ is close to unity.

Example. Table B on page 297 gives a plan for making the calculations that are necessary for comparing the empirical distribution constructed in the previous section with the normal distribution.

Column IX of Table B shows the end points of the intervals in conventional units $t^{(k)}$. Since the step in conventional units is equal to unity, we must subtract 0.5 from each of the column numbers of Table A to obtain the lower end points of the intervals and add 0.5 to obtain the upper end points.

In order to be able to calculate the probability that the random variable will assume values in each of the intervals, according to formula (11.3) of Part III, we must know the values of the probability integral at the lower and upper end point of each interval for values of the argument of the integral representing the deviations from the mean value divided by the mean square deviation of the normal law. Therefore, column X gives the values of the deviations of the end points of the intervals from the mean value, that is, the numbers $t^{(k)} - \bar{t}$ (where $\bar{t} = -0.450$). Column XI gives the quotients resulting from dividing these numbers by $\sigma_t$ (where $\sigma_t = 1.036$). These quotients will be the values of the argument for the probability integral.

Column XII. For each of the numbers

$$\frac{t^{(k)} - \bar{t}}{\sigma_t}$$

in column XI, we determine from the table of the probability integral (Table III at the end of the book) the number

$$\Phi\left(\frac{t^{(k)} - \bar{t}}{\sigma_t}\right);$$

If the argument of the function $\Phi$ is negative, $\Phi$ is taken for the absolute value of the argument and the number obtained is assigned the sign —.

Column XIII gives the probabilities $p_k^{(c)}$ of falling into each of the intervals. If the end points of any of the intervals are $\alpha$ and $\beta$ in conventional units, the probability of falling into that interval is computed from the formula

$$p(\alpha < t < \beta) = p_k^{(c)} = \Phi\left(\frac{\beta - \bar{t}}{\sigma_t}\right) - \Phi\left(\frac{\alpha - \bar{t}}{\sigma_t}\right).$$

Therefore, to obtain the numbers $p_k^{(c)}$, we must subtract the immediately preceding number of the same column from each number in column XII (that is, we must calculate the first-order differences of the numbers in column XII). Here, we need to note the point in this column at which the sign changes from minus to plus, since for that interval we must add the absolute values of the two obtained values of the function $\Phi$. The probabilities (obtained in this manner) of falling in the different intervals are shown with a superscript $(c)$ to emphasize that these probabilities are calculated (under the assumption that the distribution satisfactorily approximates a normal distribution law). As a check, the sum of the numbers in the column should be approximately equal to unity.

Column XIV. In order to avoid dealing with fractions, we multiply the numbers in column XIII by the total number of observations; that is, we assume that the numbers define probabilities and we calculate the theoretical multiplicity in the intervals, which are denoted by $n_k(c)$. As a check, the sum of the numbers $n_k(c)$ must differ only slightly from the total number of observations $n$. A discrepancy of several units is possible because in the case of a normal theoretical distribution, the random variable may formally take values from $-\infty$ to $+\infty$, and we are confining ourselves to a finite region. In the present example, the sum differs from $n$ only by a unit in the reserve digit. (The numbers $n_k(c)$ are counted with tenth parts, which gives a reserve digit.)

Column XV. From every term in column II, we subtract the corresponding number in column XIV. The differences obtained are denoted by $0 - c$ (the observed minus the computed). The sum of the numbers obtained must be equal to the difference between the sums of the numbers in columns II and XIV. In the calculation of the numbers in column XV, the first and last two intervals of the table were combined because the theoretical multiplicities were small, which would have made more difficult the determination of the precision coefficient.* This column can be used for a qualitative comparison of the observed distribution with the corresponding normal distribution.

In columns XVI and XVII, preparation is made for calculating the precision coefficient, which is one of the criteria of reliability of the theoretical distribution (in the present problem, a normal distribution). To calculate it, we need the sum of the numbers in column XVII.

Column XVIII gives the values $N_k^{(c)}$ of the theoretical distribution function. These values are obtained by adding the adjacent numbers in column XIV. (Thus, column XIV consists of the first-order differences of the numbers in column XVIII.)

Comparison of the Empirical with the Normal Distribution

*The use of the asymmetry and the excess.* This is the simplest method. It requires no supplementary calculations other than those made for obtaining the parameters of the empirical distribution. In a normal distribution, the asymmetry and the excess are both equal to zero. In the present problem, the asymmetry has a sufficiently small numerical value, but the excess cannot be considered sufficiently small. Thus, the distribution is approximately symmetric about its center, like a normal distribution, but close to the center, the probability density is greater than it is with a normal distribution.

*The use of column XV* (for $0-c$). Here, we have the differences between the observed and computed multiplicities under the assumption that a normal law holds. Examination of these numbers confirms the conclusion obtained from the excess that there will be a large positive deviation about the center and small negative deviations in all the remaining intervals except the one adjacent to the center, where we obtain -8.3. Consequently, the behavior of the numbers in the $0-c$ column is to some degree systematic.

*Calculation of the precision coefficient.* From formula (18.15), where $s'$ is the number of intervals in which the numbers $0-c$ are given, we use the sum of the numbers in column XVII to obtain

$$H=\frac{5.94}{6-1}=1.2.$$

Since $H$ differs slightly from unity, a normal distribution may be considered an admissible approximation for the empirical distribution under consideration.

*Kolmogorov's criterion.* Comparing the numbers in column XVIII with the numbers in column VIII of the table on page 296, we find the maximum $D$ of the absolute value of the difference $N_k - N_k^{(c)}$, namely, 8.9.

We calculate the value of the argument:

$$\lambda=\frac{D}{\sqrt{n}}=\frac{8.9}{\sqrt{189}}=0.65.$$

From the table on page 300, we find the probability that the deviation $D$ will exceed the number 8.9 that we have obtained above. Specifically, $P(\lambda)=0.78$. Since the probability of obtaining an even greater deviation than in the case that we have been examining is considerably greater than 1/2, the approximation by a normal law can be considered satisfactory.

## 97. CONFIDENCE PROBABILITIES AND CONFIDENCE LIMITS

The numerical characteristics of an empirical distribution considered above (the average value, the mean square deviation, the coefficient of variability, the mode, the median, the asymmetry, the excess) are sufficient for an overall description of various distributions, and some of them are sufficient also for comparing the distributions of different variables. Thus, their purpose is to replace the raw material (that is, the observational data) with numbers that as completely as possible characterize the entire set of observations. However, taken alone, these characteristics do not

---

*The first two intervals above give $n(0)=4$ and $n(c)=4.5$. Therefore, $(0-c)$ becomes -0.5. An analogous situation holds in the last two intervals.

enable us to predict the possible results of future observations of the random variable. As was mentioned above, such a prediction may consist in calculating the probability that the value of the variable will be contained within certain limits. In practice, it is assumed that such a specification of these limits can be considered as reliable if the probability is close to unity (for example, 0.99 or 0.999). In connection with this, we introduce the concepts of confidence probabilities and confidence limits.

*Definition:* The *confidence probability* that a random variable will assume some value between specified limits is a value of this probability that (by agreement) will be considered sufficiently close to unity for the purposes of the problem. The corresponding limits are called *confidence limits*.

If the confidence probability is close to unity, this means that the event (falling within the limits) is virtually certain; that is, only rarely will it fail to happen. For example, if the probability is equal to 0.99, the law of large numbers (J. Bernoulli's theorem) indicates that when a large number of observations is made, the percentage of failures of the event is close to 0.01 or 1%.

To calculate the confidence probabilities and the confidence limits, we must construct a theoretical distribution law by solving the problem of the approximation of the empirical distribution by means of a theoretical law chosen on some basis or other. The parameters of this law are determined by the method shown in Section 96. The distribution law that we construct (the probability density) must be checked against observations. With the help of the theoretical distribution function that we choose, we may set up tables for calculating the confidence probability from the given confidence limits and for solving the inverse problem.

With the aid of Table II (at the end of the book), it is easy to obtain, for a normal distribution, a table of confidence limits for certain confidence probabilities (the average value $\bar{x}$, the mean square deviation $\sigma$) (see Table A). We also give a table of confidence probabilities for the confidence limits (see Table B).

Table A

| Confidence probabilities | Lower limit | Upper limit |
|---|---|---|
| 0.9 | $\bar{x} - 1.645\sigma$ | $\bar{x} + 1.645\sigma$ |
| 0.99 | $\bar{x} - 2.577\sigma$ | $\bar{x} + 2.577\sigma$ |
| 0.999 | $\bar{x} - 3.291\sigma$ | $\bar{x} + 3.291\sigma$ |

Table B

| Confidence limits | Confidence probabilities |
|---|---|
| $\bar{x} \mp 1\sigma$ | 0.6827 |
| $\bar{x} \mp 2\sigma$ | 0.9545 |
| $\bar{x} \mp 3\sigma$ | 0.9973 |
| $\bar{x} \mp 4\sigma$ | 0.9999 |

Similar tables are constructed for the Charlier and Pearson distributions.

## 98. GRAPHICAL REPRESENTATION OF AN EMPIRICAL SET

A graphical representation is made along with the numerical analysis of an empirical set. The graphs made are then compared with the accepted theoretical distribution.

Let us first examine the graphs of a discrete distribution.

The graph of a table of an empirical distribution is of a simple form (see Fig. 12). The discrete values $x_k$ are laid off along the horizontal axis and the corresponding values of the empirical probabilities $p_k$ are laid off along the vertical axis. The graph consists of isolated points. They can be connected by dashed lines (as shown in the figure) in order to make the change in $p_k$ with respect to $x_k$ clearer from a visual standpoint. In the intervals between the points representing the $x_k$ and outside the interval $[x_1, x_s]$, the values of $p$ are equal to 0.

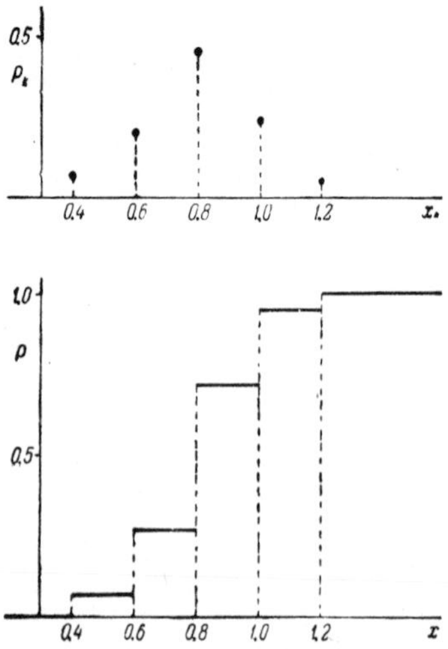


Fig. 12. Graphs of a probability distribution and of a distribution function of a discrete random variable.

The graph of a distribution function is of the following form: From $x = -\infty$ to $x = x_1$, the graph coincides with the horizontal axis. There is a discontinuity at $x = x_1$: To the left, $P = 0$, and to the right, $P = P_1 = p_1$ up to the value $x = x_2$. At that point, there is another discontinuity: To the left, the value is $p_1$, and to the right it is $p_1 + p_2$ up to the value $x = x_3$, etc. Thus, the graph consists of a horizontal semi-axis, of a line parallel to the horizontal axis at a distance $p_1$ above it between the values $x_1$ and $x_2$ of the argument, of another line segment parallel to the horizontal axis at a distance $p_1+p_2$ above it between the values $x_2$ and $x_3$, and so on until we obtain a segment between $x=x_{s-1}$ and $x=x_s$ parallel to the horizontal axis at a distance $1-p_s$ above it, and finally another horizontal semi-axis at unit distance above it from $x_s$ to $\infty$. Such a graph is frequently referred to as a "step graph."

In the case of a continuous distribution, the values of the random variable are laid off on the horizontal axis. To construct the graph of the distribution function at those points on the horizontal axis that represent the upper end points of the intervals, we construct ordinates of length $N_k$ or $N_k/n$. At the lower end point of the first interval, we put a dot on the horizontal axis. If $N_k$ is laid off on the ordinates, the length of the last ordinate will be equal to the total number of cases. However, if the empirical probabilities are laid off, the length will be equal to unity.

In contrast with the graph of a discrete variable, here the points must be joined, since arbitrary intermediary values of our variable are possible. Ordinarily, the points in question are connected by straight line segments. The graph consists of a broken line beginning on the horizontal axis and ending at the point whose ordinate is equal to $n$ or 1. No ordinate of the broken line can be lower than the preceding one. A graph of this form is called an *ogive* (see Fig. 13). The ogive is used for determining the median. A straight line parallel to the horizontal axis is drawn through the midpoint of the last ordinate on the right and is extended until it intersects the ogive and a perpendicular is dropped from the point of intersection to the horizontal axis. The point at which this perpendicular intersects the horizontal axis approximately represents the median.

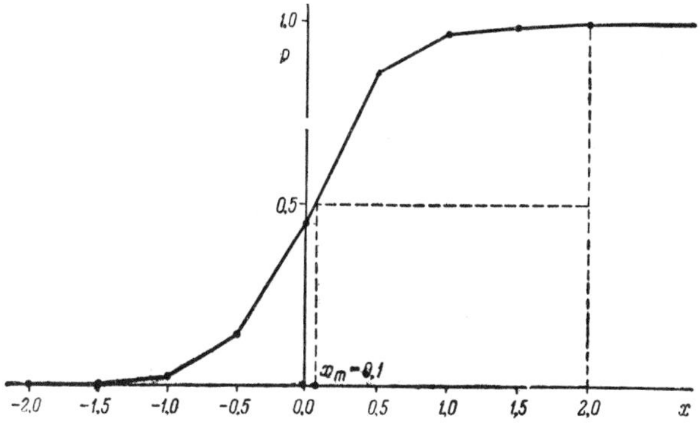


Fig. 13. The graph of an empirical distribution function. The dashed lines show how the median is determined graphically (see the example on page 296).

To construct the graph of an empirical probability density on each interval and on the base, we construct a rectangle whose area is equal either to the number of events or to the relative frequency. In the first case, the area of the entire graph is equal to the number of outcomes, and in the second case it is equal to unity. It follows from the method of construction that the altitude of each rectangle represents the average number of outcomes that take place per unit of the corresponding interval or the mean statistical probability per unit of interval. We may say that the altitude of the rectangle is the average density of the empirical probability that the value of the variable will fall in that interval.

Graphs of such a shape are called *histograms*. Sometimes, instead of a histogram, we construct a polygon, which can be obtained from a histogram if we draw straight line segments connecting the midpoints of the upper sides of adjacent rectangles (see Fig. 14). A graphical comparison of the empirical distribution with the theoretical distribution can be made by means of the histograms of these distributions and polygons.

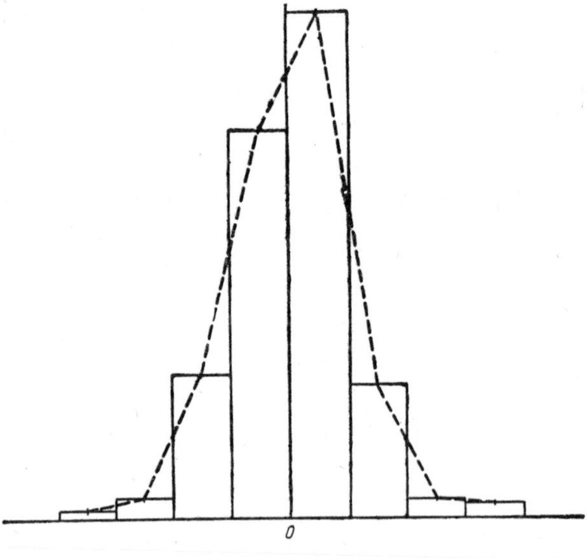


Fig. 14. A histogram (solid lines) and a polygon (dashed lines) of the distribution of a continuous random variable. The areas of the rectangles are proportional to the probabilities of the values of the variable represented by the bases of the rectangles.

Example. Let us compare the empirical with the theoretical distribution for the example examined in Sections 95 and 96 (see Tables A and B on pages 296 and 297.

Let us draw the histograms of the empirical and normal distributions on a single diagram (Fig. 15). The empirical histogram is drawn in solid lines from the table of values of $n_k$ (column II). The histogram of the normal distribution, which approximates the given distribution, is drawn in dashed lines, using the numbers $n_b(c)$ (column XIV). On such a graph, it is not necessary that the total area be equal to unity or to the total number of observations, since this requirement can always be satisfied by a suitable choice of scale on the coordinate axis. Therefore, the altitudes of the rectangles can be taken in proportion to the number of cases (for the observed distribution, the numbers in column II, and for the theoretical distribution, those in column XIV).

Figure 15 shows a comparison of the histograms.

Figure 16 shows the Gaussian curve and the polygon of the frequencies. This polygon may be treated as the graph of the probability density of the empirical distribution.

The polygon of the frequencies is a broken line drawn through the basic points (that is, the points $M_k$, $n_k$ ). Additional calculations necessary for drawing the Gaussian curve in a form convenient for making the comparison are given in the following table:

| 1 | 2 | 3 | 4 | 5 | 6 | 7 |
|---|---|---|---|---|---|---|
| $M$ | $M-\overline{M}$ | $\frac{M-\overline{M}}{\sigma}$ | $\Phi'\left(\frac{M-\overline{M}}{\sigma_M}\right)$ | $\Phi' : \sigma_M$ | $y_c$ | $y_0$ |
| -1.75 | -1.775 | -3.427 | 0.0011 | 0.0021 | 0.4 | 2 |
| -1.25 | -1.275 | -2.461 | 0.0193 | 0.0373 | 7.0 | 6 |
| -0.75 | -0.775 | -1.496 | 0.1303 | 0.2515 | 47.5 | 44 |
| -0.25 | -0.275 | -0.531 | 0.3465 | 0.6689 | 126.4 | 120 |
| +0.025 | 0 | 0 | 0.3989 | 0.7701 | 145.6 | — |
| +0.25 | +0.225 | +0.434 | 0.3631 | 0.7010 | 132.5 | 156 |
| +0.75 | +0.725 | +1.400 | 0.1497 | 0.2890 | 54.6 | 40 |
| +1.25 | +1.225 | +2.365 | 0.0243 | 0.0469 | 8.9 | 6 |
| +1.75 | +1.725 | +3.330 | 0.0016 | 0.0031 | 0.6 | 4 |

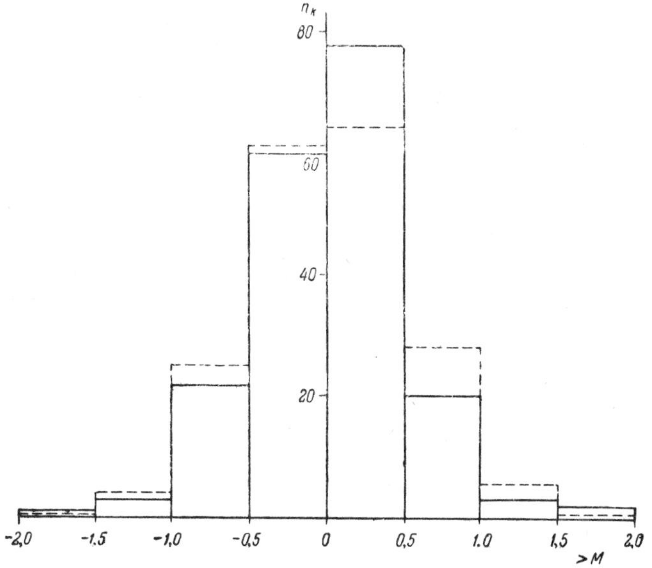


Fig. 15. Comparison of the histograms of the empirical (solid lines) and the theoretical (dashed lines) distributions.

The fifth column gives the values of the probability density at the points shown in the first column. The sixth column gives the products $y_c$ of these densities and the total number of observations.

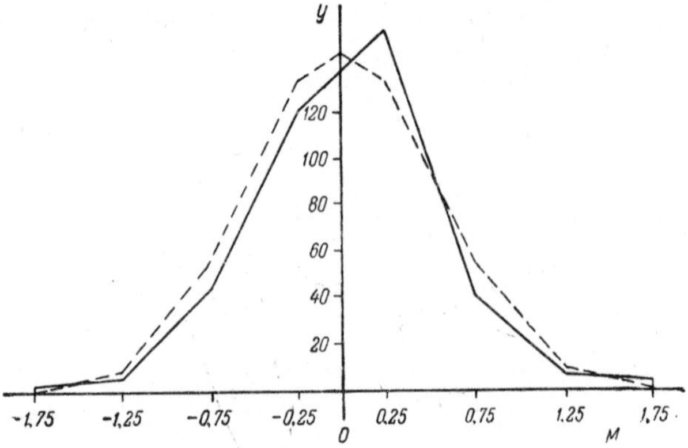


Fig. 16. Comparison of the polygons of the empirical (solid line) and the normal (dashed line) distributions.

The last column gives the numbers $y_0$. for comparison with them. These numbers are proportional to the empirical probability density and are obtained by dividing the multiplicities by the length of the step (namely, 0.5).*

Both drawings confirm the conclusions that the overall agreement with the normal distribution is satisfactory.

## 99. THE AVERAGE ERRORS OF THE PARAMETERS OF A SAMPLE SET

As was stated above, in the majority of problems the empirical sets are sample sets. Therefore, the conclusions drawn from empirical distributions cannot be considered sufficiently reliable without supplementary investigation.

On the basis of the law of large numbers, when the sample is sufficiently large, we may expect with a probability close to unity that the parameters of the sample set will be arbitrarily close to the parameters of the total set. Therefore, the numerical characteristics of a sufficiently large sample may be considered as approximate values of those probability parameters of the distribution that have to be calculated for the total set. For the same reason, those probabilities that are computed from an empirical distribution should be considered as approximate values of the probabilities which we would need to calculate from data concerning the whole set (if this were possible).

We can get some idea of the unknown total set if we find, at least approximately, the mean square errors of the parameters of

*The fifth row, corresponding to $M = 0.025$, is included to indicate the center of the theoretical distribution. In the empirical material, there is no corresponding interval, hence the dash.

the sample set, that is, the variance of these parameters with respect to the parameters of the general set.

To evaluate these mean errors, we reason as follows. Let us suppose that we can consider every possible sample of the total set. In each sample, we would obtain some value $\bar{x}$. (For brevity, we shall speak only of $\bar{x}$ though our remarks apply also to other distribution parameters.) The set of the sample values $\bar{x}$ represents a certain distribution. If we derive the function of the distribution of $\bar{x}$, we can evaluate the probabilities of various sample values of $\bar{x}$. However, when we have one sample value, we can use the distribution parameters to find out how much the sample mean value may differ from the overall one.

Study of the sample values of $\bar{x}$ and $\sigma_x$ in the overall set, which obeys a normal law, has yielded the following conclusions:

The law of distribution of the sample mean values $\bar{x}$ is a *normal law*, and the expression for the mean square error of the value of $\bar{x}$ is

$$\sigma_{\bar{x}} = \frac{\sigma_x}{\sqrt{n}}. \tag{18.16}$$

However, the law of distribution of the sample values of the variance $\sigma_x$ is not a normal law. For the mean square error $\sigma(\sigma_x)$ of the sample mean square deviation, we have the following value:

$$\sigma(\sigma_x) = \frac{\sigma_x}{\sqrt{2n}}. \tag{18.17}$$

Example. In the example examined above,

$$\overline{M} = +0.025, \quad \sigma_M = 0.513, \quad n = 189.$$

Therefore,

$$\sigma_{\overline{M}} = \frac{0.513}{\sqrt{189}} \approx 0.037,$$

$$\sigma(\sigma_M) = \frac{0.513}{\sqrt{378}} \approx 0.026.$$

We may summarize the contents of this chapter with the following procedure for analyzing a one-dimensional statistical set:

1. An initial processing.
2. Determination of the numerical characteristics of the empirical set (the average value, the mean square deviation, the asymmetry, the excess, the mode, and the median).
3. Determination of the parameters of the chosen theoretical distribution by the method of moments.
4. Construction of the theoretical distribution from the parameters found.
5. Numerical comparison of the theoretical distribution with the empirical distribution by use of the agreement criteria.

6. Construction of the graphs of the empirical and theoretical distributions and comparison of these.

7. Calculation of the average errors of the parameters of the empirical set (if it is a sample set).

Chapter 19

# ELEMENTARY THEORY OF THE CORRELATION OF TWO VARIABLES

## 100. THE EMPIRICAL DISTRIBUTION OF TWO RANDOM VARIABLES

Suppose that a statistical set consisting of objects (observations) is given and that for each of them we have obtained empirically numerical values for the random variables $X$ and $Y$. We confine ourselves to the case of continuous variables. The results of the observations can be first written in a simple table giving the corresponding values of $x_k$ and $y_k$. In what follows, we shall denote a table of this kind by the letter A:

$$\begin{array}{c||cccc} X & x_1 & x_2 & \ldots & x_n \\ Y & y_1 & y_2 & \ldots & y_n. \end{array} \qquad \text{(A)}$$

Table A is of exactly the same form as the table (the list of the results of observations) from which we derived an empirical formula relating $X$ and $Y$ in a preceding chapter. However, at that time, it was assumed that the variables $X$ and $Y$ were related by a functional dependence whose nature we did not know and which was distorted by observational errors. In the present case, we shall not make this assumption regarding the variables $X$ and $Y$.

The distinctive feature of the statistical relation that we shall study in the present chapter consists in the fact that to each value of one variable there corresponds an indefinite number of values of the other, among which there may be both unequal and equal values. This characteristic can be made clearer if we make two other tables, which we shall denote by $B_1$ and $B_2$. For this, let us choose *different* values of the variable $X$, take them for the values of the argument, and assign to each of these values all the values of the variable $Y$ that appear with it in Table A. We thus obtain Table $B_1$:

$$\begin{array}{ll} x^{(1)} & y_{11}, \; y_{12}, \; \ldots, \; y_{1r_1}, \\ x^{(2)} & y_{21}, \; y_{22}, \; \ldots, \; y_{2r_2}, \\ \cdot & \cdot \quad \cdot \quad \cdot \quad \cdot \quad \cdot \\ x^{(l)} & y_{l1} \; y_{l2}, \; \ldots, \; y_{lr_l}. \end{array} \qquad (B_1)$$

In this table, $x^{(1)}, x^{(2)}, \ldots, x^{(l)}$ are different values of $X$. The numbers with double subscripts represent the corresponding values of $Y$.

In just the same way, we obtain Table B2, which differs from Table B1 in that the places of the values of $X$ and $Y$ are reversed:

$$\begin{matrix} y^{(1)} & x_{11}, & x_{12}, & \ldots, & x_{1s_1}, \\ \cdot & \cdot & \cdot & \cdot & \cdot \\ y^{(m)} & x_{m1}, & x_{m2}, & \ldots, & x_{ms_m}. \end{matrix} \qquad (B_2)$$

Table A is used directly for analysis of the material when the amount of data is quite small. We rarely construct Table B. Tables of that sort are needed for making clearer certain fundamental concepts.

If the number of observations in Table A is great (a hundred or more), we construct Table C, which is the two-dimensional analogue of the distribution table of probabilities that we constructed in the preceding chapter for a single continuous variable. Table C is constructed as follows. As in the case of a single variable, we partition the interval of variation of each variable into a number of equal subintervals and we count the number of times that $X$ and $Y$ assume values in each of the pairs of corresponding intervals:

| $Y$ \ $X$ | $x_1$ | $x_2$ | ... | $x_k$ | ... | $x_r$ | Distribution of $Y$ |
|---|---|---|---|---|---|---|---|
| $y_1$ | $n_{11}$ | $n_{21}$ | ... | $n_{k1}$ | ... | $n_{r1}$ | $n_{01}$ |
| $y_2$ | $n_{12}$ | $n_{22}$ | ... | $n_{k2}$ | ... | $n_{r2}$ | $n_{02}$ |
| $\vdots$ | | | | | | | $\vdots$ |
| $y_l$ | $n_{1l}$ | $n_{2l}$ | ... | $n_{kl}$ | ... | $n_{rl}$ | $n_{0l}$ |
| $\vdots$ | | | | | | | $\vdots$ |
| $y_s$ | $n_{1s}$ | $n_{2s}$ | ... | $n_{ks}$ | ... | $n_{rs}$ | $n_{0s}$ |
| Distribution of $X$ | $n_{10}$ | $n_{20}$ | ... | $n_{k0}$ | ... | $n_{r0}$ | $n$ \ $n$ |

(C)

The first row of the table contains values of $X$ corresponding to the midpoints of the intervals of that variable. (The end points of the intervals are not written down.) The first column contains the midpoints of the intervals of the variable $Y$. The quantities with double subscripts are the multiplicities of the part of the total set having values of $x$ and $y$ in intervals corresponding to the rectangle in which the number is written. If the steps of the variables $X$ and $Y$ are equal to $g$ and $h$, respectively, the number $n_{kl}$ is the number of observations in which $X$ takes values from $x_k - \frac{1}{2}g$ to $x_k + \frac{1}{2}g$ and $Y$ at the same time takes values from $y_l - \frac{1}{2}h$ to $y_l + \frac{1}{2}h$. The last column is obtained by adding all the numbers $n_{kl}$ in each row. The resulting column gives the distribution of the variable $Y$ for arbitrary values of $X$. The last row is obtained by adding the numbers $n_{kl}$ in the individual columns. It represents the distribution of the variable $X$. The sum of all the numbers $n_{kl}$ (for $k \neq 0,\ l \neq 0$) must be equal to the number of observations $n$.

Tables of this kind are called correlational tables (or joint tables). Setting up such a table is not recommended when the number of events is small, since it is assumed in the analysis that the number of events in each rectangle refers to the midpoints of the intervals and this may give appreciable errors when the number of observations is small.

The empirical distribution of two continuous variables can be represented graphically. We take the numbers $x$ and $y$ in Table A as rectangular plane coordinates and we plot the points with coordinates $x_m$, $y_m$ (for $m = 1, 2, \ldots, n$). We then obtain a set of points scattered over the plane. This set is known as the *field of correlation*.

Let us find the average values $\bar{x}$ and $\bar{y}$ of each of the variables separately. The point in the field with coordinates $\bar{x}$ and $\bar{y}$ is called the *center of distribution*. When a field of correlation has been set up, it is easy to make a correlational table like Table C. For this it is sufficient to construct a coordinate net passing through the points that determine the end points of the intervals. The plane is partitioned into rectangles. If we count the number of points in each rectangle, we obtain a correlational table.

On each rectangle we construct parallelepipeds of height such that the volume of each parallelepiped is equal to the ratio of the number of events in the rectangle to the total number of events. The three-dimensional step figure thus obtained may be called the empirical surface of the distribution or the histogram of the two-dimensional problem. This is a natural generalization of the method of graphical representation of the distribution of a single variable, as described above.

## 101. CORRELATIONAL DEPENDENCE. PROBLEMS IN THE THEORY OF CORRELATION

The relationship between $X$ and $Y$ defined by their distribution is usually quite different from what we call a functional relationship between two variables. In the case of a one-to-one functional dependence, to each value of $x$ there corresponds one and only one value of $y$ and vice versa. It is clear from Tables B1 and B2 that to one value of $x$ there may correspond any number of values of $y$ and to one value of $y$ there may correspond several values of $x$. Also, they may be quite different one from the other. The alternation in the number of these different values is such that it is not convenient to speak of a multiple-valued functional dependence.

Examination of the correlational Table C also shows a deviation from a functional dependence. When the values of one of the variables lie in some interval, the other variable may take values between rather wide bounds. This characteristic becomes more obvious when we consider the field of correlation.

In the case of an exact functional relationship between $X$ and $Y$, the points in the field must lie along some quite definite curve. If there is an exact functional relationship between $X$ and $Y$, but the numbers in Table A are obtained from observations, the presence of random errors will still keep the points of the field from lying precisely on the theoretical curve. Nonetheless, if the errors are small, the points must lie in some narrow strip along the theoretical curve. In the case of a correlational dependence, however, the points of the field are located more or less at random in the plane.

To study the pecularities of a correlational connection, we supplement Table B with another column giving the average values of the variable $Y$ for each of the values of $X$ that appear in the first column. The first and last columns of Table $B_1$ in its extended form determine the dependence of the average values $\bar{y}_x$ of the variable $Y$ on the corresponding values of the variable $X$. We extend Table $B_2$ in the same manner and obtain the empirical dependence of the average values $\bar{x}_y$ of the variable $X$ on the corresponding values of the variable $Y$. The two tables $(x, \bar{y}_x)$ and $(y, \bar{x}_y)$, respectively, are said to define the empirical regression of $Y$ with respect to $X$ and of $X$ with respect to $Y$.

Examination of similiar tables leads to the following conclusion. When the variable $x$ increases, the corresponding values of $y$ in the individual observations may both increase and decrease. To a single value of $x$ there may correspond both large and small values of $y$. The same statement holds if we reverse the letters $x$ and $y$. Even so, in many problems, the average values of a single variable corresponding to the values of the other disclose a certain dependence on the values of the second variable. Sometimes we may even speak of a quasi-functional dependence of the average values of one variable on the corresponding values of the other.

In those cases in which the distribution of the two variables exhibits these features, we say that there is a correlational dependence, or simply a correlation, between the variables. Thus, there is a correlation between two random variables if to every value of one there corresponds an indefinite number of values of the other, but the averages of these values depend on the values of the first variable.

A one-to-one functional relationship between the variables $X$ and $Y$ can be considered as a special case of correlational dependence. If to each value of $x$ there corresponds only one well-defined value of $y$ and vice versa and if all points of the field are located on the curve no matter how greatly we increase the number of them, a correlational dependence becomes a functional dependence.

Construction of fields of correlation for different pairs of random variables yields varied results. Sometimes, the points of the field are scattered at random and at other times they are almost all located along some imaginary curve or straight line. Thus, the correlational dependence can to a greater or lesser degree deviate from a functional dependence. In connection with this, the first problem in the theory of correlation is the derivation of a numerical criterion for evaluating the degree of closeness of a correlational dependence to a functional dependence. If out of all the observations we pick only two quantities, there can of course be no functional relationship between them since these quantities are related with others that we have not taken into consideration. In applications, it is important for us to know how to choose those quantities that are most closely related with each other. Specifically, a numerical criterion for the degree of connection is introduced for solving such problems.

It was shown in the preceding section that the average values of one variable that are calculated for a finite interval of the other disclosed a dependence on the values of the second variable. Therefore, the second problem to be considered in the theory of correlation consists in deriving empirical formulas for determining the average values of one variable from the values of the other. There are two such formulas. They are called the equations of regression.

We shall confine ourselves to the theory of linear correlation. This means, first, that we shall derive a criterion for the degree of deviation of the correlational dependence from a linear functional dependence and, second, that we shall derive linear empirical formulas of the form

$$\bar{y}_x = a + bx, \quad \bar{x}_y = c + dy \tag{19.1}$$

for determining the average value of each variable from the values of the other variable.

## 102. DERIVATION OF A LINEAR EMPIRICAL FORMULA

To solve the problem of deriving the equations of regression, we first solve the problem of setting up a linear empirical formula in a form that will be convenient for obtaining the lines of regression.

Suppose that we obtain from observations a table like Table A giving the values of $x_k$ and the values of $y_k$ (for $k = 1, 2, \ldots, n$) corresponding to them. We need to construct an empirical formula of the form

$$Y = a + bX. \tag{19.2}$$

According to Section 90, to determine the coefficients $a$ and $b$, we obtain the conditional equations

$$a + bx_k - y_k = 0 \qquad (k = 1, 2, \ldots, n). \tag{19.3}$$

From these, we set up two normal equations whose coefficients it is convenient to write not in Gauss' notation but in the form of the sums

$$na + b\sum_{k=1}^{n} x_k - \sum_{k=1}^{n} y_k = 0, \qquad (19.4)$$

$$a\sum_{k=1}^{n} x_k + b\sum_{k=1}^{n} x_k^2 - \sum_{k=1}^{n} x_k y_k = 0. \qquad (19.5)$$

Let us now suppose that all the $x_k$ and $y_k$ are equally probable. Then, if we divide $\sum x_k$ by $n$, we get the average value of $x$ and if we divide $\sum y_k$ by $n$, we get the average value of $y$. Therefore, the normal equation (19.4), after division by $n$, can be written in the form

$$a + b\bar{x} - \bar{y} = 0. \qquad (19.6)$$

To transform equation (19.5), we also divide it by $n$. The coefficient

$$\left(\sum_{k=1}^{n} x_k^2\right) : n$$

can be replaced with the expression $\sigma_x^2 + \bar{x}^2$, which is formally obtained if we determine the variance by the following formula. The variance is equal to the difference between the expectation of the square of a random variable and the square of its expectation. To transform the last term in the equation (19.5), we introduce the notation

$$\nu_{11} = \frac{1}{n}\sum_{k=1}^{n} x_k y_k, \quad \mu_{11} = \nu_{11} - \bar{x}\bar{y}.$$

If we generalize the concept of moments of distribution to the set of two random variables and consider all pairs $(x_k, y_k)$ as equally probable, we may call $\nu_{11}$ the initial moment of order "one-one" of the distribution of $(X, Y)$, and $\mu_{11}$ the central moment of the same order.

After these changes are made, the second equation becomes

$$a\bar{x} + b(\sigma_x^2 + \bar{x}^2) - (\bar{x}\bar{y} + \mu_{11}) = 0.$$

Let us rewrite it as

$$a\bar{x} + b\bar{x}^2 - \bar{x}\bar{y} + b\sigma_x^2 - \mu_{11} = 0.$$

The first three terms are equal to zero because of (19.6) and we obtain the following system of equations:

$$\left.\begin{aligned} a + b\bar{x} &= \bar{y}, \\ b\sigma_x^2 &= \mu_{11}. \end{aligned}\right\} \qquad (19.7)$$

Therefore,

$$\left.\begin{aligned} b &= \frac{\mu_{11}}{\sigma_x^2}, \\ a &= \bar{y} - \frac{\mu_{11}\bar{x}}{\sigma_x^2}. \end{aligned}\right\} \tag{19.8}$$

The linear empirical formula (19.6) derived from the table of $(x_k, y_k)$ can now be written in the form

$$Y - \bar{y} = \frac{\mu_{11}}{\sigma_x^2}(X - \bar{x}); \tag{19.9}$$

Its parameters can be calculated from the formulas

$$\left.\begin{aligned} \bar{x} &= \frac{1}{n}\sum_{k=1}^{n} x_k, & \bar{y} &= \frac{1}{n}\sum_{k=1}^{n} y_k, \\ \sigma_x^2 &= \frac{1}{n}\sum_{k=1}^{n} x_k^2 - \bar{x}^2, & \mu_{11} &= \frac{1}{n}\sum_{k=1}^{n} x_k y_k - \bar{x}\bar{y} \end{aligned}\right\} \tag{19.10}$$

It was assumed in the derivation that all the pairs $(x_k, y_k)$ are equally probable. This is equivalent to the assumption that every pair occurs exactly once in the table of values. If each pair of numbers $(x_k, y_k)$ is encountered $n_k$ times in the table and if the number of different pairs is equal to $s$, the probability of each pair and of each of the numbers taken separately must be considered equal to $n_k / n$. Therefore, the above equations are replaced with the following ones:

$$\left.\begin{aligned} \bar{x} &= \frac{1}{n}\sum_{k=1} n_k x_k, & \bar{y} &= \frac{1}{n}\sum_{k=1}^{n} n_k x_k, \\ \sigma_x^2 &= \frac{1}{n}\sum_{k=1} n_k x_k^2 - \bar{y}^2, & \mu_{11} &= \frac{1}{n}\sum_{k=1}^{s} n_k x_k y_k - \bar{x}\bar{y}. \end{aligned}\right\} \tag{19.11}$$

These formulas may be called the "weight equations" since the numbers $n_k$ play the role of weights in the calculations.

We have constructed an empirical linear formula expressing $Y$ in terms of $X$. Of course, $X$ and $Y$ may represent different *physical* quantities, but from a computational point of view, they are completely equivalent. Therefore, besides the empirical formula that we have constructed, we may also construct an empirical formula expressing $X$ in terms of $Y$. Obviously, it will be a consequence of the first formula only if $X$ and $Y$ are related by an exact linear dependence. Otherwise, the second formula will not be a consequence of the first, but will have an independent significance. We shall not derive the second formula (it is recommended that the reader do this himself) and shall give only its final form for the case of equal probability of $(x_k, y_k)$:

$$X-\bar{x}=\frac{\mu_{11}}{\sigma_y^2}(Y-\bar{y}), \tag{19.12}$$

where

$$\sigma_y^2=\frac{1}{n}\sum_{k=1}^{n} y_k^2-\bar{y}^2; \tag{19.13}$$

The remaining parameters have the same expressions as in the preceding case. Here, the quantity $\mu_{11}$ does not change since it is symmetric with respect to $X$ and $Y$.

If the pairs of numbers $(x_k, y_k)$ appear $n_k$ times, the form of the formula does not change and the parameters are calculated from the weight formulas. Here, the formula for $\sigma_y^2$ undergoes the obvious change.

## 103. DERIVATION OF THE LINEAR EQUATIONS OF REGRESSION

In the preceding section, we derived formulas for determining the coefficients in the linear empirical formulas

$$Y=a+bX \text{ and } X=c+dY.$$

We obtained the equations for the straight lines

$$Y-\bar{y}=\frac{\mu_{11}}{\sigma_x^2}(X-\bar{x}) \text{ and } X-\bar{x}=\frac{\mu_{11}}{\sigma_y^2}(Y-\bar{y}); \tag{19.14}$$

It is clear from these equations that both lines pass through the center of distribution.

We need not emphasize the fact that we derived these formulas by using Table A because, if necessary, we could obtain the empirical formulas for expressing $Y$ in terms of $X$ and vice versa. In the meantime, by definition, the equations of regression must be empirical formulas for determining the average value of $\bar{y}$ as a function of $x$ and the average value of $\bar{x}$ as a function of $y$. Starting with the determination of the equations of regression, let us show that these equations are of the same form as the empirical formula (19.14). Let us set up tables like Table $B_1$ and Table $B_2$. In each row, we calculate the average values of $Y$ and $X$ and denote them respectively by $\bar{y}_x$ and $\bar{x}_y$.

We must set up the equations of regression for these averages and the values of $X$ and $Y$ corresponding to them by using the formulas of the preceding section. However, in so doing, we need to take into consideration the fact that if, for example, three values of $y$ correspond to some value $x_m$, the pair of numbers $(x_m, \bar{y}_{x,m})$ obtained after determining the average value $\bar{y}$ must be considered equivalent to three pairs of numbers and we must determine the average values from the weight formulas. Suppose that Table B1 (extended as described earlier) is of the form

$$\begin{array}{c|cccc|c} x^{(1)} & y_{11} & y_{12} & \cdots & y_{1r_1} & \bar{y}_{x1} \\ x^{(2)} & y_{21} & y_{22} & \cdots & y_{2r_2} & \bar{y}_{x2} \\ \vdots & \cdot & \cdot & \cdot & \cdot & \\ \vdots & \cdot & \cdot & \cdot & \cdot & \\ x^{(l)} & y_{l1} & y_{l2} & \cdots & y_{lr_l} & \bar{y}_{xl}. \end{array} \qquad (B_1)$$

In this table, $l$ is the number of different values of $x$ that appear in Table A and $r_1, r_2, \ldots, r_l$ represent the number of values of $y$ corresponding to the quantities $x^{(1)}, x^{(2)}, \ldots, x^{(l)}$. Obviously,

$$r_1 + r_2 + \ldots + r_l = n, \quad l \leqslant n.$$

Thus, we need to construct an empirical formula for the table

| $X$ | $Y$ | Weight |
|---|---|---|
| $x^{(1)}$ | $\bar{y}_{x1}$ | $r_1$ |
| $x^{(2)}$ | $\bar{y}_{x2}$ | $r_2$ |
| . | . . | . . |
| . | . . | . . |
| $x^{(l)}$ | $\bar{y}_{xl}$ | $r_l$ |

The numbers $\bar{y}_{x1}, \bar{y}_{x2}, \ldots$ in this table are obtained from the formulas

$$\bar{y}_{x1} = \frac{y_{11} + y_{12} + \cdots + y_{1r_1}}{r_1}, \quad \bar{y}_{x2} = \frac{y_{21} + y_{22} + \cdots + y_{2r_2}}{r_2}, \ldots$$

The weighted average value $\bar{y}$ will be

$$\bar{y} = \frac{r_1\bar{y}_{x1} + r_2\bar{y}_{x2} + \cdots + r_l\bar{y}_{xl}}{r_1 + r_2 + \cdots + r_l} =$$
$$= \frac{y_{11} + y_{12} + \cdots + y_{1r_1} + y_{21} + \cdots + y_{2r_2} + \cdots + y_{lr_l}}{n}.$$

Since the numerator of the last fraction is simply the sum of all possible values of $y$, the weighted mean is equal to the ordinary average, which is obtained from Table A. An analogous phenomenon holds for $x$.

Furthermore, from the weight formula,

$$\sigma_x^2 = \frac{r_1(x^{(1)})^2 + r_2(x^{(2)})^2 + \cdots + r_l(x^{(l)})^2}{r_1 + r_2 + \cdots + r_l} - \bar{x}^2.$$

But from such a formula we would need to calculate the simple mean square deviation of $X$ from Table A, since the number of values $x^{(1)}$ in it is $r_1$, etc. To determine $\mu_{11}$ from Table B$_1$, we would need to write

$$\mu_{11}=\frac{r_1x^{(1)}\bar{y}_{x1}+r_2x^{(2)}\bar{y}_{x2}+\ldots+r_lx^{(l)}\bar{y}_{xl}}{r_1+r_2+\ldots+r_l}-\bar{x}\bar{y};$$

If we remember the expression for $\bar{y}_{x1}, \bar{y}_{x2}, \ldots$, then

$$\mu_{11}=$$

$$=\frac{x^{(1)}y_{11}+x^{(1)}y_{12}+\ldots+x^{(1)}y_{1r_1}+x^{(2)}y_{21}+\ldots+x^{(2)}y_{2r_2}+\ldots+x^{(l)}y_{lr_l}}{n}-\bar{x}\bar{y}.$$

The numerator again contains the sum of the products of all values of $x$ (including the repeated ones) multiplied by the corresponding values of $y$; that is, $\mu_{11}$ would have to be calculated just as for Table A.

Thus, when we set up the empirical formula for determining $Y$ from $X$, we obtain the same result as when we set up the equations of regression for $\bar{y}_x$ as a function of $x$.

Thus, the equations of regression are of the form

$$\bar{y}_x-\bar{y}=\frac{\mu_{11}}{\sigma_x^2}(X-\bar{x}),\quad \bar{x}_y-\bar{x}=\frac{\mu_{11}}{\sigma_y^2}(Y-\bar{y}). \tag{19.15}$$

For simplicity, we often replace $\bar{y}_x$ and $\bar{x}_y$ with $y$ and $x$, respectively. As was just shown, this involves no error. The numbers

$$\frac{\mu_{11}}{\sigma_x^2}=\rho_{yx},\quad \frac{\mu_{11}}{\sigma_x^2}=\rho_{xy} \tag{19.16}$$

are called the *coefficients of regression.*

## 104. THE CORRELATION COEFFICIENT

To make the following derivations simpler, let us assume that the center of distribution $(\bar{x}, \bar{y})$ has been determined and that all the numbers $x$ and $y$ have been replaced with their deviations from their mean values. We denote these deviations by $u$ and $v$. The numbers $u$ and $v$ are related to $x$ and $y$ by the obvious equations

$$u=x-\bar{x},\quad v=y-\bar{y}. \tag{19.17}$$

If we change from $x$ and $y$ to $u$ and $v$, the equations of regression (19.15) become

$$\bar{v}_u=\frac{\mu_{11}}{\sigma_u^2}u,\quad \bar{u}_v=\frac{\mu_{11}}{\sigma_v^2}v. \tag{19.18}$$

For brevity, we may write $v$ and $u$ to represent the left sides of these equations, respectively. Since, from (19.17),

$$x=u+\bar{x},\quad y=v+\bar{y}$$

and since $\bar{x}$ and $\bar{y}$ are constants, we have

$$\bar{u} = \bar{v} = 0, \quad \sigma_x^2 = \sigma_u^2, \quad \sigma_y^2 = \sigma_v^2. \tag{19.19}$$

The number $\mu_{11}$ and the variances $\sigma_u$ and $\sigma_v$ can be calculated from the formulas

$$\mu_{11} = \sum_{k=1}^{n} \frac{u_k v_k}{n}, \tag{19.20}$$

$$\left.\begin{aligned} \sigma_u^2 &= \frac{\sum_{k=1}^{n} u_k^2}{n}, \\ \sigma_v^2 &= \frac{\sum_{k=1}^{n} v_k^2}{n}. \end{aligned}\right\} \tag{19.21}$$

It is convenient to make calculations from these formulas by using the table directly if $n$ is small. If $n$ is large, it is better to use (19.11).

For simplicity, we shall assume the deviations from the averages, that is, the numbers $u_k$ and $v_k$, as given.

We have obtained two straight lines of regression, which, as we stated, pass through the center of distribution. Their directions are determined by the coefficients of regression. The first is the tangent of the angle formed by the line of regression $v$ (expressed in terms of $u$) and the $u$-axis. The second is the tangent of the angle between the line of regression $u$ (expressed in terms of $v$) and the $v$-axis, since in this equation $u$ and $v$ have switched positions. We denote these angles by $\alpha$ and $\beta$ (Fig. 17).

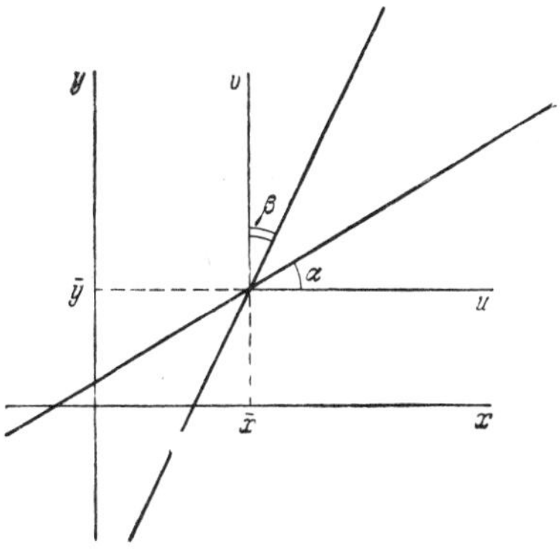


Fig. 17. The lines of regression.

The coefficients of regression may be both positive ($\mu_{11} > 0$) or both negative ($\mu_{11} < 0$). The two lines of regression generally do not coincide. If the correlational dependence becomes a perfectly linear functional relation, the two lines of regression must then coincide, because in that case it does not matter whether $v$ is expressed in terms of $u$ or vice versa. In the case of coinciding lines of regression,

$$\tan\alpha \tan\beta = 1$$

because then

$$\alpha + \beta = \frac{\pi}{2} \qquad (\mu_{11} > 0).$$

If there is no connection between $u$ and $\bar{v}$, on the average, $\bar{v}_u$ will change only slightly when $u$ changes and vice versa. In this case, $\alpha$ and $\beta$ are close to zero and in the limit, $\tan\alpha \tan\beta = 0$. The square root of the number

$$\tan\alpha \tan\beta = \frac{\mu_{11}^2}{\sigma_u^2 \sigma_v^2} \qquad (19.22)$$

is taken for the degree of closeness of the correlational dependence to a linear functional dependence.

*Definition.* The *linear correlation coefficient* of two random variables $x$ and $y$ is the number $r$ defined by

$$r = \frac{\mu_{11}}{\sigma_u \sigma_v}, \qquad (19.23)$$

where $u$ and $v$ are the deviations of $x$ and $y$ from their average values and

$$\mu_{11} = \frac{\sum_{k=1}^{n} u_k v_k}{n}. \qquad (19.24)$$

It is clear from formula (19.23) that $r$ is a dimensionless quantity; that is, it does not depend on the units in which the quantities that we are studying are being measured. It is also independent of the coordinate origin, since only the central moments appear in the expression.

It is clear from (19.16) and (19.23) that the correlation coefficient is equal to the square root of the product of the coefficients of regression. If we solve for $\mu_{11}$ in (19.23), we may make the substitution

$$\mu_{11} = r\sigma_u \sigma_v;$$

in the equations of regression (19.18). These then become

$$\bar{v}_u = \frac{\sigma_v}{\sigma_u} ru, \quad \bar{u}_v = \frac{\sigma_u}{\sigma_v} rv. \tag{19.25}$$

As we have seen, the correlational dependence becomes a linear functional relationship if $\tan\alpha \tan\beta = 1$, that is, if $r = \pm 1$ (the sign depending on the sign of $\mu_{11}$).

On the other hand, if we assume, for example, that the points in the field of correlation are pairwise symmetric about the coordinate axis, the lines of regression will coincide with the coordinate axis and $r$ will vanish. In this case, we may consider $u$ and $v$ independent.

We obtain all gradations between complete independence and a linear functional dependence when the sum $\alpha + \beta$ varies from 0 to $\pi/2$ with $\mu_{11} > 0$. Here, $r$ varies monotonically from 0 to $\pm 1$. (We exclude the theoretically possible case of $\alpha \to 0$, $\beta \to \pi/2$ since this case is of no significance in practice.)

If $\mu_{11}$ is positive, $v$ will increase on the average with increasing $u$ and vice versa. In this case, the choice of the formula for $r$ yields $r > 0$, which is somewhat convenient.

The number $\mu_{11}$ in the formula for $r$ can be calculated in various ways. From (19.24),

$$\mu_{11} = \frac{1}{n} \sum_{k=1}^{u} u_k v_k;$$

Here, $u_k$ and $v_k$ are the deviations from the averages. In the majority of cases, it is not convenient to use the deviations from the averages. Therefore, we use formulas containing $x_k$ and $y_k$:

$$\mu_{11} = \frac{1}{n} \sum_{k=1}^{n} x_k y_k - \bar{x}\bar{y}, \tag{19.26}$$

if Table A is being compiled. However, this should be done only when $n$ is small.

If we compile the correlational Table C, let us agree to relate all the cases shown in each rectangle to the midpoints of the intervals $x$ and $y$, just as in the case of the distribution of a single variable.

Let us recall the notations used above: $x_k$ and $y_k$ are the values of $x$ and $y$ corresponding to the midpoints of the intervals of the variables $x$ and $y$; $r$ is the number of intervals of the variable $x$; $s$ is the number of the intervals of the variable $y$; $n_{kl}$ is the number of outcomes in a rectangle corresponding to $x_k$ and $y_l$. Then, to calculate $\mu_{11}$, we may write the formula

$$\mu_{11} = \frac{1}{n} \sum_{k=1}^{r} \sum_{l=1}^{s} n_{kl} x_k y_l - \bar{x}\bar{y}. \tag{19.27}$$

The numbers $\bar{x}$, $\bar{y}$, $\sigma_x$, and $\sigma_y$ are calculated from the rules for determining the characteristics of the distribution of a single variable:

$$\left.\begin{aligned} \bar{x}=\frac{1}{n}\sum_{k=1}^{n} n_{k0}x_k, \quad \bar{y}=\frac{1}{n}\sum_{l=1}^{s} n_{0l}y_l, \\ \sigma_x^2=\frac{1}{n}\sum_{k=1}^{r} n_{k0}x_k^2-\bar{x}^2, \quad \sigma_y^2=\frac{1}{n}\sum_{l=1}^{s} n_{0l}y_l^2-\bar{y}^2. \end{aligned}\right\} \qquad (19.28)$$

## 105. THE AVERAGE ERRORS IN THE EQUATIONS OF REGRESSION. BOUNDS FOR THE VALUES OF THE CORRELATION COEFFICIENT

If we use the equation of regression for determining $y$ from a given value of $x$ (or vice versa), the computed value $y_c$ will differ from each of the values of $y$ that in actuality correspond to the number $x$ in the observations.

We may say that when we substitute $x$ into the equation of regression for calculating $y$, we will obtain $y_c$ with an error (more precisely, with a deviation from observations). The question naturally arises as to the value of the average "error" in the equation of regression, so that we may judge the extent to which the points of the field are dispersed about the line of regression. In determining the average error (that is, the mean square deviation), it is convenient to deal not with the values of the variable, but with the deviations of these values from the average values. Therefore, we write the equation of regression (19.18) in the form (19.25):

$$v=\frac{\sigma_v}{\sigma_u}ru, \quad u=\frac{\sigma_u}{\sigma_v}rv.$$

Here, we drop the macrons and the subscripts from the left side of each of these equations, since we are interested only in comparing $v_c$, calculated from the equation of regression in order to determine $u$, with all the values $v$ obtained from observations (Table A).

We denote the mean square errors in the equations of regression by $s_v$ and $s_u$. By definition,

$$ns_v^2=\sum_{k=1}^{n}\left(v_k-\frac{\sigma_v}{\sigma_u}ru_k\right)^2=\sum_{k=1}^{n}v_k^2-2\frac{\sigma_v}{\sigma_u}r\sum_{k=1}^{n}u_kv_k+\frac{\sigma_v^2}{\sigma_u^2}r^2\sum_{k=1}^{n}u_k^2 .$$

Since $u_k$ and $v_k$ are the deviations from the average values,

$$\left.\begin{aligned} \sum_{k=1}^{n} v_k^2=n\sigma_v^2, \\ \sum_{k=1}^{n} u_k^2=n\sigma_u^2, \\ \sum_{k=1}^{n} u_kv_k=n\mu_{11}=nr\sigma_u\sigma_v. \end{aligned}\right\} \qquad (19.29)$$

Therefore,

$$s_v^2 = \sigma_v^2 (1 - r^2), \qquad s_v = \sigma_v \sqrt{1 - r^2}. \tag{19.30}$$

In an analogous manner, we obtain

$$s_u = \sigma_u \sqrt{1 - r^2}. \tag{19.31}$$

From formulas (19.30), we may draw the following conclusions. If we use the equation of regression for determining the value of one variable from the value of the other, the average error in this determination is less than the average error in the first variable, provided its value is replaced with the average value obtained from the entire distribution.

Formulas (19.30) and (19.31) enable us to determine exactly the limits between which $r$ can vary. The quantity $s_v^2$ is a positive number. Therefore, it follows from the formula for $s_v^2$, that $r^2 \leqslant 1$ or

$$-1 \leqslant r \leqslant +1. \tag{19.32}$$

We may obtain a similiar conclusion regarding $s_u^2$.

The correlation coefficient $r$ can be equal to -1 or 1 only if $s_v^2 = 0$ or $s_u^2 = 0$. The quantity $ns_v^2$ is the sum of the squares of the deviations and it can be equal to 0 only when each deviation is equal to 0. The same is true of $ns_u^2$. Thus, if $r = \pm 1$, this means that the equations of regression give the *exact* values of $v$ in terms of $u$ and vice versa. This in turn means that we have a linear functional relationship.

We note in particular that the correlation coefficient should indicate the degree of connection between two random variables. It should be clearly understood that this number alone is not sufficient to characterize the distribution in this respect.* Therefore, we should be careful in forming conclusions based on the value of the correlation coefficient. If $r \approx 0$, this still does not mean that there is no relationship. The relationship may be close to a nonlinear one, in which the value of $r$ plays no role.

## 106. AVERAGE ERRORS OF SAMPLE COEFFICIENTS OF CORRELATION AND REGRESSION

The concept of a general set can be extended to the case in which we study the distribution of several random variables (in particular, two). For example, if we are interested in the correlation

*In practice, we usually assume that the variables are sufficiently related if $|r| > 0.7$ or 0.6. However, we may conclude that there is a relationship even when $r$ is less than this, if physical considerations substantiate this view. On the other hand, even when $|r| = 0.9$, one should not categorically speak of a dependence if it cannot be explained on a physical basis.

between the visible magnitude and the distance of stars of a certain spectral class, we should consider all those observations that we might theoretically perform (by observing all stars) as belonging to the general set. In the study of the relationship between the height of men called into the army and their weight, the general set consists of the total data on the height and weight of all persons examined. In practice, the study of the general set either is too tedious, as in the second example, or is in practice impossible, as in the first example, where the concept of the general set is only of a theoretical nature. Ordinarily, we deal with a sample taken from the general set. Thus, for example, four standard observations of temperature and humidity during a year represent a choice from the theoretical general set of these quantities.

However, it is of interest to form a picture of the nature of the general set on the basis of the sample. To do this, we need to find out to what extent the sample correlation coefficient and the sample coefficients of regression represent the same quantities in the general set.

On the basis of the law of large numbers, we can only say that for a sufficiently large sample, the sample parameters can differ by an arbitrarily small amount from the parameters of the general set and that we can expect this with a probability close to unity.

Pearson investigated the distribution of the sample values of $r$ in a general set obeying a normal law of distribution (see Chapter 12). The law of distribution turned out to be rather complicated. The distribution of the sample correlation coefficients differs from a normal distribution and approximates it only if the sample is large (but here, the value of the correlation coefficient is not close to unity). From the distribution function, we may derive an approximate expression for the average error of the sample correlation coefficient:

$$\sigma_r = \frac{1 - r^2}{\sqrt{n}}, \tag{19.33}$$

where $n$ is the size of the sample (the number of observations).

From what was said concerning the distribution of the sample values of $r$, we can assign the variable $\sigma_r$ the same value as in a normal distribution if the sample is large. In the opposite case, $\sigma_r$ approximates the possible bounds for the general coefficient only very crudely (for example, according to the three-sigma rule).

For the average errors of the sample coefficients of regression, we obtain the following approximate expressions:

$$\left.\begin{aligned} \sigma(\rho_{yx}) &= \frac{\sigma_y}{\sigma_x}\sqrt{\frac{1-r^2}{n}}, \\ \sigma(\rho_{xy}) &= \frac{\sigma_x}{\sigma_y}\sqrt{\frac{1-r^2}{n}} \end{aligned}\right\} \tag{19.34}$$

for the regression of $Y$ with respect to $X$ and $X$ with respect to $Y$, respectively.

If the sample is very small, calculation of the average errors from these formulas gives virtually no results. In such cases, it is necessary to estimate the correlation from the theory of a small sample by using Fischer's investigations. A very clear exposition of this problem can be found in the book by V. I. Romanovskii *Elementarnyĭ kurs matematicheskoĭ statistiki* (Elementary Course in Mathematical Statistics).

## 107. THE PROBABILISTIC SIGNIFICANCE OF THE ELEMENTARY THEORY OF CORRELATION

In the preceding sections of this chapter, we constructed linear empirical formulas approximately representing the dependence of the average values of each of the variables on the corresponding values of the other variables. We also introduced the correlation coefficient as a measure of the deviation of the relationship between the two variables from a linear relationship.

We have discussed the problem of studying statistical relationships between two variables on the basis of observed pairs of their values, without considering the relationship of this approach to probability theory. We must show the relationship between Chapter 12 (dealing with sets of two random variables) and the present chapter in order to determine the conditions under which we may apply the computing procedures that we have now developed.

The apparatus of the theory of correlation that we have developed gives five numbers that serve as overall characteristics of the sample set being considered: the average values of each of the variables, the mean square deviations of each variable in particular, and the correlation coefficient. Under what conditions are these five numbers sufficient to describe the sample set and to determine approximately the parameters of the general set from which the sample was taken?

In Chapter 12, we examined a normal distribution of a set of two random variables. It was shown there that the conditional expectation of each variable (when the value of the other variable was given) is a linear function of the second variable. This corresponds to the condition taken in the present chapter of constructing linear equations of regression.

The coefficient of correlation $r$, which was introduced earlier in the chapter, can be formally defined as the quotient that results when we divide the average value of the products of the deviations of both variables from their average values by the product of their mean square deviations.

As was shown in Section 64, the parameter $R$ of a two-dimensional normal law is equal to the quotient that results when we divide the expectation of the product of the deviations of the variables from their expectations by the product of the mean square deviations of these variables. If we remember that the expectation of a random variable is its average value, we obtain a complete correspondence between the numbers $r$ and $R$. We may say that $r$ is an approximate value of $R$ obtained from the sample set, if we assume that the general set obeys a normal law of distribution.

From what has been said about the equations of regression and the correlation coefficient, it follows that study of a linear correlation is admissible if the variables in question have a normal distribution. The parameters of the distribution ($\bar{x}$, $\bar{y}$, $\sigma_x$, $\sigma_y$, $r$) can then be considered sufficient to describe the set of two variables that we are studying (provided we can assume the distribution to be normal).

Calculation of the mean square errors in these parameters is necessary, since this makes it possible for us to evaluate the reliability of the values of the parameters after they are calculated.

If our results can be considered reliable, we may write the probability density with the approximate values of the parameters and we may calculate the probability that the values of the variables will belong to some given region by integrating the density over that region.

## 108. THE PROCEDURE FOR INVESTIGATING THE CORRELATION IN THE CASE OF A LARGE NUMBER OF OBSERVATIONS. AN EXAMPLE

If there are no more than about fifty observations, the parameters can be calculated from the formulas given in Sections 103 and 104.

| | I | II | III | | | | | | | IV | V | VI | VII | VIII | IX | X | XI |
|---|---|---|---|---|---|---|---|---|---|---|---|---|---|---|---|---|---|
| (1) | $m$ / $P$ | | 1.5 | 2.5 | 3.5 | 4.5 | 5.5 | 6.5 | 7.5 | Distribution $P$ | $(y)$ | $n_{0l} \cdot y_l$ | $n_{0l} \cdot y_l^2$ | $\sum_k n_{kl} x_k$ | $y_l \sum_k n_{kl} x_k$ | VIII : V | $\bar{x}_y$ from Eqs. of regression |
| (2) | | $X$ / $Y$ | -4 | -3 | -2 | -1 | 0 | +1 | +2 | $y_l$ | $n_{0l}$ | | | | | | |
| (3) | 1.1 | -4 | 2 | | | | | | | -4 | 2 | - 8 | 32 | - 8 | +32 | -4.00 | -3.80 |
| | 1.3 | -3 | 2 | 4 | | | | | | -3 | 6 | - 18 | 54 | -20 | +60 | -3.33 | -3.06 |
| | 1.5 | -2 | | 3 | 3 | | | | | -2 | 6 | - 12 | 24 | -15 | +30 | -2.50 | -2.32 |
| | 1.7 | -1 | | | 25 | 7 | | | | -1 | 32 | - 32 | 32 | -57 | +57 | -1.78 | -1.58 |
| | 1.9 | 0 | | | 7 | 64 | 37 | 1 | | 0 | 109 | 0 | 0 | -77 | 0 | -0.71 | -0.84 |
| | 2.1 | +1 | | | 4 | 16 | 143 | 14 | | +1 | 177 | +177 | 177 | -10 | -10 | -0.06 | -0.09 |
| | 2.3 | +2 | | | | 4 | 20 | 16 | 2 | +2 | 42 | + 84 | 168 | +16 | +32 | +0.38 | +0.65 |
| | 2.5 | +3 | | | | | | 1 | 1 | +3 | 2 | + 6 | 18 | + 3 | + 9 | +1.50 | +1.39 |
| (4) | Distribution $(x_k)$ | $x_k$ | -4 | -3 | -2 | -1 | 0 | +1 | +2 | | Sum | Sum | Sum | | Sum | | |
| (5) | Distribution $m$ | $n_{k0}$ | 4 | 7 | 39 | 91 | 200 | 32 | 3 | Sum | 376 / 376 | +197 | 505 | | 210 | | |
| (6) | $n_{k0} \cdot x_k$ | | -16 | -21 | -78 | -91 | 0 | +32 | +6 | Sum | -168 | | | | | | |
| (7) | $n_{k0} \cdot x_k^2$ | | 64 | 63 | 156 | 91 | 0 | 32 | 12 | Sum | 418 | | | | | | |
| (8) | $\sum_l n_{kl} y_l$ | | -14 | -18 | -27 | +17 | +183 | +49 | +7 | | | | | | | | |
| (9) | $x_k \sum_l n_{kl} y_l$ | | +56 | +54 | +54 | -17 | 0 | +49 | +14 | Sum | 210 | | | | | | |
| (10) | (8) : (5) | | -3.50 | -2.57 | -0.69 | +0.19 | +0.92 | +1.53 | +2.33 | | | | | | | | |
| (11) | $\bar{y}_x$ from Eqs. of regression | | -2.56 | -1.70 | -0.83 | -0.04 | +0.91 | +1.78 | +2.65 | | | | | | | | |

Let us now examine the method of calculating the correlation coefficient and of setting up the equations of regression when there is a large amount of observational material.

Let us calculate the correlation coefficient and derive the equations of regression for visible stars of magnitudes $m$ and the logarithms of the distances in parsecs $P$ of the stars of the spectral type B5–B9.

The calculations should be arranged as shown in the diagram on page 328.

### Description and Explanation of the Diagram

Column I gives the values of the variable $P$ at the midpoints of its intervals. Since the step is equal to 0.2, the first interval contains stars with values of $P$ from 1.0 to 1.2; the second contains those from 1.2 to 1.4, etc. Row (1) gives the values $m$ of the variable at the midpoints of the intervals. Here, the step is equal to unity. Therefore, the first interval contains those stars whose visible size lies between 1 and 2, the second contains those from 2 to 3, etc. Column II contains the values of the midpoints of the intervals of the variable $P$ in conventional units as measured from the zero point agreed on. Row (2) contains the same values for the variable $m$. Both these rows are filled out after calculating column V and row (5) just as in the case of a one-dimensional distribution.

The numerical matrix, denoted by III–(3), is a correlational table of type C. It is obtained by calculating from a catalogue the number of stars whose visible brightness and whose values of $P$ lie in the intervals corresponding to each rectangle in the diagram. The sum of all the elements in the matrix must be equal to the total number of observations. The correlational table is surrounded by heavy lines. Directly to the right of it is column IV and then column V. Column IV is a repetition of column II and consequently is filled out after column V. The diagram can be simplified somewhat by eliminating either column II or column IV. It is more convenient to keep column IV next to column V. Column V is obtained by adding all the numbers in every row of the matrix III. Column V and column I together show the distribution of the single variable $P$. These columns together with columns II and IV give the distribution of the same variable in conventional units (that is, of the variable $Y$, as is indicated by the column heads in the diagram). The same may be said with regard to rows (4) and (5) with the difference that we must speak of the variable $m$ or $X$.

Calculations of the numbers in column V and row (5) can be checked by adding all the numbers in the line. The sum must be equal to the total number of observations. Therefore, the number 376 appears twice in the diagram—once in column V and once in the continuation of row (5). The places, such as here, where we need to perform this addition are indicated by the word "sum." A diagonal line is drawn across those rectangles where we do not need to take the sum.

After computing column V, we must choose our zero point for the variable $P$. The maximum of the distribution of this variable, that is, the largest value of the multiplicity (of the numbers $n_{0l}$ appears in that interval in which the midpoint has the value 2.1. We could take our zero point here, but the preceding value of $n_{0l}$ is rather large. There are also several lower values in the table. Therefore, it would be better to take our zero point at the midpoint of the interval in which $n_{0l}$ is equal to 109.* For the variable $m$, we take the zero point at the midpoint of the interval in which $n_{k0}$ has its maximum.

Columns IV and V and rows (4) and (5), which adjoin the matrix III, give the distributions of the variables $Y$ and $X$ in question taken separately. Therefore, they are bounded by heavy lines.

Column VI gives the figure we need for calculating the average value of the variable $P$ in conventional units (that is, of the variable $Y$). Therefore, the column is labelled $n_{0l} \cdot y_l$ ; that is, every number in column V must be multiplied by the number next to it in column IV. The numbers obtained are then added. A completely analogous operation is done in the case of row (6).

In column VII, the preparatory calculations are made for determining the second-order initial moment of the variable $Y$. This is necessary for calculating the mean square deviation of that variable. The numbers in column VII are obtained by multiplying the numbers in column VI by the numbers in column IV. Analogous operations are performed in row (7). They give the sum that is necessary for calculating the mean square deviation of the variable $m$. Columns VI and VII and rows (6) and (7) contain the final result for one-dimensional distributions of the variables $P$ and $m$.

---

*As computations show, such a choice is not altogether felicitous, but this is of no great significance because if the point taken as the zero point is poorly chosen, the calculations are made only slightly more complicated.

To calculate the correlation coefficient from a table of type C and to calculate the coefficients of regression, we must evaluate the double sum

$$\sum_k \sum_l n_{kl} x_k y_l = \sum_l \left[ y_l \left( \sum_k n_{kl} x_k \right) \right].$$

This could be calculated directly by multiplying every number in the matrix III by the values of $x_k$ and $y_l$ corresponding to this number and adding all the elements of the matrix thus formed. Since in so doing we would need to write down the transformed correlational table and since there would not be a check, we usually prefer another method for making the calculations. The summation is made first over one argument and then over the other. By reversing the orders of the arguments, we can obtain the double sum a second time. Since all the operations are carried out in a formally exact manner (that is, with no approximations), the second sum must be exactly equal to the first and this ensures a reliable check on the calculations. Let us examine in detail the calculations of columns VIII and IX, which give the double sum. As indicated in the column head of column VIII, the numbers $n_{kl}$ in each row are multiplied by the corresponding values of $x_k$ and the resulting products are added. These operations may be done in one's head or, if the numbers $n_{kl}$ are great, on a calculating machine. In the present problem, all these operations can be done in one's head. The first row is

$$2 \times (-4) = -8;$$

the second row is

$$2 \times (-4) + 4 \times (-3) = -20, \ldots;$$

the sixth row is

$$4 \times (-2) + 16 \times (-1) + 143 \times (0) + 14 \times 1 = -10.$$

After multiplying each of the numbers in column VIII by $y_l$, we obtain column IX. Addition of the numbers in column IX gives the double sum above. In just the same way, rows (8) and (9) give the same sum, but the summation is made first over $y$ and then over $x$. For example, the number 49 in row (8) is obtained thus:

$$1 \times 0 + 14 \times 1 + 16 \times 2 + 1 \times 3 = 49.$$

If we multiply by + 1, we obtain the result of summing over y when $x = 1$. Addition of all the numbers in the ninth row completes the calculation of the double sum carried out first over $y$ and then over $x$. The exact same number should be obtained in both cases. Columns VIII and IX and rows (8) and (9), together with the sixth and seventh lines give all the necessary parameters of the empirical distribution of the set of two variables (under the condition that it is sufficient to examine the linear equations of regression). With this, we may conclude the work from the diagram and turn to the calculation of the coefficients of regression, to the derivation of the equations of regression, and to the calculation of the correlation coefficient. The tenth and eleventh lines in the diagram are filled out when it is necessary to compare the empirical with the theoretical (linear) regression constructed by them. As indicated in the heading of the tenth lines, every number in the eighth line must be divided by the corresponding number in the fifth line. Since, for example, $n_{0l}$ is the number of stars corresponding to a given value of $y_l$, the ratio $n_{kl} / n_{0l}$ is the empirical probability of every $x_k$ under the same conditions. Therefore, the numbers in column X represent the weighted means of the value $\bar{x}_y$ for consecutive values of $y$. This means that we have obtained the empirical regression of $X$ with respect to $Y$. Analogously, row (10) gives the sequence of average values of $y$ for given values of $x$, that is, the empirical regression of $Y$ with respect to $X$. It should be recalled that in making these calculations we assume that we have $n_{kl}$ stars for which the values of the variables are equal to $x_k$ and $y_l$. The eleventh lines give the values of the averages of $X$ for successive values of $y_l$ and of the averages of $Y$ for different values of $x_k$, calculated from the equations of regression. Comparison of the empirical regression with the regression calculated from the equations of regression is shown rapidly in Figure 18. The empirical relationship is indicated by the broken lines drawn through the points representing the numbers in the tenth lines (columns and rows).

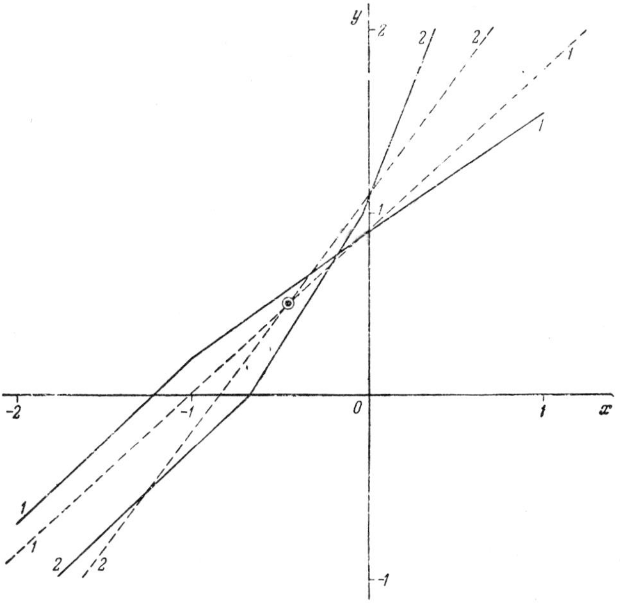


Fig. 18. The empirical (solid lines) and theoretical (dashed lines) lines of regression close to the center of distribution. The center of distribution is indicated by the rosette. The numbers denote the corresponding lines of regression: 1, $y$ with respect to $x$ and 2, $x$ with respect to $y$.

Calculation of the Parameters of the Distribution

(a) *The average values.* Division of the sum of the numbers in column VI by the total number of observations gives the average value of $Y$:

$$\bar{y} = \frac{+197}{376} = 0.524.$$

When we take into account the position of the zero point and the size of the step in the catalogue units, we obtain

$$P = 1.9 + 0.2 \times 0.524 = 2.005.$$

Division of the sum of the numbers in the sixth row gives the average value of $X$:

$$\bar{x} = \frac{-168}{376} = -0.447;$$

$$\bar{m} = 5.5 + 1 \times (-0.447) = 5.05.$$

since the step in the table with respect to $m$ is equal to unity and the zero point is taken at the midpoint of the interval with visible magnitude 5.5.

(b) *The mean square deviations.* The sum of the numbers in the seventh column divided by the number of observations gives the initial moment of order zero-two, that is, the second-order initial moment of the variable $Y$. When we subtract the square of the average value of this variable from this moment (in accordance with the variance formula), we obtain the variance of the variable $Y$; the square root of the variance gives, by definition, the mean square deviation:

$$\sigma_y^2 = \frac{505}{376} - (0.524)^2 = 1.068. \quad \sigma_y = \sqrt{1.068} = 1.033.$$

Analogously, from the seventh row,

$$\sigma_x^2 = \frac{418}{376} - (0,447)^2 = 0,912, \quad \sigma_x = \sqrt{0,912} = 0,955.$$

(c) *The correlation coefficient.* Division of the sum of the numbers in column IX (or row (9)) by the total number of observations gives the initial moment of order one-one of the given two-dimensional distribution:

$$\nu_{11} = \frac{210}{376} = 0,559.$$

To obtain the central moment of the same order, we must subtract from the initial moment the product of the average values of the variables in question:

$$\mu_{11} = 0,559 - (-0,447) \times (+0,524) = 0,793.$$

To calculate the correlation coefficient, we form the product of the mean square deviations:

$$\sigma_y \sigma_x = 1,033 \cdot 0,955 = 0,987;$$

We then obtain

$$r = \frac{0,793}{0,987} = 0,803.$$

(d) *The coefficients of regression and the equations of regression.* We calculate these in conventional units from the formulas containing the correlation coefficient. As a preliminary, we find the ratios of the mean square deviations:

$$\frac{\sigma_y}{\sigma_x} = 1,082, \quad \frac{\sigma_x}{\sigma_y} = 0,924.$$

We then find for the coefficients of regression the values

$$\rho_{yx} = 0,803 \times 1,082 = 0,869, \quad \rho_{xy} = 0,803 \times 0,924 = 0,742.$$

The equations of regression are as follows:

The regression of $y$ with respect to $x$:

$$\bar{y}_x - 0,524 = 0,869 \times (x + 0,447)$$

or

$$\bar{y}_x = 0,869x + 0,912$$

(The notation $\bar{y}_x$ can be replaced with just $y$, but if we do this, we should not forget the meaning and origin of the equations of regression.)

The regression of $x$ with respect to $y$:

$$\bar{x}_y + 0,447 = 0,742 \times (y - 0,524)$$

or

$$\bar{x}_y = 0,742y - 0,836.$$

The eleventh column and row of the matrix were obtained from these equations. The values of $x$ and $y$ in the fourth row and column, respectively, of the matrix were substituted one after the other into the right members of these equations for that purpose.

(e) *The mean square errors in the parameters.* The extra calculations to be described now are carried out in those problems in which the statistical material is a sample from an infinite general set that obeys a normal law of distribution.

In Sections 99 and 106, we presented without proof formulas according to which the mean square deviations of the basic parameters of one- and two-dimensional distributions can be calculated.

Some of these formulas are known to the reader from the theory of random errors.

1. The mean square errors of the arithmetic means:

$$\sigma_{\bar{x}} = \frac{\sigma_x}{\sqrt{n}}, \qquad \sigma_{\bar{y}} = \frac{\sigma_y}{\sqrt{n}};$$

in our case $\sqrt{n} = 19.4$. Therefore,

$$\sigma_{\bar{x}} = \frac{0.955}{19.4} = 0.049; \qquad \sigma_{\bar{y}} = \frac{1.033}{19.4} = 0.053.$$

2. The mean square errors of the sample mean square errors:

$$\sigma(\sigma_x) = \frac{\sigma_x}{\sqrt{2n}}, \qquad \sigma(\sigma_y) = \frac{\sigma_y}{\sqrt{2n}};$$

In our example, $\sqrt{2n} = 27.4$. Therefore,

$$\sigma(\sigma_x) = \frac{0.955}{27.4} = 0.035, \qquad \sigma(\sigma_y) = \frac{1.033}{27.4} = 0.038.$$

These variables characterize the reliability of the parameters in the one-dimensional case. The following numbers give an evaluation of the reliability of the parameters in a two-dimensional distribution.

3. The mean square errors in the equations of regression ($s_y$ and $s_x$ are calculated from formulas (19.30) given above). In the present case, $r^2 = 0.645$; $1 - r^2 = 0.355$; $\sqrt{1 - r^2} = 0.596$; $s_y = 1.033 \cdot 0.596 = 0.616$; $s_x = 0.955 \cdot 0.596 = 0.569$. The numbers $s_y$ and $s_x$ are the mean square errors that are obtained if we compare the values calculated from the equations of regression with the individual (but complete) values obtained from observations.

4. The mean square error of the correlation coefficient. From formula (19.33) we obtain for the distribution in question,

$$\sigma_r = \frac{0.355}{19.4} = 0.018.$$

5. The mean square errors in the coefficients of regression are calculated from formulas (19.34). The results are

$$\frac{\sqrt{1 - r^2}}{\sqrt{n}} = \frac{0.596}{19.4} = 0.0307. \qquad \sigma(\rho_{yx}) = 1.082 \cdot 0.0307 = 0.033,$$
$$\sigma(\rho_{xy}) = 0.924 \cdot 0.0307 = 0.028.$$

SUMMARY OF THE RESULTS

We write the results of the computation of the parameters of the distribution, taking into consideration the mean square deviations, just as we did in the theory of random errors.

A. *Summary in conventional units:*

$$\bar{x} = -0.447 \pm 0.049, \qquad \bar{y} = 0.524 \pm 0.053$$
$$\sigma_x = 0.955 \pm 0.035, \qquad \sigma_y = 1.033 \pm 0.038$$
$$\rho_{yx} = 0.869 \pm 0.033, \qquad \rho_{xy} = 0.742 \pm 0.028$$
$$\bar{y}_x = 0.869x + 0.912, \qquad \bar{x}_y = 0.742y - 0.836$$
$$r = +0.803 \pm 0.018.$$

B. *Summary in basic units.* In most problems, we must have the parameters not only in conventional units, but also in those units in which the investigated quantities are usually given. The values are measured from the chosen zero point.

The method of changing from conventional units and the conventional zero point to basic units and a new zero point for a one-dimensional distribution was explained in the preceding chapter. Therefore, it will be sufficient to show how the change in the parameters is made in the case of a two-dimensional distribution. Since the coefficients of regression and the coefficient of correlation depend on the central moments, changing the zero point has no effect on them and we need to consider only the size of the steps. The correlation coefficient remains completely unchanged, since this is a dimensionless quantity, as was shown in the introduction to this section. Therefore, let us consider only the problem of the change in the coefficients of regression. It is clear from the expressions for these coefficients

$$\rho_{yx} = r\frac{\sigma_y}{\sigma_x}, \qquad \rho_{xy} = r\frac{\sigma_x}{\sigma_y}$$

that in converting to basic units, we must multiply the numerator in the first one by the step of the second variable in basic units, and the denominator by the step of the first variable. In the second coefficient, the order of the transformations is just the opposite. Here, the first variable is assumed to be the one that is denoted by $x$ in conventional units. Let us perform the conversion in the example that we have been studying. Since the conventional zero of the variable $x$ corresponds to a value of 5.5 of the visible magnitude and the step for this variable is equal to unity, the zero point for the variable $y$ corresponds to a value of 1.9 of the variable $P$, and the step of this variable is equal to 0.2. Therefore,

$$\bar{m} = 5.5 - 0.447 \times 1 = 5.053, \qquad \bar{P} = 1.9 + 0.524 \times 0.2 = 2.005$$
$$\sigma_m = 0.955 \times 1 = 0.955, \qquad \sigma_P = 1.033 \times 0.2 = 0.207$$
$$\rho_{Pm} = 0.869 \times \frac{0.2}{1} = 0.174, \qquad \rho_{mP} = 0.742 \times \frac{1}{0.2} = 3.71.$$

We transform the equations of regression directly by using the coefficient of regression and the average values that we have obtained. The equation of regression of $P$ with respect to $m$ is

$$\bar{P}_m - 2.005 = 0.174 \times (m - 5.053) \quad \text{or} \quad \bar{P}_m = 0.174m + 1.126.$$

The equation of regression of $m$ with respect to $P$ is

$$\bar{m}_P - 5.053 = 3.71 \times (P - 2.005)$$

or

$$\bar{m}_P = 3.71P - 2.39.$$

These calculations make it possible for us to draw the following conclusions about the correlation of the variables $P$ and $m$. It is clear from the values of the mean square errors in the parameters that sufficiently accurate values were obtained for all of them, especially the correlation coefficient. Therefore, the connection between $P$ and $m$ can be considered (on the basis of the investigated material) as being close to linear on the average. This is confirmed by a comparison of the numbers in columns X and XI and also in rows (10) and (11). However, in the case of the rows, we may find more appreciable deviations on the part of the theoretical averages from the empirical ones near the left edge of the distribution. The obvious explanation is the small number of bright stars.

It follows from what has been said that the equations of regression can be used for calculating the values of a single variable from the values of the other variable. The results of the calculations give on the average a small discrepancy with the empirical averages.

It is recommended that the reader make his own comparison of the empirical regressions with the theoretical ones in basic units. To do this, he will need to set up the tenth column and row in basic units and to check the eleventh row and column from the theoretical equations of regression in basic units. If we find the deviations on the part of the numbers in the tenth column from the numbers in the eleventh column and calculate the weighted mean square deviation, we obtain an overall evaluation of the quality of the approximation of the data (on the average) by the equations of regression.

## 109. AN EXAMPLE OF INVESTIGATING THE CORRELATION FROM A SMALL NUMBER OF OBSERVATIONS

Analysis of a two-dimensional statistical set when the number of observations is small can be considerably simplified. The example that we are about to consider is taken from the book by V. I. Romanovskii.

We wish to study the correlation between the amount of precipitation in millimeters in January for nine consecutive years in Tashkent and at the agricultural experimental station twelve kilometers away from Tashkent. Since the two stations are close to each other, we may expect that the relation will be close, but it is necessary to check this since local peculiarities distorting the relation are possible. The results of the observations in Tashkent are denoted by $x$ and those at the station by $y$.

We make a diagram showing the results of observations and certain calculations made from them:

| | $x^2$ | $x$ | $xy$ | $y$ | $y^2$ |
|---|---|---|---|---|---|
| | 7 569 | 87 | 7 482 | 86 | 7 396 |
| | 2 209 | 47 | 2 632 | 56 | 3 136 |
| | 5 476 | 74 | 6 216 | 84 | 7 056 |
| | 7 396 | 86 | 6 192 | 72 | 5 184 |
| | 1 444 | 38 | 1 786 | 47 | 2 209 |
| | 225 | 15 | 255 | 17 | 289 |
| | 1 681 | 41 | 1 763 | 43 | 1 849 |
| | 64 | 8 | 152 | 19 | 361 |
| | 6 241 | 79 | 6 952 | 88 | 7 744 |
| Total | 32 305 | 475 | 33 430 | 512 | 35 224 |

The diagram is simple and the column heads are self-explanatory. Note that the totals shown at the bottom, which are necessary for what follows, can be obtained on a calculating machine by the method of accumulation without writing the individual addends. Here, the calculations are made in detail in order to show completely the order in which the calculations are made. From the formulas of Sections 103 and 104, we make the following calculations:

$$\bar{x} = \frac{475}{9} = 52.8, \qquad \bar{y} = \frac{512}{9} = 56{,}9$$

$$\nu_{20} = \frac{32305}{9} = 3589.44, \qquad \nu_{02} = \frac{35224}{9} = 3913.78,$$

$$\mu_{20} = 3589.44 - 52.8^2 = 801.60, \qquad \mu_{02} = 3913.78 - 56.9^2 = 676.17,$$

$$\sigma_x = \sqrt{801.60} = 28.3 \qquad \sigma_y = \sqrt{676.17} = 26.0,$$

$$\nu_{11} = \frac{33430}{9} = 3710, \qquad \bar{x}\,\bar{y} = 52.8 \cdot 56.9 = 3000,$$

$$\mu_{11} = 3710 - 3000 = 710, \qquad \sigma_x\sigma_y = 28.3 \times 26.0 = 736,$$

$$r = \frac{710}{736} = 0.965, \qquad r^2 = 0.931, \qquad 1 - r^2 = 0.069,$$

$$\sigma_r = \frac{0.069}{\sqrt{9}} = 0.023, \qquad r = 0.965 \pm 0.023.$$

The correlation coefficient is close to unity and its mean square error is very small despite the very small number of observations. The calculations were first made in a formally exact manner, that is, as if the values of $x$ and $y$ were exact. Beginning with the mean square deviations, the calculations are taken to three digits.

The result of the determination of the correlation coefficient shows that the equations of regression can be used to calculate the values of one variable from the values of the other with a small mean square error.

It is suggested that the reader derive for himself the equations of regression and compare the results of calculation from the equations of regression with observations. Answer (incomplete): $\rho_{yx} = 0.887$, $\rho_{xy} = 1.050$.

# BIBLIOGRAPHY

Part I

Bezikovich, Ya. S., *Priblizhennye vychisleniya* (Approximate Calculations), 6th ed., Gostekhizdat, 1949.

Krylov, A. N., *Lektsii o priblizhennykh vychisleniyakh* (Lectures on Approximate Calculations), 6th ed., Gostekhizdat, 1954; *Sobranie trudov* (Collected Works), vol. III, part 1, Izdatel'stvo Akad. Nauk, USSR, 1949.

Yakovlev, K. P., *Matematicheskaya obrabotka rezul'tatov izmereniǐ* (Mathematical Processing of the Results of Measurements), 2nd ed., Gostekhizdat, 1953.

Part II

Blazhko, S. N., *Kurs sfericheskoi astronomii* (Course in Spherical Astronomy), 2nd ed., Gostekhizdat, 1954, ch. II.

Goncharov, V. L., *Teoriya interpolirovaniya i priblizheniya funktsiǐ* (Theory of Interpolation and Approximation of Functions), 2nd ed., Gostekhizdat, 1954.

Kazakov, S. A., *Kurs sfericheskoi astronomii* (Course in Spherical Astronomy), with supplement on interpolation, 2nd ed., Gostekhizdat, 1940.

(See also the bibliography for Part I.)

Part III

Bernstein, S. N., *Teoriya veroyatnosteǐ* (Probability Theory) 4th ed., Gostekhizdat, 1946.

Gnedenko, B. V., *Kurs teorii veroyatnosteǐ* (Course in Probability Theory), 2nd ed., Gostekhizdat, 1954.

Gnedenko, B. V., and Khinchin, A. Ya., *Elementarnoe vvedenie v Teoriyu veroyatnosteǐ* (Elementary Introduction to Probability Theory), 3rd ed., Gostekhizdat, 1952.

Goncharov, V. L., *Teoriya veroyatnosteǐ* (Probability Theory), Oborongiz, 1939.

Kolomogorov, A. N., *Osnovnye ponyatiya teorii veroyatnosteǐ* (Basic Concepts of Probability Theory) ONTI, 1936.

Romanovskii, V. I., *Elementarnyĭ kurs matematicheskoĭ statistiki* (Elementary Course in Mathematical Statistics), Gosplanizdat, 1939.

Part IV

Idel'son, N. I., *Sposob naimen'shikh kvadratov i teorya matematicheskoi nablyudeniĭ* (The Method of Least Squares and the Theory of Mathematical Analysis of Observations) Geodezizdat, 1947.
Kolmogorov, A. N., "*K obosnovaniyu metoda naimen'shikh kvadratov*" (The Basis of the Method of Least Squares), *Uspekhi matematicheskikh nauk*, 1, No. 1, 1946.
Lakhtin, L. K., *Kurs teorii veroyatnosteĭ* (Course in Probability Theory) Gosudarstvennoe izdatel'stvo, 1924.
Makover, S. G., "Reshenie sistemy normal'nykh uravneniĭ pri pomoshchi matrits" (Solution of Systems of Normal Equations by Means of Matrices), *Astronomicheskiĭ zhurnal*, 33, No. 3, 1956.
Reznikovskii, P. T., "Ob odnom variante resheniya sistemy normal'nykh uravneniĭ v metode naimen'shikh kvadratov (A Variation in the Solution of Systems of Normal Equations by the Method of Least Squares), *Soobshch. Gos. astron. instituta im. Shternberga*, No. 54, 1950.
Romanovskii, V. I., *Osnovnye zadachi teorii oshibok* (Basic Problems in the Theory of Errors), Gostekhizdat, 1947.
Semendyev, K. A., *Empiricheskie formuly* (Empirical Formulas), ONTI, 1933.
Whittaker, E. and Robinson, G., Mathematical analysis of the results of measurements.
Faddeeva, V. N., *Vychislitel'nye metody lineĭnoĭ algebry* (Computational Methods of Linear Algebra), Gostekhizdat, 1950.
(See also the bibliography to Part I and the books by Gnedenko and Khinchin in Part III.)

Part V

Cramer, H., Mathematical Methods of Statistics, Princeton University Press, Princeton, 1946.
Romanovskii, V. I., *Matematicheskaya statistika* (Mathematical Statistics), ONTI, 1938.
Slutskii, E. E., *Teoriya korrelyatsii i elementy ucheniya o krivykh raspredeleniya* (The Theory of Correlation and Elements in the Study of Distribution curves), Kiev, 1912.
Smirnov, N. Y., "Priblizhenie zakonov raspredeleniya sluchainykh velichin po empiricheskim dannym" (Approximation of the Laws of Distribution of Random Variables from Empirical Data), *Uspekhi matematicheskikh nauk*, No. 10, 1944.
(See also the books by Gnedenko and Romanovskii in Part III).

z

# APPENDIX

Table I gives the values of the Laplace-Gauss function, which is used as an approximate expression for the probability of the number of occurrences in the problem of repeated trials. This function is the probability density of a normal distribution with center equal to zero and mean square deviation equal to unity. Suppose that $n$ is the number of trials, $p$ is the probability of an occurrence in a single trial, and $k$ is the given number of occurrences whose probability we wish to compute. The calculation is made on the basis of the formula

$$P_{k,n} \approx \frac{1}{\sqrt{npq}} \Phi'\left(\frac{k-np}{\sqrt{npq}}\right), \quad q = 1 - p,$$

$$\Phi'(z) = \frac{1}{\sqrt{2\pi}} e^{-\frac{z^2}{2}}.$$

Table II gives the approximate values of the probability in the case of the problem of repeated trials when the probability of an event is small.* In this table, $k$ is the number of occurrences, $a = np$, $n$ is the number of trials, and $p$ is the probability of an occurrence in a single trial. In this case,

$$P_{k,n} \approx P_k(a) = \frac{a^k e^{-a}}{k!}.$$

Table III gives the values of the probability integral that are used for calculating the probability that a random variable will assume a value in a given interval if it obeys a normal law of distribution. If $\bar{x}$ is the average value of the random variable $X$ (the center of distribution) and $\sigma$ is the mean square deviation, the probability of obtaining a value between $\alpha$ and $\beta$ is calculated from the formula

$$P(\alpha < X < \beta) = \Phi\left(\frac{\beta - \bar{x}}{\sigma}\right) - \Phi\left(\frac{\alpha - \bar{x}}{\sigma}\right),$$

$$\Phi(z) = \frac{1}{\sqrt{2\pi}} \int_0^z e^{-\frac{t^2}{2}} dt.$$

In using this table, we should bear in mind that $\Phi(-z) = -\Phi(z)$.

---

*The table in B. V. Gnedenko's book *Kurs teorii veroyatnosteĭ* (Course in Probability Theory) was used.

If a number in Table I or II ends with the digit 5 and a plus sign appears after it, the number is an approximation that is less than the actual value. If the digit 5 is to be discarded, the preceding digit should be increased by one unit. If a minus sign appears after the 5, the value shown is in excess of the actual value. If the 5 is to be discarded, the preceding digit should be left unchanged.

Table I

$$\Phi'(z) = \frac{1}{\sqrt{2\pi}} e^{-\frac{z^2}{2}}$$

| z | Φ' | z | Φ' | z | Φ' | z | Φ' | z | Φ' |
|---|---|---|---|---|---|---|---|---|---|
| 0.00 | 0.399 | 0.50 | 0.352 | 1.00 | 0.242 | 1.50 | 0.130 | 2.00 | 0.054 |
| 0.01 | 0.399 | 0.51 | 0.350 | 1.01 | 0.240 | 1.51 | 0.128 | 2.01 | 0.053 |
| 0.02 | 0.399 | 0.52 | 0.348 | 1.02 | 0.237 | 1.52 | 0.126 | 2.02 | 0.052 |
| 0.03 | 0.399 | 0.53 | 0.347 | 1.03 | 0.235 | 1.53 | 0.124 | 2.03 | 0.051 |
| 0.04 | 0.399 | 0.54 | 0.345 | 1.04 | 0.232 | 1.54 | 0.122 | 2.04 | 0.050 |
| 0.05 | 0.398 | 0.55 | 0.343 | 1.05 | 0.230 | 1.55 | 0.120 | 2.05 | 0.049 |
| 0.06 | 0.398 | 0.56 | 0.341 | 1.06 | 0.228 | 1.56 | 0.118 | 2.06 | 0.048 |
| 0.07 | 0.398 | 0.57 | 0.339 | 1.07 | 0.225+ | 1.57 | 0.116 | 2.07 | 0.047 |
| 0.08 | 0.398 | 0.58 | 0.337 | 1.08 | 0.223 | 1.58 | 0.114 | 2.08 | 0.046 |
| 0.09 | 0.397 | 0.59 | 0.335+ | 1.09 | 0.220 | 1.59 | 0.113 | 2.09 | 0.045- |
| 0.10 | 0.397 | 0.60 | 0.333 | 1.10 | 0.218 | 1.60 | 0.111 | 2.10 | 0.044 |
| 0.11 | 0.396 | 0.61 | 0.331 | 1.11 | 0.216 | 1.61 | 0.109 | 2.11 | 0.043 |
| 0.12 | 0.396 | 0.62 | 0.329 | 1.12 | 0.213 | 1.62 | 0.107 | 2.12 | 0.042 |
| 0.13 | 0.396 | 0.63 | 0.327 | 1.13 | 0.211 | 1.63 | 0.106 | 2.13 | 0.041 |
| 0.14 | 0.395 | 0.64 | 0.325+ | 1.14 | 0.208 | 1.64 | 0.104 | 2.14 | 0.040 |
| 0.15 | 0.394 | 0.65 | 0.323 | 1.15 | 0.206 | 1.65 | 0.102 | 2.15 | 0.040 |
| 0.16 | 0.394 | 0.66 | 0.321 | 1.16 | 0.204 | 1.66 | 0.101 | 2.16 | 0.039 |
| 0.17 | 0.393 | 0.67 | 0.319 | 1.17 | 0.201 | 1.67 | 0.099 | 2.17 | 0.038 |
| 0.18 | 0.392 | 0.68 | 0.317 | 1.18 | 0.199 | 1.68 | 0.097 | 2.18 | 0.037 |
| 0.19 | 0.392 | 0.69 | 0.314 | 1.19 | 0.196 | 1.69 | 0.096 | 2.19 | 0.036 |
| 0.20 | 0.391 | 0.70 | 0.312 | 1.20 | 0.194 | 1.70 | 0.094 | 2.20 | 0.036 |
| 0.21 | 0.390 | 0.71 | 0.310 | 1.21 | 0.192 | 1.71 | 0.092 | 2.21 | 0.035- |
| 0.22 | 0.389 | 0.72 | 0.308 | 1.22 | 0.190 | 1.72 | 0.091 | 2.22 | 0.034 |
| 0.23 | 0.388 | 0.73 | 0.306 | 1.23 | 0.187 | 1.73 | 0.089 | 2.23 | 0.033 |
| 0.24 | 0.388 | 0.74 | 0.303 | 1.24 | 0.185- | 1.74 | 0.088 | 2.24 | 0.032 |
| 0.25 | 0.387 | 0.75 | 0.301 | 1.25 | 0.183 | 1.75 | 0.086 | 2.25 | 0.032 |
| 0.26 | 0.386 | 0.76 | 0.299 | 1.26 | 0.180 | 1.76 | 0.085- | 2.26 | 0.031 |
| 0.27 | 0.385- | 0.77 | 0.297 | 1.27 | 0.178 | 1.77 | 0.083 | 2.27 | 0.030 |
| 0.28 | 0.384 | 0.78 | 0.294 | 1.28 | 0.176 | 1.78 | 0.082 | 2.28 | 0.030 |
| 0.29 | 0.382 | 0.79 | 0.292 | 1.29 | 0.174 | 1.79 | 0.080 | 2.29 | 0.029 |
| 0.30 | 0.381 | 0.80 | 0.290 | 1.30 | 0.171 | 1.80 | 0.079 | 2.30 | 0.028 |
| 0.31 | 0.380 | 0.81 | 0.287 | 1.31 | 0.169 | 1.81 | 0.078 | 2.31 | 0.028 |
| 0.32 | 0.379 | 0.82 | 0.285+ | 1.32 | 0.167 | 1.82 | 0.076 | 2.32 | 0.027 |
| 0.33 | 0.378 | 0.83 | 0.283 | 1.33 | 0.165- | 1.83 | 0.075 | 2.33 | 0.026 |
| 0.34 | 0.376 | 0.84 | 0.280 | 1.34 | 0.163 | 1.84 | 0.073 | 2.34 | 0.026 |
| 0.35 | 0.375+ | 0.85 | 0.278 | 1.35 | 0.160 | 1.85 | 0.072 | 2.35 | 0.025+ |
| 0.36 | 0.374 | 0.86 | 0.276 | 1.36 | 0.158 | 1.86 | 0.071 | 2.36 | 0.025- |
| 0.37 | 0.373 | 0.87 | 0.273 | 1.37 | 0.156 | 1.87 | 0.069 | 2.37 | 0.024 |
| 0.38 | 0.371 | 0.88 | 0.271 | 1.38 | 0.154 | 1.88 | 0.068 | 2.38 | 0.023 |
| 0.39 | 0.370 | 0.89 | 0.268 | 1.39 | 0.152 | 1.89 | 0.067 | 2.39 | 0.023 |
| 0.40 | 0.368 | 0.90 | 0.266 | 1.40 | 0.150 | 1.90 | 0.066 | 2.40 | 0.022 |
| 0.41 | 0.367 | 0.91 | 0.264 | 1.41 | 0.148 | 1.91 | 0.064 | 2.41 | 0.022 |
| 0.42 | 0.365+ | 0.92 | 0.261 | 1.42 | 0.146 | 1.92 | 0.063 | 2.42 | 0.021 |
| 0.43 | 0.364 | 0.93 | 0.259 | 1.43 | 0.144 | 1.93 | 0.062 | 2.43 | 0.021 |
| 0.44 | 0.362 | 0.94 | 0.256 | 1.44 | 0.141 | 1.94 | 0.061 | 2.44 | 0.020 |
| 0.45 | 0.361 | 0.95 | 0.254 | 1.45 | 0.139 | 1.95 | 0.060 | 2.45 | 0.020 |
| 0.46 | 0.359 | 0.96 | 0.252 | 1.46 | 0.137 | 1.96 | 0.058 | 2.46 | 0.019 |
| 0.47 | 0.357 | 0.97 | 0.249 | 1.47 | 0.135+ | 1.97 | 0.057 | 2.47 | 0.019 |
| 0.48 | 0.356 | 0.98 | 0.247 | 1.48 | 0.133 | 1.98 | 0.056 | 2.48 | 0.018 |
| 0.49 | 0.354 | 0.99 | 0.244 | 1.49 | 0.131 | 1.99 | 0.055+ | 2.49 | 0.018 |

Table I (continued)

| $z$ | $\Phi'$ | $z$ | $\Phi'$ | $z$ | $\Phi'$ | $z$ | $\Phi'$ | $z$ | $\Phi'$ | $z$ | $\Phi'$ |
|---|---|---|---|---|---|---|---|---|---|---|---|
| 2.50 | 0.018 | 2.60 | 0.014 | 2.70 | 0.010 | 2.80 | 0.008 | 2.90 | 0.006 | 3.00 | 0.004 |
| 2.51 | 0.017 | 2.61 | 0.013 | 2.71 | 0.010 | 2.81 | 0.008 | 2.91 | 0.006 | | |
| 2.52 | 0.017 | 2.62 | 0.013 | 2.72 | 0.010 | 2.82 | 0.007 | 2.92 | 0.006 | | |
| 2.53 | 0.016 | 2.63 | 0.013 | 2.73 | 0.010 | 2.83 | 0.007 | 2.93 | 0.005+ | | |
| 2.54 | 0.016 | 2.64 | 0.012 | 2.74 | 0.009 | 2.84 | 0.007 | 2.94 | 0.005+ | | |
| 2.55 | 0.015 | 2.65 | 0.012 | 2.75 | 0.009 | 2.85 | 0.007 | 2.95 | 0.005+ | | |
| 2.56 | 0.015 | 2.66 | 0.012 | 2.76 | 0.009 | 2.86 | 0.007 | 2.96 | 0.005- | | |
| 2.57 | 0.015 | 2.67 | 0.011 | 2.77 | 0.009 | 2.87 | 0.006 | 2.97 | 0.005- | | |
| 2.58 | 0.014 | 2.68 | 0.011 | 2.78 | 0.008 | 2.88 | 0.006 | 2.98 | 0.005- | | |
| 2.59 | 0.014 | 2.69 | 0.011 | 2.79 | 0.008 | 2.89 | 0.006 | 2.99 | 0.005- | | |

Table II

$$P(a) = \frac{a^k e^{-a}}{k!}$$

| $k$ \ $a$ | 0.1 | 0.2 | 0.3 | 0.4 | 0.5 | 0.6 | 0.7 | 0.8 | 0.9 | 1.0 |
|---|---|---|---|---|---|---|---|---|---|---|
| 0 | 0.905 | 0.819 | 0.741 | 0.670 | 0.607 | 0.549 | 0.497 | 0.449 | 0.407 | 0.368 |
| 1 | 0.090 | 0.164 | 0.222 | 0.268 | 0.303 | 0.329 | 0.348 | 0.359 | 0.366 | 0.368 |
| 2 | 0.005- | 0.016 | 0.033 | 0.054 | 0.076 | 0.099 | 0.122 | 0.144 | 0.165- | 0.184 |
| 3 | 0.000 | 0.001 | 0.003 | 0.007 | 0.013 | 0.020 | 0.028 | 0.038 | 0.049 | 0.061 |
| 4 | | | 0.000 | 0.001 | 0.002 | 0.003 | 0.005 | 0.008 | 0.011 | 0.015+ |
| 5 | | | | | | 0.000 | 0.001 | 0.001 | 0.002 | 0.003 |
| 6 | | | | | | | | | 0.000 | 0.001 |

| $k$ \ $a$ | 1 | 2 | 3 | 4 | 5 | 6 | 7 | 8 | 9 |
|---|---|---|---|---|---|---|---|---|---|
| 0 | 0.368 | 0.135+ | 0.050 | 0.018 | 0.007 | 0.002 | 0.001 | 0.000 | 0.000 |
| 1 | 0.368 | 0.271 | 0.149 | 0.073 | 0.034 | 0.015 | 0.006 | 0.003 | 0.001 |
| 2 | 0.184 | 0.271 | 0.224 | 0.147 | 0.084 | 0.045- | 0.022 | 0.011 | 0.005- |
| 3 | 0.061 | 0.180 | 0.224 | 0.195+ | 0.140 | 0.089 | 0.052 | 0.029 | 0.015- |
| 4 | 0.015+ | 0.090 | 0.168 | 0.195+ | 0.175+ | 0.134 | 0.091 | 0.057 | 0.034 |
| 5 | 0.003 | 0.036 | 0.101 | 0.156 | 0.175+ | 0.161 | 0.128 | 0.092 | 0.061 |
| 6 | 0.001 | 0.012 | 0.050 | 0.104 | 0.146 | 0.161 | 0.149 | 0.122 | 0.091 |
| 7 | 0.000 | 0.003 | 0.022 | 0.060 | 0.104 | 0.138 | 0.149 | 0.140 | 0.117 |
| 8 | | 0.001 | 0.008 | 0.030 | 0.065+ | 0.103 | 0.130 | 0.140 | 0.132 |
| 9 | | 0.000 | 0.003 | 0.013 | 0.036 | 0.069 | 0.101 | 0.124 | 0.132 |
| 10 | | | 0.001 | 0.005+ | 0.018 | 0.041 | 0.071 | 0.099 | 0.119 |
| 11 | | | 0.000 | 0.002 | 0.008 | 0.023 | 0.045+ | 0.072 | 0.097 |
| 12 | | | | 0.001 | 0.003 | 0.011 | 0.026 | 0.048 | 0.073 |
| 13 | | | | 0.000 | 0.001 | 0.005+ | 0.014 | 0.030 | 0.050 |
| 14 | | | | | 0.000 | 0.002 | 0.007 | 0.017 | 0.032 |
| 15 | | | | | | 0.001 | 0.003 | 0.009 | 0.019 |
| 16 | | | | | | 0.000 | 0.001 | 0.005 | 0.011 |
| 17 | | | | | | | 0.001 | 0.002 | 0.006 |
| 18 | | | | | | | 0.000 | 0.001 | 0.003 |
| 19 | | | | | | | | 0.000 | 0.001 |
| | | | | | | | | | 0.001 |
| | | | | | | | | | 0.000 |

Table III

$$\Phi(z) = \frac{1}{\sqrt{2\pi}} \int_0^z e^{-\frac{z^2}{2}} dz$$

| z | 0 | 1 | 2 | 3 | 4 | 5 | 6 | 7 | 8 | 9 |
|---|---|---|---|---|---|---|---|---|---|---|
| 0.0 | 0.00000 | 00399 | 00798 | 01197 | 01595 | 01994 | 02392 | 02790 | 03188 | 03586 |
| 0.1 | 03983 | 04380 | 04776 | 05172 | 05567 | 05962 | 06356 | 06749 | 07142 | 07535 |
| 0.2 | 07926 | 08317 | 08706 | 09095 | 09483 | 09871 | 10257 | 10642 | 11026 | 11409 |
| 0.3 | 11791 | 12172 | 12552 | 12930 | 13307 | 13683 | 14058 | 14431 | 14803 | 15173 |
| 0.4 | 15542 | 15910 | 16276 | 16640 | 17003 | 17364 | 17724 | 18082 | 18439 | 18793 |
| 0.5 | 19146 | 19497 | 19847 | 20194 | 20540 | 20884 | 21226 | 21566 | 21904 | 22240 |
| 0.6 | 22575 | 22907 | 23237 | 23565 | 23891 | 24215 | 24537 | 24857 | 25175 | 25490 |
| 0.7 | 25804 | 26115 | 26424 | 26730 | 27035 | 27337 | 27637 | 27935 | 28230 | 28524 |
| 0.8 | 28814 | 29103 | 29389 | 29673 | 29955 | 30234 | 30511 | 30785 | 31057 | 31327 |
| 0.9 | 31594 | 31859 | 32121 | 32381 | 32639 | 32894 | 33147 | 33398 | 33646 | 33891 |
| 1.0 | 34134 | 34375 | 34614 | 34850 | 35083 | 35314 | 35543 | 35769 | 35993 | 36214 |
| 1.1 | 36433 | 36650 | 36864 | 37076 | 37286 | 37493 | 37698 | 37900 | 38100 | 38298 |
| 1.2 | 38493 | 38686 | 38877 | 39065 | 39251 | 39434 | 39617 | 39796 | 39973 | 40147 |
| 1.3 | 40320 | 40490 | 40658 | 40824 | 40988 | 41149 | 41309 | 41466 | 41621 | 41774 |
| 1.4 | 41924 | 42073 | 42220 | 42364 | 42507 | 42647 | 42786 | 42922 | 43056 | 43189 |
| 1.5 | 43319 | 43448 | 43574 | 43699 | 43822 | 43943 | 44062 | 44179 | 44295 | 44408 |
| 1.6 | 44520 | 44630 | 44738 | 44845 | 44950 | 45053 | 45154 | 45254 | 45352 | 45449 |
| 1.7 | 45543 | 45637 | 45728 | 45818 | 45907 | 45994 | 46080 | 46164 | 46246 | 46327 |
| 1.8 | 46407 | 46485 | 46562 | 46638 | 46712 | 46784 | 46856 | 46926 | 46995 | 47062 |
| 1.9 | 47128 | 47193 | 47257 | 47320 | 47381 | 47441 | 47500 | 47558 | 47615 | 47670 |
| 2.0 | 47725 | 47778 | 47831 | 47882 | 47932 | 47982 | 48030 | 48077 | 48124 | 48169 |
| 2.1 | 48214 | 48257 | 48300 | 48341 | 48382 | 48422 | 48461 | 48500 | 48537 | 48574 |
| 2.2 | 48610 | 48645 | 48679 | 48713 | 48745 | 48778 | 48809 | 48840 | 48870 | 48899 |
| 2.3 | 48928 | 48956 | 48983 | 49010 | 49036 | 49061 | 49086 | 49111 | 49134 | 49158 |
| 2.4 | 49180 | 49202 | 49224 | 49245 | 49266 | 49286 | 49305 | 49324 | 49343 | 49361 |
| 2.5 | 49379 | 49396 | 49413 | 49430 | 49446 | 49461 | 49477 | 49492 | 49506 | 49520 |
| 2.6 | 49534 | 49547 | 49560 | 49573 | 49585 | 49598 | 49609 | 49621 | 49632 | 49643 |
| 2.7 | 49653 | 49664 | 49674 | 49683 | 49693 | 49702 | 49711 | 49720 | 49728 | 49736 |
| 2.8 | 49744 | 49752 | 49760 | 49767 | 49774 | 49781 | 49788 | 49795 | 49801 | 49807 |
| 2.9 | 49813 | 49819 | 49825 | 49831 | 49836 | 49841 | 49846 | 49851 | 49856 | 49861 |
| | 3.0 | 0.49865 | 3.1 | 49903 | 3.2 | 49931 | 3.3 | 49952 | 3.4 | 49966 |
| | 3.5 | 49977 | 3.6 | 49984 | 3.7 | 49989 | 3.8 | 49993 | 3.9 | 49995 |
| | 4.0 | 499968 | | | | | | | | |
| | 4.5 | 499997 | | | | | | | | |
| | 5.0 | 49999997 | | | | | | | | |

# INDEX